S0-ALE-565

THE EYE
Volume 3

THE EYE

EDITED BY HUGH DAVSON

*Physiology Department, University College
London, England*

VOLUME 3

Muscular Mechanisms

1962

ACADEMIC PRESS, *New York and London*

ACADEMIC PRESS INC.
111 FIFTH AVENUE
NEW YORK 3, N.Y.

United Kingdom Edition
Published by
ACADEMIC PRESS INC. (LONDON) LTD.
BERKELEY SQUARE HOUSE, BERKELEY SQUARE,
LONDON W.1.

Copyright © 1962, by Academic Press Inc.

ALL RIGHTS RESERVED

NO PART OF THIS BOOK MAY BE REPRODUCED IN
ANY FORM, BY PHOTOSTAT, MICROFILM, OR ANY
OTHER MEANS, WITHOUT WRITTEN PERMISSION
FROM THE PUBLISHERS

Library of Congress Catalog Card Number 61–10694

PRINTED IN GREAT BRITAIN

List of Contributors

MATHEW ALPERN, *University of Michigan, Ann Arbor, Michigan, U.S.A.*

OTTO LOWENSTEIN, *Columbia University College of Physicians and Surgeons, New York, U.S.A.*

IRENE E. LOEWENFELD, *Columbia University College of Physicians and Surgeons, New York, U.S.A.*

WILLIAM K. MCEWEN, *Francis I. Proctor Foundation for Research in Ophthalmology, University of California San Francisco Medical Center, San Francisco, California, U.S.A.*

Foreword

THE study of the physiology of the eye employs a wide variety of scientific disciplines; for example, its vegetative physiology and biochemistry bring us into the realms of electron-microscopy of such structures as the ciliary epithelium, vitreous body and cornea; the active transport mechanisms concerned with the function of the aqueous humour; the special problem of a vascular circulation in a semi-rigid cavity; the metabolism of avascular tissues, and so on. Similarly with other aspects, so that the compilation of an authoritative treatise on the eye is best carried out by a group of research workers who are experts in particular aspects. In the present work the Editor has attempted to provide a well-integrated and authoritative account of the physiology of the eye, and to this end the fractionation of the subject, necessary in a multi-author work, has been minimized as far as practicable, so that it is hoped that the book will be read more as an advanced text than consulted as a "Handbook". The emphasis has been on function so that the Editor has been content with an elementary introductory outline of the anatomy and embryology of the eye, detailed descriptions of the anatomy of any part being postponed until they could be given in their immediate physiological context.

Whilst the emphasis has been on readability rather than exhaustiveness, the various accounts are sufficiently well documented to make the treatise valuable not only to teachers in physiology, psychology and ophthalmology, but also to research workers in all branches of ocular physiology.

HUGH DAVSON

Acknowledgment

FIGURE 2 on page 35 is a slightly modified version of the diagram by F. H. Adler in " Physiology of the Eye ", 1959, and is reproduced by kind permission of the publishers, The C. V. Mosby Company, St. Louis, U.S.A.

Contents

Part I: Movements of the Eyes

1. Introduction to Movements of the Eyes

MATHEW ALPERN

2. Specification of the Direction of Regard

MATHEW ALPERN

3. Kinematics of the Eye

MATHEW ALPERN

4. Anatomical Aspects

MATHEW ALPERN

5. Types of Movement
MATHEW ALPERN

6. Physiological Characteristics of the Extra-Ocular Muscles
MATHEW ALPERN

7. Strabismus

MATHEW ALPERN

Part II: Accommodation and the Pupil

8. Accommodation

MATHEW ALPERN

9. The Pupil
OTTO LOWENSTEIN AND IRENE E. LOEWENFELD

Part III: Secretion of Tears and Blinking

10. Secretion of Tears and Blinking
WILLIAM K. McEWEN

THE EYE
(COMPLETE IN 4 VOLUMES)

PART I

Movements of the Eyes

by

Mathew Alpern

University of Michigan, Ann Arbor, Michigan, U.S.A.

CHAPTER 1

Introduction to Movements of the Eyes †

I. Copepod Ocellus

The axial length of the ocellus of the copepod crustacean *Copilia* occupies almost one half of the length of its body. This ocellus consists of a cuticle and a lens which form an image in the plane of the dotted line in Fig. 1. In this

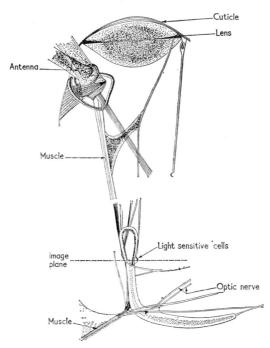

FIG. 1. The ocellus of the copepod crustacean *Copilia*. (Modified after Grenacher, 1879.)

† The lectures of Professors Elizabeth Caroline Crosby and John W. Henderson at the University of Michigan were of very great help to me in the preparation of much that is written here. Moreover, each of them has graciously read certain sections of the manuscript and offered very valuable suggestions for the revision. Professor Meredith W. Morgan Jr., of the University of California, made a number of comments on an early draft of the section on vergence movements which were quite useful in the preparation of the final form of this section.

plane is a small cluster of three retinula cells surrounded by a pigment sheath. The contraction of a long slender muscle on the side of the eye, and certain accessory muscles, can produce a shifting of this cluster of cells so that now this, and now that, part of the image of the object of regard can be examined by these photoreceptors. Thus, in a very simple way, the components that allow for the inspection of objects in different parts of the visual field are found in this small invertebrate plankton. These are: an optical system, a group of light-sensitive cells, and a motor system (i.e., muscles and the related nervous system). This last brings about a shift of the sensitive cells so that various parts of the image of an object can be examined in detail.

II. Fovea Centralis

Vertebrate eyes, in general, and the highly mobile human eye, in particular, are much more complex than this. Nevertheless, in some respects the basic problems for vision are strikingly similar in the two cases. One important reason is that the human retina, unlike the photographic plate to which it is so frequently compared, does not have the same spatial sensitivity throughout. Figure 2 illustrates this fact although it represents measurements made

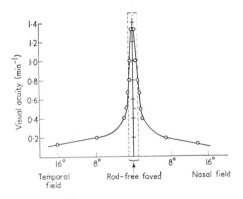

Fig. 2. The visual acuity in the horizontal meridian of the visual field of the normal eye. The data are the mean of results on two observers.

over only a very small per cent of the sensitive field and in only one (the horizontal) meridian. At the very centre of the visual field, acuity is exceptionally good but it begins to drop off even while the chief-ray image of the test letter is still well within the rod-free fovea. As a matter of fact, except for this geographically minute spot, slightly smaller than 35′ of arc, the visual acuity of the entire retina is quite low. While this small central area represents physically an insignificant fraction of the total visual field, physiologically it is the most important, since it is this tiny area with which the eye does all of its critical seeing.

If the visual field were imaged on a perfectly stationary retina only that part of the image which stimulated this insignificant 35′ area in the centre could be seen in great detail. The rest of the image would show fewer and fewer details the farther from the centre it was and it would be seen as completely blurred only a few degrees out. Obviously, such an arrangement would be highly inefficient. It becomes remarkably effective, however, merely by allowing mobility to the eye so that it is free to rotate about its centre and to point its most sensitive central area at first one part of the image and then at another. Just as in the eye of *Copilia*, in the human eye, the motor activity produces a scanning of the image of the object of regard by the most sensitive photoreceptors.

Since one cannot examine the retinal image in a moving human eye, one has only good presumptive evidence that this is the case: if one examines the fundus of the normal eye and asks the subject to fixate directly into the ophthalmoscope, one sees the geographic feature characteristic of the area centralis correctly centred in the illuminated area. Moreover, there are a number of rather ingenious methods of demonstrating to an observer certain anatomical features of his own area centralis entoptically (Maxwell, 1856; Haidinger, 1844) and it will suffice to point out that when normal observers participate in such a demonstration they invariably see the centre of the entoptic macula centred over the fixation point regardless of where it may appear in the field of fixation.

A variety of evidence of this sort makes it quite evident that the human eye fixates by positioning itself in such a way that the image of the object of regard always falls at the centre of the region of most acute vision in the area centralis.† This is the basis of the physiology of the movement of the eye.

References

Grenacher, H. (1879). "Untersuchungen ueber das Sehorgan der Arthropoden, insbesondere der Spinnen, Insecten und Crustaceen." Vanderhoeck u. Ruprecht, Goettingen.
Haidinger, W. (1844). Ueber das directe Erkennen des polarischen Lichts und der Lage der Polarisationsebene. *Ann. Phys. chem.* Ser. 2, **63**, 29–39.
Maxwell, J. C. (1856). On the unequal sensibility of the foramen centrale to light of different colours. *Rep. Brit. Ass.* **26**, Notices and Abstracts, p. 12.

† In certain types of abnormalities of binocular vision, the region of the retina used for fixation may not coincide precisely with this centre of the area centralis. There is evidence, however, that even in these cases the region of the retina used for fixation is always the same and so the arrangement is not essentially different.

Chapter 2

Specification of the Direction of Regard

I. Definitions

Before attempting a discussion of the motor aspects of vision it seems worthwhile to specify the precise meaning of some of the relevant technical terms. Of necessity this discussion must be brief. Fortunately a more detailed analysis of some of these questions has been given elsewhere (Fry *et al.*, 1945, 1947a, 1947b).

A. Entrance Pupil

The entrance pupil is the image of the real pupil formed by refraction at the cornea.

B. Object of Regard

The object of regard is the point at which an observer directs his gaze. According to the principle described in the introduction, it can be assumed that under these conditions the observer positions his eye so that the image of this object falls at the centre of the area centralis (i.e., at the fovea).

C. The Line of Sight

The line of sight is a line passing from the centre of the entrance pupil to the object of regard. In normal fixation of the type already described, it represents that part of the foveal chief ray which can be specified in object space.

D. Visual Axis

The visual axis is a line in image space from the centre of the fovea through the second nodal point of the eye. In object space it is a line which passes through the first nodal point. These two lines (in object and image space, respectively) must be parallel to each other, and are collectively called the visual axis.

E. Pupillary Axis

A line passing from the centre of the entrance pupil normal to the cornea (and hence through the centre of curvature of the cornea).

F. Angle Lambda

The angle formed at the centre of the entrance pupil by the intersection of the pupillary axis and the line of sight. While conventional physiological optics has specified other angles (alpha, kappa, gamma) they are designated as the intersection of lines which cannot be operationally defined and so they

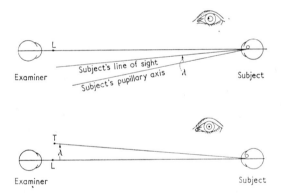

Fig. 1. Method of measurement of the angle lambda.

have little clinical value. The angle lambda, as defined above, was introduced by Lancaster (1943). The easiest way of measuring this angle is to have the subject look directly at a small flashlight (L) held by the examiner underneath his lower eyelid (Fig. 1). The examiner stands at a convenient distance from the subject and the other eye of each is occluded. The examiner sees the corneal image of the flashlight along a line (his own line of sight) that intersects the centre of curvature of the anterior surface of the cornea of the patient's eye. He notes the relation between this image of the light and the centre of the subject's entrance pupil. A small fixation target (T) is then brought into the field of view and the subject directs his gaze at this target while the examiner moves it until the image of the light is seen centred in the subject's entrance pupil. At this moment the examiner's line of sight coincides with the pupillary axis of the subject and the angle lambda can then be determined by measuring the angle subtended by the distance between the fixation target and the light (TOL) at the centre of the subject's entrance pupil.

G. CENTRE OF ROTATION

By the centre of rotation of the eye, using the accepted terms of mechanics, we mean a point which, during rotation of the eye, has zero velocity both within the eye and within the orbit (assuming that the head is held rigidly fixed). Quite obviously the determination of such a point, or even deciding whether or not one exists, is not easy. For this reason less exacting definitions have been suggested. Mueller, for example, proposed that the centre of rotation of the eye be defined as a point fixed in the eye coincident with the geometrical centre of curvature of the posterior part of the globe.

1. EXPERIMENTAL DETERMINATION

Volkmann (1869) and Woinow (1870), among others, showed that, for various positions of the fixation point within the visual field, the line of sight of the eyes always intersected at a common point. Volkmann located a great number of straight pins along the circumferences of two concentric circles in such a way that lines joining a pin on one circle passed to the common centre by intersecting a pin on the circumference of the other. He then found that a position of the eye could always be found such that the two corresponding pins were seen exactly aligned as the eye rotated, i.e., the inside ones appearing precisely in front of the outside one. Volkmann felt that this proved that a single centre of rotation for the eye existed and that this point fell at the centre of these concentric circles at the completion of his experiment. Hering (1879; 1942) and von Kries (1925), however, have both emphasized that these results could be obtained even though the point of intersection of the various positions of the line of sight did not have a velocity of zero both with respect to the head and with respect to the eye during any given rotation.

Numerous other experimental determinations of the centre of rotation have been attempted but the most exact measurements are those of Park and Park (1933) and of Verrijp (1949). They verified the findings of Woinow and Volkmann that the line of sight intersected at a common point (let us call

1*

it the sighting centre) irrespective of the direction of gaze.† Park and Park then proceeded to measure the distance (r) of the sighting centre from the anterior corneal apex (o'), when the eye assumed fixation in various directions in the horizontal plane. These data clearly indicate that the distance from the corneal apex to the sighting centre was different for each direction of the gaze. This demonstrated that the sighting centre could not have a zero velocity during eye rotation and that Volkmann's notion that the sighting centre was coincident with the centre of rotation was erroneous. Knowing the position of the sighting centre for each position of the line of sight, Park and Park were able to compute the locus of points that, for any position of the line of sight, had zero velocity. These calculations clearly demonstrated that a single position for the centre of rotation of the eye during any horizontal rotation was not to be found. On the contrary, every motion in the horizontal plane could be represented by a *series* of pure rotations about certain points. Each of these points, while in use, is the instantaneous centre of rotation. The locus of these instantaneous centres was calculated and found to fall on two curves. The first curve, in the plane of the rotation and fixed in the orbit, can be called the *space centrode*. The other curve was fixed in the eye and may be termed the *body centrode*. At any instant the centre of rotation is the point of contact of these two centrodes, and the motion of the eye may be represented by the rolling of the body centrode upon the space centrode. The point in the eye that coincides with this point of contact at any instant is the only point in the eye that has zero velocity. Figure 2 illustrates the positions of these two centrodes.

These data show that the concept of the eye as a sphere rotating about a point which is both fixed within it and within the orbit is quite artificial.‡ More appropriately, the eye appears to move forward and backward in the orbit even when performing a purely horizontal movement.

2. SCREW MOVEMENTS

Berlin (1871) showed that the eyes also undergo "screw" motions, by which is meant a displacement parallel to the axis about which the eye is rotating.

† Earlier data of Verrijp (1930) show only an approximate intersection of the lines of sight in the various directions of horizontal gaze and this is probably the reason for the statement of Fry *et al.* (1945) that the lines of sight in the various directions intersect in a caustic surface. The more recent data confirm the earlier view and it seems more reasonable to regard the lines of sight intersecting in a single point on the basis of all the available data.

‡ It will probably come as no great surprise that movements of other parts of the body pose many similar problems. An interesting example is the movements of the mandibular bone, which were regarded as occurring about a single fixed centre of rotation. Recent studies with X-ray techniques show, however, that, on the contrary, such movements can occur only about many instantaneous centres of rotation (Superstine, 1957).

A thread was stretched horizontally in such a way as to bisect the head of three thumb tacks mounted in the horizontal plane, one each in the nasal, straight ahead, and temporal fields. Upon looking at the middle tack (the eye in the primary position), all three tacks were seen to be bisected by the string. If the eye looked either at the nasal or the temporal tack the string appeared shifted with respect to the tacks. The rotation about a supposedly vertical

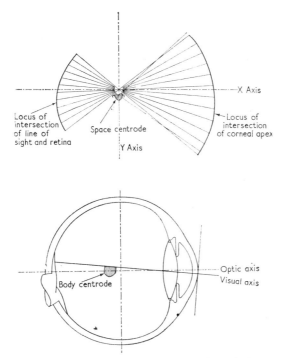

FIG. 2. Illustrating the position of the space centrode and the body centrode as computed by Park and Park (1953).

axis was associated with a vertical displacement of the globe. Similar results were obtained with oblique and vertical arrangements of the threads and corresponding movements of the eyes. For example, a plumb-line may be arranged in line with a second plumb-line at a different distance when the eye fixates the middle. However, as the eye roves up and down the plumb-line the two lines are seen in parallax. This demonstrates a displacement of the eye horizontally while it was rotating about a horizontal axis.

3. APPROXIMATE POSITION OF CENTRE

Experiments of this sort emphasize that the simplest of eye movements is quite complex. For practical purposes, however, the approximation of the eye as a sphere rotating about a single fixed point is accurate enough unless the analysis is to be made in very precise quantitative terms. Such an approximation is necessary for much that follows. In order to be specific, the centre of rotation will be designated as a point on the line of sight located 13.5 mm behind the cornea when the eye is in the straight-forward position (to be defined).

H. Base Line

The base line is a line connecting the centres of rotation of the two eyes.

I. Plane of Regard

The plane of regard is a plane that includes the base line and the object of regard.

J. Primary Position

(See below.) The primary position is the position from which either a pure horizontal movement or a pure vertical movement is not associated with any tilt of the vertical meridian of the eye with respect to objective vertical.

K. Straightforward Position of the Line of Sight

The line of sight in this position is perpendicular both to the base line and to the face plane (a plane tangent to the chin and the superciliary ridges).

References

Berlin, E. (1871). Beitrag zur Mechanik der Augenbewegungen. v. Graefes Arch. Ophthal. 17 (Abt. 2), 154–203.

Fry, G. A., Treleaven, C. L., and Baxter, R. C. (1945). Specification of the direction of regard. Special Report, No. I. Amer. J. Optom. 22, 351–360.

Fry, G. A., Treleaven, C. L., Walsh, R., Higgins, E. L., and Radde, C. A. (1947a). Definition and measurement of torsion. Special Report, No. 2. Amer. J. Optom. 24, 329–334.

Fry, G. A., Treleaven, C. L. Walsh, R., Higgins, E. L., and Radde, C. A. (1947b). Definition and measurement of cyclophoria with converged and elevated lines of sight. Special Report, No. 3. Amer. J. Optom. 24, 489–493.

Hering, E. (1879). Der Raumsinn und die Bewegungen des Auges. In "Handbuch der Physiologie" (L. Hermann, ed.), Vol. III, Teil I, pp. 343–601. F. C. W. Vogel, Leipzig.

Hering, E. (1942). "Spatial Sense and Movements of the Eye" (translated by C. A. Radde). American Academy of Optometry, Baltimore.

Lancaster, W. B. (1943). Terminology in ocular motility and allied subjects. *Amer. J. Ophthal.* **26**, 122–132.

Park, R. S., and Park, G. E. (1933). The center of ocular rotation in the horizontal plane. *Amer. J. Physiol.* **104**, 545–552.

Superstine, M. (1957). Mandibular movement in children as revealed by the use of rapid serial cephalograms. M.Sc. Thesis. The University of Michigan.

Verrijp, C. D. (1930). Ocular movements. *Arch. Ophthal.*, *N.Y.* **4**, 73–83.

Verrijp, C. D. (1949). Movements of the eyes. *In* "The Eye and Its Diseases" (C. Berens, ed.), pp. 699–713. W. B. Saunders Company, Philadelphia.

Volkmann, A. W. (1869). Zur Mechanik der Augenmuskeln. *Ber. Sächs. Ges. (Akad.) Wiss.* **21**, 28–69.

von Kries, J. (1925). Notes on ≠27 on the ocular movements. *In* "Helmholtz's Treatise on Physiological Optics", (translated from the 3rd German ed., J. P. C. Southall, ed.), Vol. III, pp. 127–154. The Optical Society of America, Rochester.

Woinow, M. (1870). Ueber den Drehpunkt des Auges. *v. GraefesArch. Ophthal.* **16**, 243–250.

Kinematics of the Eye

I. Degrees of Freedom

For purpose of discussion of the kinematics of the eye, the globe is regarded as a sphere rotating about a point that is fixed within it and also within the orbit. The laws that are then applied to such rotations are the laws of the kinematics of rigid bodies constrained to rotate about a fixed point. Under these conditions any such body has three degrees of freedom—i.e., three independent quantities are required to state the position of the body with respect to a given frame of reference. Donders was apparently the first to suggest that in the case of the human eye one did not need three degrees of freedom to specify its position in the orbit and that, on the contrary, the position of the eye with respect to a given reference frame could invariably be described by only two independent quantities. This suggestion was elaborated upon first by Listing, who suggested a way in which this could be done, and later by many others, including Helmholtz (1925) who developed the necessary theoretical equations and established the empirical data which adequately verified them.

A. REFERENCE FRAME

It is meaningless, of course, to specify any position of the eye in its orbit without using some definite reference frame. The frame of reference in the following discussion, unless otherwise specified, will be the *objective vertical*. Begin by assuming that the eye is in the primary position and defer for the moment how one defines this any more precisely. It is frequently stated that this is when the head is erect, the two eyes fixing at the horizon. Actually, the primary position cannot be operationally defined in this way although the description is not a bad estimate of the position of the eyes in the orbit when

15

they are in the primary position.† Imagine that, with the eye in the primary position, a cross with vertical and horizontal limbs is rigidly attached to the eyeball with its centre at the point where the line of sight pierces the globe anteriorly.

II. Listing's Law

Since it is assumed that the eye rotates about a single fixed centre of rotation, every point on its surface will describe the arc of a circle in a single rotation. A basic principle is that the angle that the arms of the cross make with the circle along which the centre of the cross travels must remain constant during any rotation about a single axis. Listing proposed that each movement of the eyes from the primary to any other position was the equivalent of a single rotation about an axis in the equatorial plane.‡ This axis is perpendicular to that plane which contained the initial and final positions of the line of sight. This is what Helmholtz called Listing's law although it seems likely that Helmholtz himself contributed much more to its mathematical elucidation and to its empirical verification than did Listing.

A. Primary Position

When, according to Listing's law, the eye moves in a purely horizontal way from the primary position, this is equivalent to a rotation about a vertical axis in the equatorial plane. Movements in a purely vertical direction from the primary position, according to Listing's law, occur about a horizontal axis in this same plane. Such movements bring the eye to a *secondary position* of the line of sight. Since the angle the limbs of the cross make with the circle along which the centre of the cross must travel always remains constant in a rotation about a single axis, it is at once evident that movements from the primary to any secondary position occur without any deviation of the arms of the cross from the objective vertical position. This corollary of Listing's law is a convenient way of operationally defining the primary position: the primary position is that position of the eyes from which either purely

† The line of sight is assumed to continue through the eye undeviated, to pass through the centre of rotation, and to pierce the globe posteriorly at a point that Helmholtz called the "occipital" point. For convenience, the line of sight (which has the advantage of being operationally defined) will be used to describe these movements. Most authors used the line of fixation but since the centre of rotation has been operationally defined as the point on the line of sight 13.5 mm. behind the cornea, the line of fixation will have to coincide with the line of sight and the additional term is superfluous.

‡ The equatorial plane—sometimes referred to as Listing's plane—is fixed in the orbit passing through both the centre of rotation and the equator of the eye when it is in its primary position.

horizontal or purely vertical movements do not produce any deviation of the vertical arms of the cross from objective vertical.

B. TERTIARY POSITION

The movement of the eye from the primary to any position of the line of sight other than a secondary one is known as a movement to a *tertiary position*. Another consequence of Listing's law is that each movement of the eye from the primary to a tertiary position (equivalent to a rotation about an axis in the equatorial plane between the vertical and horizontal axes used for rotations to secondary positions) is always associated with a definite tilt of the vertical limb of the cross with respect to objective vertical. This is illustrated in Fig. 1. A movement from the primary to a tertiary position

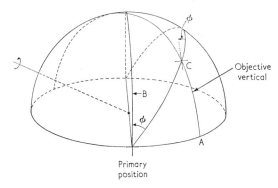

FIG. 1. Simple rotation around axis in Listing's plane is associated with a tilt of the vertical limb of the cross with respect to objective vertical although the angle that the vertical limb of the cross makes with the circle along which the centre of the cross travels (ϕ) remains fixed. (Modified from a similar sketch by Boeder, 1957.)

(according to Listing's law) occurs along a meridian and all such meridians are along great circles which pass through the occipital point. Since the angle that the limbs of the cross make with the circle along which the centre of the cross travels (ϕ in Fig. 1) remains constant and since the angle which any given meridian (other than the vertical or horizontal meridian) makes with objective vertical varies with the amplitude (the so-called eccentricity) of the movement along the meridian, each tertiary position is associated with a finite tilt of the vertical limb of the cross with respect to objective vertical.

Donders's law states further that the angle of this tilt for a given tertiary position of the eyes is always the same irrespective of the manner in which the eyes are brought to this position. Thus any tertiary position of the eyes may be fully described by specifying the position of the axis in Listing's plane about which the rotation may be regarded as occurring (i.e., the meridian $[90 - \phi]$ in Fig. 1) and the amplitude (i.e., eccentricity) of the movement. Two degrees of freedom suffice to describe the movement completely.

C. Tilt of the Vertical

The system of axes used to describe the results of a movement according to Listing's law does not include a rotation about the line of sight. Despite this fact, in a tertiary position the vertical limb of the cross on the cornea in Fig. 1 is tilted with respect to objective vertical. Now Listing's law says nothing about how the eye actually moves from the primary to the tertiary position. The law is only concerned with a description of the result of the movement and is completely "as if" in its formulation. The number of axes that can be postulated to describe the result of the rotation from the primary position to a given tertiary position are infinite. Listing's system of axes is superior to those others in one—and only one—important respect, namely, that fewer degrees of freedom are needed to describe the results of the movement than with any other system of axes that one might imagine. For example, Helmholtz (1925) suggested a system of axes that involved rotation first about a fixed horizontal axis from point P to B through the angle POB and then around a second axis to the point C through the angle BOC (Fig. 2). Fick (1854), on the other hand, proposed a system of axes according to which the eye would rotate from the point P to the point A through the angle POA and then to the point C through the angle AOC. With the rotation just described, using Fick's system, the vertical limb of the cross on the cornea still remains coincident with objective vertical since the angle that the arms of the cross make with the circle along which the anterior pole of the eye is travelling remains constant in any simple movement. We have already seen, however, that according to Listing's law the vertical limb of the cross will be tilted with respect to the objective vertical when the eye moves from point P to point C. If one is going to describe the movement according to Fick's system of axes (rather than Listing's) then one must postulate that, in addition to rotating through the angles POA and AOC, the eye makes a rotation around its own line of sight, i.e., a torsion movement.†

† The amount of this "false" torsion, or (what amounts to the same thing) the amount of tilt of the vertical limb of the cross with respect to objective vertical (ρ_v), is a function of the tertiary position of the eyes. Equations which express these functions have been derived by Helmholtz (1925); Schubert (1924); Lamb (1919) and others. Westheimer (1957) recently used a more elegant treatment afforded by quaternions. The derivation of these relations is beyond the scope of this review, but the relation between the angle of

In a similar way if one moved the eye from the point P to the point C, using Helmholtz' system, i.e., rotating through the angle POB and then through the angle BOC, the eye would arrive at the point C with the horizontal limb of the cross on the cornea coincident with the plane DBE (plane of regard). In order to bring the eye into the position it assumes under Listing's law one would have to postulate a rotation around the line of sight and it can be shown that the postulated rotation † around the line of sight with this system of axes would be opposite to that necessary to postulate using Fick's system of axes.

The orientation of the primary vertical plane of the eye with respect to the objective vertical, and the orientation of the primary horizontal plane of the eye with respect to the plane of regard, as specified by Equations (1) and (2) in the footnotes are summarized in Table 1, for the left eye. In this table the

TABLE I

	Tilt of primary horizontal plane with respect to the plane of regard	Tilt of primary vertical plane with respect to objective vertical
Upper Temporal Quadrant	In	Out
Upper Nasal Quadrant	Out	In
Lower Nasal Quadrant	In	Out
Lower Temporal Quadrant	Out	In

direction *out* refers to the condition in which the primary vertical plane appears to be rotated clockwise with respect to the objective vertical (or the primary horizontal plane appears to be rotated clockwise with respect to the plane of regard) when the eye is examined along its line of sight looking towards the centre of rotation from in front.

tilt ρ_v and the two variables in Listing's axis system (meridional direction c and eccentricity w) is:

$$\rho_v = \tan^{-1}\frac{\sin c \cos c \,(1 - \cos w)}{\cos^2 c + \sin^2 c \cos w}, \tag{1}$$

in which $\qquad c = \dfrac{\pi}{2} - \phi$

† Helmholtz's equation for this angle of rotation (ρ_h) in terms of the same quantities as equation (1) in the previous footnote is:

$$\rho_h = \tan^{-1}\frac{\sin c \,.\, \cos c \,(1 - \cos w)}{\sin^2 c + \cos^2 c \,.\, \cos w} \tag{2}$$

In this equation ρ_h is the angle the horizontal limb of the cross makes with the plane of regard.

1. "FALSE TORSION"

Some authors in order to emphasize that motion of the eye according to Listing's law produces the tilting of the vertical limb of the cross with respect to objective vertical without requiring a postulation of rotation around the line of sight at all, have called this tilting of the cross a *false* torsion. By this term they wanted to draw a clear distinction between rotations around the line of sight (i.e., torsion)—which produce a tilting of the vertical limb of the cross—and tilting of the vertical limb of the cross produced by rotation about axes other than the line of sight. It has already been emphasized that the system of axes postulated to explain any given movement is completely arbitrary. There is no way of asking the question "Which system of axes does the eye actually use in making a rotation from the primary to a tertiary position?" If one uses the Helmholtz (or the Fick) system in order to explain the movement, then indeed a rotation around the line of sight must be postulated in order to explain the actual position that one finds the eye in the tertiary position. On the other hand, Listing's system of axes explains the position of the eye in this tertiary position without requiring any rotation around the line of sight. Helmholtz's or Fick's—or any other we might choose —system of axes require at least three degrees of freedom in order to explain the movement and for this reason they are less elegant—but no less exact— than Listing's system. The latter, of course, is more parsimonious since *it* only requires two degrees of freedom in order to define the position of the eyes completely. It has no other advantage.

2. SYSTEMS OF CO-ORDINATES

It would be misleading to leave the reader with the impression that Fick's system— also used by Meissner and Wundt—or Helmholtz's system, for that matter, was developed purely to avoid the distinction between "true" and "false" torsion. They seem to have the more practical objective of permitting the development of a system of co-ordinates that permit specification of the fixation point in the tertiary position relative to the primary position. This was a preliminary to the development of ophthalmic instruments such as tangent screens, major amblyoscopes, etc., which must specify points in space with reference to the straightforward position. Helmholtz's system consists of a fixed horizontal axis which is coincident with the lines connecting the centres of rotation of the two eyes, and a vertical axis which moves about this horizontal axis. The rotation around the horizontal axis (angle *POB* in Fig. 2) is known as an angle of *elevation*. The rotation around the vertical axis (angle *BOC* in Fig. 2) is known as the angle of *azimuth*. Fick assumed that the line of sight first turned through an angle which he termed *longitude* (angle *POA* in Fig. 2), the vertical axis being fixed and analogous to the polar axis of a terrestrial globe. Then the line of sight ascends through an angle of *latitude* (angle *AOC* of Fig. 2) by rotation around a horizontal axis which itself rotates about the fixed vertical axis.

Helmholtz preferred his system to that of Fick because ". . . the values of both *longitude* and *latitude* depend upon the initial position that is chosen for the plane of fixation; and as there is no satisfactory way of defining a fixed initial position of this plane, every time it is changed trigonometrical calculations have to be made for the other two angles. On the other hand, the *azimuth angle* used in my work is entirely independent of the primary position of the plane of fixation; while the angle of *elevation* merely has to be corrected by addition or subtraction when it is measured from a new origin."

It is of interest to point out that Listing's system of axes can also be used to specify the position of points in visual space with reference to the primary position; and certain ophthalmic instruments—notably the perimeter—use this system to advantage. It uses the angle of *meridional* direction, to specify the position of the axis of rotation in Listing's plane about which the rotation is imagined to occur, and the angle of *eccentricity*, to specify the amplitude of the rotation.

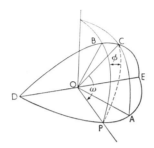

FIG. 2. Diagram illustrating the relation of the two parameters of Listing's system ϕ and ω to those proposed by Helmholtz and Fick.

Various names have been suggested in the past to describe the failure of the vertical limb of the cross to coincide with the objective vertical when the eye is in a tertiary position. The angle of "false" torsion has already been alluded to. Helmholtz suggested *Raddrehung* (i.e., wheel rotation) and this is usually described in the textbooks "as an unfortunate choice of terms." It was, however, von Kries (1925), in what some textbooks regard as a "clarification," who contributed most to the confusion. He emphasized a sharp distinction between *Raddrehung* and *Rollung* (suggested by Hering, 1879), the latter term being reserved for exclusive use as description of rotations around the line of sight. As has been pointed out, this distinction is purely a matter of arbitrary selection of systems of axes. Other terms used to describe the tilting of the vertical limb of the cross from the objective vertical in the tertiary position include: *kinematic inclination* by Tschermak-Seysenegg (1952), *cyclorotation* by Boeder (1957), *aberration* by Meinong (1898). It seems likely, however, that the term "false torsion" is so ingrained in the literature that it will continue to be used.

D. MOVEMENT FROM TERTIARY POSITION

As originally stated, Listing's law specifically requires that the movement of the eye must start from the primary position. This is indeed a highly artificial situation because rarely does the eye find itself in the primary position at the beginning of a movement unless special efforts are made to arrange matters in this way. On the other hand, Donders's law specifies that "For any given position of the globe the angle of tilt (or false torsion) is precisely the same irrespective of the manner in which the eye has been rotated in order to achieve the position that it assumes." This means that rotation of the eye from one tertiary position to another results in the same amount of tilt of the vertical limb of the cross as though the eye had been rotated to this end position from the primary position. Some authors have interpreted this as meaning that all such movements (i.e., from one tertiary position to another) must contain a component of rotation around the line of sight (Tschermak-Seysenegg, 1952; Quereau 1954, 1955; Duke-Elder, 1939—p. 601). Boeder (1957) has shown, however, that this need not be the case. He analysed such a movement—not in terms of a single simple rotation—but in terms of a series of simple rotations. Each of these component simple rotations is along the arc of a direction circle and is about the axis of this direction circle.† In this analysis the axis of rotation is constantly changing. The instantaneous axis of rotation will not lie in Listing's plane unless the arc of the direction circle at that instant coincides with a meridian. While it is not obvious, kinematic considerations show that the vertical limb of the cross at the end of any one of these component simple rotations will make precisely that angle of tilt with respect to objective vertical that it would have if the eye had been brought to this position from the primary position according to Listing's law.

E. Validity of Listing's Law

How accurately does Listing's law actually describe the position of living human eyes? About this there is still a certain amount of disagreement (Marquez, 1949). Even Helmholtz was not as fixed about this as is commonly believed. He admitted that discrepancies were to be found from individual to individual even for the rather impractical case of the two eyes gazing at infinity. He stated the matter:

† A direction circle was the term used by Helmholtz to describe a circle which passes through the following three points: (a) the centre of the cross on the cornea at the beginning of the minute component simple rotation, (b) the centre of the cross on the cornea at the end of the minute component simple rotation, and (c) the occipital point, which is a point fixed in the orbit which coincides with the point where the line of sight pierces the globe posteriorly when the eye is in the primary position. According to Boeder's scheme, the eye only moves along arcs of direction circles whenever it moves between any two points. Whenever the two points between which the eye must move do not lie on the arc of a single direction circle, the movement is broken up into a series of component rotations and each of these components is along the arc of a direction circle.

"Accordingly, we must not expect quite the same precision in the eye as in a scientific instrument, although under ordinary conditions normal eyes do obey the laws of Donders and Listing pretty accurately."

Berthold (1865) who was 10 diopters myopic, found that his eyes did not follow Listing's law but that the deviations were never very large.

1. EXPERIMENTAL VERIFICATION

In practice it is inconvenient to affix a cross to a cornea but one can place the after-image of a centrally fixated cross on the retina. Much of the data has been obtained in this way. Confusion persists to this day because after-images projected onto a flat surface when the eyes are in a tertiary position will undergo a distortion due to perspective problems (which, of course, have nothing whatsoever to do with Listing's law) (Le Conte, 1881; Marquez, 1949). Various authors have stated, that since the projection of an after-image on a flat surface will distort its perception due to perspective factors, that such distortions are the sole cause of tilt of after-images in these classical experiments, and that Listing's law does not describe the position of living eyes. The available evidence certainly fails to justify this point of view. Le Conte (1881, and even earlier) emphasized this distortion of the after-image by perspective factors and arranged to project after-images in a tertiary position on a surface that was perpendicular to the line of sight. In this way he eliminated this problem. If one projects the after-image upon a hollow concave spherical surface with the eye located at its centre, this difficulty is also eliminated and the results of the experiments done in these ways clearly verify the predictions of Listing's law. (Tscherning, 1900; Le Conte, 1881; Tschermak-Seysenegg, 1952; Quereau, 1954.)

a. Photographic Method

Furthermore, it is easy to verify Listing's law by other means. Moses (1950) photographed the eyeball in a movement along the 45° meridian and measured the amount of tilt of the vertical meridian of the cornea with respect to the objective vertical as indicated by a plumb-line placed next to the eye. For a movement of 20°, he found a tilt of the vertical meridian of the cornea of about 2° (eq. 1 in the footnote on p.19 which is derived from Listing's law predicts 1° 47') and for a movement of 30°, he found a tilt of about 5° (eq. 1 in the footnote on p.19 predicts 4° 6'). The agreement seems quite good.

b. Direct Observation

Another method of demonstrating the validity of Listing's law is to observe the eye directly (Quereau, 1954). The procedure may be described as follows

"... the lids should be separated widely, exposing a large area of the eyeball; the opposite eye should be covered. With use of a bright light, a conjunctival vessel is selected such that an imaginary line from it to the centre of the pupil coincides exactly with the proposed direction of rotation ... the eye is (then) made to rotate along this imaginary line ... (while) the observer sights along this line, in line with it and the centre of the eye ...."

Following this procedure, if the eye follows Listing's law, then the meridian along which the eye moves and the imaginary line from the vessel to the centre of the pupil will remain coincident.† Measurements made in this way by Quereau have shown that in normal eyes Listing's law does remain valid.

c. Blind Spot

Still another way of showing the validity of Listing's law was described by Quereau (1955) who adapted the method of plotting the blind spot in the tertiary positions of gaze, originally described by Fick (1854), and later used by Meissner (1860), to a concave hemispherical perimeter. Measurements on eight subjects were very nearly identical. In the movements in the field of fixation within which the eyes move in everyday seeing, Listing's law was found to be quite valid. Far out in the superior and inferior temporal quadrants, a small (3° to 5°) amount of deviation from the position predicted by Listing's law was found. A deviation did not appear in either the nasal inferior or the nasal superior quadrants presumably because the line of sight was obstructed by the contours of the bones of the face before the extreme position of rotation was reached at which such a deviation might be found.

The recent photographic measurements of Weale (1959) on seven subjects showed that (contrary to Listing's law), in rotations of the eye through an amplitude of 45° in the 45° meridian the vertical meridian of the eye coincided with the objective vertical. These data are subject to possibility of several sources of error, however, and it seems likely that for the single eye fixating at infinity the appraisal made by Helmholtz (and quoted above) remains quite accurate even to this day.

2. CONVERGENCE

In the case of convergence of the lines of sight, however, there is a variety of evidence that suggests that Listing's law breaks down completely, as Helmholtz was well aware. Since convergent positions of the eyes are quite a high percentage of eye positions in normal use of the two eyes, this exception to the generality of Listing's law is not an inconsiderable one. Experiments demonstrating phenomena of this kind were carried out by some of the more

† The same procedure is used to detect small amounts of rotation about the line of sight such as may occur in the tertiary position of gaze in some patients with defects of of the ocular muscles.

famous physiologists of the last century. The phenomenon seems to have been reported very early by Volkmann in unpublished correspondence with Helmholtz (cf., Helmholtz, 1925, p. 51). Further experiments by Hering (1868), Donders (1876) and especially Landolt (1876) left little doubt as to the facts, however. In the present century the experiments of Hermans (1943), Carow (1939) and recently Allen (1954) all lead to the conclusion that considerable deviations from Listing's law occur when the eyes converge, and that the extent of this deviation increases with increasing angles of convergence. Figure 3 shows some very old data of Landolt's which have been

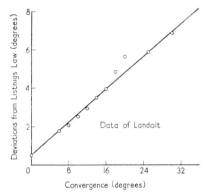

Fig. 3. Effect of convergence at zero degrees of elevation on the amount of cyclophoria. (Data from Landolt, 1876.)

largely confirmed by recent work (Allen, 1954). The ordinate in this figure shows the amount of cyclophoria, i.e., the deviation of the vertical meridians of the two eyes from parallelism, the abscissa represents the various convergent positions of the eyes. In the experiment in which the data illustrated were obtained, the convergence was maintained on the horizontal plane, but the deviations from Listing's law during convergence were not confined to the horizontal meridian but were true of all other planes tested as well. The magnitude of the increase of excyclophoria with increasing convergence was found to increase with increased elevation of the plane of regard and to decrease with depression of the plane of regard. Interpretation of such results is, of course, complicated by the fact that one must first correct for the tilting of the vertical meridians predicted by Listing's law. On the other hand, if one considers only the measurements in the horizontal plane and can assume that the eyes were in the primary position when the convergence angle was zero,† then, according to Listing's law, the values for cyclophoria should, of

† Curiously enough when the plane of regard was depressed 40°, Landolt found almost no increase of cyclophoria with increased convergence. It seems quite improbable that this extreme position represents the primary position.

course, be the same irrespective of the angle of convergence. The data in the figure clearly show greater and greater amounts of excyclophoria with increasing convergence and the amount of the increase in cyclophoria can be regarded as a measure of the amount that Listing's law is invalid for the two eyes, under these particular conditions. The data suggest that the vertical meridians of each eye will deviate from the position predicted by Listing's law by more than one degree in each ten degrees of convergence of the eyes in the horizontal plane. Hering showed that positions of the vertical meridians of the two eyes with respect to each other in asymmetric convergence were essentially those assumed in equally large amounts of symmetrical convergence movements.

References

Allen, M. J. (1954). The dependence of cyclophoria on convergence, elevation and the system of axes. *Amer. J. Optom.* **31**, 297–307.

Berthold. (1865). Ueber die Bewegungen des kurzsichtigen. Auges. *v. Graefes Arch. Ophthal.* **11** (Abt. 3). 107–141.

Boeder, P. (1957). An analysis of the general type of uniocular rotations. *A.M.A. Arch. Ophthal.* **57**, 200–206.

Carow, R. (1939). Untersuchungen ueber die Naeherungsrollung und die Hebungs-Senkungsrollung der Augen. *v. Graefes Arch. Ophthal.* **140**, 86–115.

Donders, F. C. (1876). Versuch einer genetischen Erklaerung der Augenbewegungen. *Pflug. Arch. ges. Physiol.* **13**, 373–421.

Duke-Elder, W. S. (1939). "Textbook of Ophthalmology", Vol. IV. C. V. Mosby Company, St. Louis.

Fick, A. (1854). Die Bewegungen des menschlichen Augapfels. *Ztschr. rat. Medz. N. F.* **4**, 101–128.

Helmholtz, H. L. F. von (1925). "Helmholtz's Treatise on Physiological Optics" (Translated from the 3rd German Ed., J. P. C. Southall, ed.), Vol. III, pp. 37–123. The Optical Society of America, Rochester, New York.

Hering, E. (1868). "Die Lehre vom Binocularen Sehen", pp. 92–102. W. Engelmann, Leipzig.

Hering, E. (1879). Der Raumsinn und die Bewegungen des Auges. *In* "Handbuch der Physiologie" (L. Hermann, ed.), Vol. III, Teil 1, pp. 343–601. F. C. W. Vogel, Leipzig.

Hermans, T. G. (1943). Torsion in persons with no known eye defect. *J. exp. Psychol.* **32**, 307–324.

Lamb, H. (1919). The kinematics of the eye. *Phil. Mag.* Ser. 6, **38**, 685–695.

Landolt, E., cited by Aubert, H. (1876). Physiologische Optik. *In* "Handbuch der gesammten Augenheilkunde". (A. Graefe and T. Saemisch, eds.), Vol. II, p. 662. W. Engelmann, Leipzig.

Le Conte, J. (1881). "Sight; An Exposition of the Principles of Monocular and Binocular Vision", pp. 164–177. D. Appleton & Company, New York.

Marquez, M. (1949). Supposed torsion of the eye around the visual axis in oblique directions of gaze. *Arch. Ophthal., N.Y.* **41**, 704–717.

Meinong, A. (1898). Ueber Raddrehung, Rollung und Aberration; Beitraege zur Theorie der Augenbewegungen. *Z. Psychol. Physiol. Sinnesorg.* **18**, 161–204.

Meissner, G. (1860). Ueber die Bewegungen des Auges. *Ztschr. f. rat. Med.* 3rd ser. **8**, 1–47.

Moses, R. A. (1950). Torsion of the eye on oblique gaze. *Arch. Ophthal. N.Y.* **44**, 136–139.

Quereau, J. V. D. (1954). Some aspects of torsion. *A.M.A. Arch. Ophthal.* **51**, 783–788.

Quereau, J. V. D. (1955). Rolling of the eye around its visual axis during normal ocular movements. *A.M.A. Arch. Ophthal.* **53**, 807–810.

Schubert, G. (1924). Studien ueber das Listingsche Bewegungsgesetz am Auge. *Pflüg. Arch. ges. Physiol.* **205**, 637–668.

Tschermak-Seysenegg, A. (1952). "Introduction to Physiological Optics" (translated by P. Boeder). Charles C. Thomas, Springfield, Illinois.

Tscherning, M. H. E. (1900). "Physiologic Optics, Dioptrics of the Eye. Functions of the Retina, Ocular Movements, and Binocular Vision" (translated by C. Weiland). The Keystone Publishing Company, Philadelphia.

von Kries, J. (1925). Notes on #27 on the ocular movements. *In* "Helmholtz's Treatise on Physiological Optics" (translated from the 3rd German edition, J. P. C. Southall, ed.), Vol. III, pp. 127–154. The Optical Society of America, Rochester.

Weale, R. A. (1959). The problem of false torsion. *Proc. roy. Soc. Med.* **52**, 183–184.

Westheimer, G. (1957). Kinematics of the eye. *J. opt. Soc. Amer.* **47**, 967–974.

Chapter 4

Anatomical Aspects

I. Gross Anatomy of the Muscles that Move the Eye

There are six striated muscles attached to the outside of the eye. These contribute by their contraction to rotation of the globe. They are the so-called extra-ocular muscles and they have been named according to their location on the eyeball. They are: the medial (or internal) rectus, the superior rectus, the inferior rectus, the lateral (or external) rectus, the superior oblique and the inferior oblique.

A. Annulus of Zinn

The levator palpebrae (the muscle that elevates the upper eyelid) and five of the six extra-ocular muscles originate at the apex of the orbit. Here is formed a tendinous "ring" surrounding the optic foramen and its contents as well as the inferior and medial part of the superior orbital fissure and its contents. In general, any given muscle arises from that portion of the ring which roughly corresponds to the region of the eye into which that muscle inserts. The tendinous origin of these muscles at the orbital apex was called the *annulus tendineus communis* by Zinn. The inner and superior part, which is larger, surrounds the optic nerve while the lower and outer part surrounds the oculomotor nerve as it enters the orbit. The upper part of the annulus (or "ligament") of Zinn, as it is now frequently called, is formed mostly by the origin of the superior rectus with a portion of the origin running between the oculomotor and optic nerves as they enter, and emerge from the orbit, respectively. The median portion is formed first of all by the tendon of the medial rectus while superior to it and to the tendon of the superior rectus is the origin of the levator palpebrae superiorus. The tendon of the superior

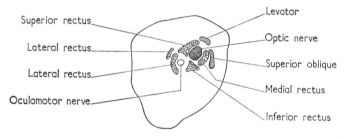

Superior rectus
Lateral rectus
Lateral rectus
Oculomotor nerve

Levator
Optic nerve
Superior oblique
Medial rectus
Inferior rectus

FIG. 1. The origin of the extra-ocular muscles at the apex of the orbit.

oblique is the most medial of all the tendons, being somewhat superior to the tendon of the medial rectus, perhaps a bit inferior to the tendon of the levator but considerably medial to both. The inferior rectus forms the lower portion of the annulus and some writers describe a portion of its tendon passing between the IInd and IIIrd cranial nerves also. The outer part of the annulus is formed by one of the heads of the lateral rectus, which also has a second origin, this one in the outer margin of the superior orbital plate of the sphenoid bone. These relationships are illustrated in Fig. 1 which has been modified after Howe (1907). The inner surface of the annulus is thickened in its upper and lower parts by two strong bands or *common tendons*.

The extra-ocular muscles as they emerge from their origins in the annulus of Zinn, move forward to attach to the globe, and since the eyeball is larger than the annulus, the muscles diverge as they go farther and farther forward. This divergence of the muscles as they leave the apex of the orbit forms a muscle cone which encloses a considerable amount of connective tissue, motor nerves, blood vessels and fat, in addition to the optic nerve and the posterior part of the globe. Since the roof of the orbit slopes, the origins of the medial and superior rectus muscles are on a plane somewhat anterior to that of the other four. The rectus muscles pass forward through the orbit fairly close to the walls of the cavity and insert into the sclera (after penetrating Tenon's capsule) with various widths of tendon and at various distances from the corneo-scleral margin.

B. MEDIAL RECTUS

The largest of the extra-ocular muscles is the medial rectus. Its tendon insertion in the globe is 8.8 mm. long and forms a line of insertion which is straight or, perhaps, slightly convex to the margin of the cornea and 5.5 mm. from it. The line of insertion is 10.3 mm. wide. The muscle itself is over 40 mm. in length, has a thickness of 1.6 mm., a volume of 709 mm.³, and weighs 0.747 g.† As it passes from the origin in the annulus of Zinn to the insertion in the sclera, the muscle lies close to the medial orbital wall and the plane of the muscle is such that its insertion in the sclera is more or less symmetrically distributed above and below the horizontal meridian of the eye.

C. LATERAL RECTUS

The same essential relation also exists for the lateral rectus muscle which inserts into the temporal sclera with a somewhat smaller line of insertion but again symmetrically distributed above and below the horizontal plane of the eye. The effect of these relations is that contraction of either the medial or lateral rectus muscle produces pure horizontal movements without vertical or torsional components when fixation is maintained in the horizontal plane.

The lateral rectus arises from both the lower and upper parts of the common tendon that bridges the sphenoidal fissure. The origin has the form of a U, the opening directed toward the optic foramen and the upper and lower heads of the muscle forming the limbs of the U. The muscle passes forward, separated from the lateral wall of the orbit at first only by a small amount of periorbital fat. Farther forward, however, it turns inward and passes along the outer surface of the globe, penetrating Tenon's capsule and inserting into the sclera at a distance of 6.9 mm. from the corneo-scleral margin with a tendon of 3.7 mm. long and a line of insertion of 9 mm. The muscle itself is longer than the medial and may be as long as 49 mm. in length. Its cross-sectional area, however, is less, being only around 26 mm.² instead of the 39 mm.² reported for the medial rectus.

---

† It hardly needs mentioning that all of these measurements will show wide individual differences. The quoted values should be regarded as a reasonable representation, useful for comparing values of one muscle to those of another.

D. Superior Rectus

The superior rectus arises in the superior part of the annulus with a slightly concave curve downward. Its position at the point of origin (as is also the case for the inferior rectus) lies considerably medial to the globe. Consequently, as the muscle moves forward towards its insertion, it also moves outwards, and the line connecting the middle of the origin and insertion actually makes an angle of about 23° with the medial orbital wall. Since the line of sight, when the eyes are in the straightforward position, is more or less parallel to the medial orbital wall, the line of action of the muscle also makes an angle of 23° to 25° with the line of sight when the eyes are in the straightforward position. This is of some importance for the understanding of the action of the vertical rectus muscles. The superior rectus muscle passes through the orbit above the globe but beneath the levator palpebrae. The muscle inserts into the sclera after passing over the tendon of insertion of the superior oblique muscle. The line of insertion of the superior rectus is somewhat oblique on the globe. It is 10.8 mm. long while the tendon is some 5.8 mm. long and terminates about 7.7 mm. from the limbus. This line is in the form of an arc slightly convex anteriorly, the centre of the line being rather to the inner side of the vertical meridian of the eye—and its inner end nearer the cornea than the outer end. The muscle has been described as 41.8 mm. long and 9.2 mm. wide. Contained within the superior rectus are considerably more elastic connective-tissue fibres than are found in the other eye muscles.

E. Inferior Rectus

It has already been emphasized that the inferior rectus, like the superior, has a line of action which makes an angle of about 23° with the line of sight when the eye is in the straightforward position. The inferior is the shortest of all the rectus muscles, being about 40 mm. long and 15.85 mm.[2] in cross-section according to the measurements of Volkmann. The centre of the line of insertion of this muscle is some 5.5 mm. from the cornea, the line of insertion being from 9.8 mm. to 10.3 mm. long but markedly convex anteriorly and always somewhat oblique (its inner end lies nearer to the cornea than does its temporal edge). The inferior oblique crosses beneath the inferior rectus muscle. The fascial sheath of the inferior rectus passes to that of the inferior oblique muscle as well as into the lower lid.

F. Obliques

In addition to the four rectus muscles there are two oblique muscles, one above the eyeball (the superior oblique) and one below (the inferior oblique).

Both oblique muscles effectively originate with the anterior medial corners of the orbit and the line of each muscle passes obliquely posteriorly to the posterior lateral part of the eyeball making an angle of from 50° to 55° with the medial wall of the orbit (and hence with the line of sight when the eye is in the primary position).

1. SUPERIOR OBLIQUE

The superior oblique, like all of the rectus muscles, originates at the apex of the orbit. It runs forward above the medial rectus almost to the orbital margin where at the angle between the roof and medial wall it becomes tendinous. At this point it passes through a cartilaginous pulley (the trochlea). Leaving the trochlea, it turns sharply backward laterally and downwards in the manner described above, passing back to the globe above the eyeball but beneath the superior rectus. This muscle thus has the longest tendon of any of the extra-ocular muscles. This tendon spreads out in a fan shaped manner to become attached obliquely in the posterior superior quadrant of the globe virtually directly lateral to the mid-vertical plane. The line of insertion is 10.7 mm. long convex backward and laterally. The anterior end of the line of insertion of the tendon falls about on the same meridian as the temporal end of the superior rectus.

2. INFERIOR OBLIQUE

The effective lines of action of the inferior and superior oblique muscles fall at about the same angle to the line of sight when the eye is in the straightforward position. The inferior oblique muscle, however, is the only one of the extra-ocular muscles which does not originate in the apex of the orbit at all. Its origin is a shallow depression in the orbital surface of the superior maxilla, a little behind the lower orbital margin and just external to the orifice of the naso-lacrimal duct. The muscle passes backward and laterally between the inferior rectus muscle and the floor of the orbit, and inserts into the eyeball after passing between this and the lateral rectus. Its insertion in the globe is the shortest tendon of any of the extra-ocular muscles. Some authorities state that it has no tendon at all. The line of insertion is oblique in the outer lower quadrant of the posterior part of the globe, concave downward, and some 7 to 9.5 mm. long. The anterior end of the tendon lies in approximately the same meridian as the lower end of the insertion of the lateral rectus. The posterior end of this tendon is about 3 mm. temporalward from the optic nerve and hence in the neighbourhood of the region of the sclera over the macula area of the retina. The muscle, like the other extra-ocular muscles, has very little connective tissue at its origin, but the closer that it approaches to its insertion the more the fibrous coverings increase in thickness and give off attachments to adjacent structures. In this way, the sheaths of

2

the two inferior extra-ocular muscles are connected to each other and to the suspensory ligament of Lockwood. Because the insertion of the inferior oblique is usually a few millimetres farther back than that of the superior oblique, the muscle planes of these two muscles do not exactly coincide (Fink, 1950). For clinical purposes, the discrepancy is ignored even though the differences in positions of these two planes may not always be small.

II. Innervation

The levator palpebrae and the superior rectus muscle are innervated by the superior division of the oculomotor (IIIrd cranial) nerve. The medial rectus, inferior rectus and inferior oblique muscles are innervated by the inferior division of this same nerve. The superior oblique muscle is innervated by the trochlear (IVth cranial) nerve and the lateral rectus muscle is innervated by the abducens (VIth cranial) nerve. Moreover, the motor nerve supplies to the extra-ocular muscles run concurrently with sensory fibres. Some of these sensory fibres are connected to the ophthalmic division of the trigeminal (N V) nerve—and in this way probably to the mesencephalic nucleus of N V (Cooper *et al.*, 1954). It has been suggested that other sensory fibres continue to the mid-brain in the oculomotor nerve, although afferent discharges in the intracranial portions of N III and N IV have not yet been demonstrated (Whitteridge, 1960).

III. Actions of the Ocular Muscles

A. Medial and Lateral Rectus

For convenience, the actions of the six extra-ocular muscles can be considered by looking at three distinct muscle groups. In the first group are the two horizontal rectus muscles. Since the line of action of these two muscles is coincident with the horizontal plane of the eye, the sole action of these muscles when the eye is in the straightforward position is to rotate the globe about a vertical axis, i.e., to produce a horizontal rotation of the eyeball. The medial rectus, of course, rotates the eye nasally, the lateral rectus, temporally.† In the straightforward position each of these muscles has only one action.

If the globe is in an elevated position, however, then contraction of either of the muscles in this group also acts to increase the elevation of the globe, and similarly when the eyeball is depressed, contraction of either of these two muscles acts to depress further the globe in addition to its effects on horizontal rotation.

† Nasal rotation is termed adduction; temporal rotation abduction.

B. Superior and Inferior Rectus

The second group consists of the two vertical rectus muscles. It has already been pointed out that the lines of action of these two muscles fall into essentially the same plane. This plane makes an angle of about 23° with the vertical plane through the line of sight when the eyes are in the straightforward position. The relationship is indicated in Fig. 2. It is clear from this figure that when the globe is in the straightforward position contraction of the vertical rectus muscles does not produce a simple deviation of the eye in only one plane (as does contraction of the horizontal rectus muscles). Rather,

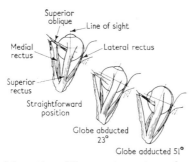

Fig. 2. The relation of the action of the superior rectus and superior oblique muscles to the various positions of the eyeball. (Modified after Adler, 1959.)

contraction of either vertical rectus muscle by itself would produce a movement in an oblique direction together with a rotation of the globe about the line of sight.† For convenience one can divide this complex movement into a horizontal, a vertical and a torsional component. Furthermore, one can classify these components into the *primary* actions of the muscle and *secondary* actions depending on the relative magnitude of the three components. When the eye is in the straightforward position, the primary action of the inferior and superior rectus muscles is in the vertical plane: the superior rectus elevating the globe when it contracts and the inferior rectus depressing the globe when it contracts. The secondary actions of the vertical rectus muscles, when the eye is in the straightforward position, are in the horizontal plane and in a rolling motion about the line of sight. Both the superior and inferior rectus muscles adduct the eye from the straightforward position but this secondary action, in each case, is rather slight; it increases, however, in each case as the eyes move nasally from the straightforward position. It reduces to zero as the eyes are abducted to 23°. If the eyes are abducted

† Rotations around the line of sight (i.e., torsions) are classified as *in*torsion or *ex*torsion as the top of the vertical corneal meridian moves nasalward or temporalward, respectively.

farther than 23°, the contraction of the vertical rectus muscles has a secondary action which effectively *abducts* the eyes.

1. TORSION

Torsional components are to be found in the contraction of the vertical rectus muscles also. In the straightforward position the contraction of the superior rectus produces an intorsion and the magnitude of this component of the movement increases as the eye is adducted. When the eye is adducted 67°, contraction of the superior rectus produces primarily an intorsion although some degree of further adduction should also occur. On the other hand, if the eye were abducted 23°, the contraction of the superior rectus would produce no torsion at all and if the eye were further abducted, contraction of the superior rectus muscles would produce an extorsion. The torsion component produced by contraction of the inferior rectus muscle is exactly opposite to that just described because this latter muscle is attached on the eye inferiorly. Hence, in the straightforward position, the contraction of the inferior rectus muscle produces a small amount of extorsion which gradually increases as the eye is adducted and this becomes the primary action of the muscle provided the eye is adducted 67°. When the eye is abducted 23°, contraction of the inferior rectus produces no torsion component at all and if the eye is abducted beyond this point, the torsional component produced by contraction of the inferior rectus is intorsion and the magnitude of this component increases the farther out the eye is abducted.

C. Oblique Muscles

The third group includes the two oblique muscles. The plane of action of these two muscles makes an angle of about 51° with the line of sight when the eye is in the straightforward position. Thus the primary action of both muscles with the eye in this position is the torsion component. For the superior oblique this is *in*torsion; for the inferior oblique this is *ex*torsion.

The primary action of either muscle is maximal when the eye is abducted 39° and becomes zero when the eye is adducted 51°. Since the oblique muscles attach to the posterior part of the globe, contraction causes the anterior part of the globe, i.e., the cornea, to move away from the muscle. Thus, in the straightforward position the contraction of the superior oblique has a secondary action of depression; contraction of the inferior oblique one of elevation. This secondary action increases as the eye is adducted and becomes maximum at the very position that the torsion component is a minimum (i.e., when the eye is adducted 51°). Temporal rotation, on the other hand, decreases the magnitude of this secondary action and it becomes zero when the line of pull of the muscle is normal to the line of sight, i.e., when the eye is abducted

39°. Contraction of the oblique muscles also has a component in the horizontal direction; in the straightforward position this is an abduction which decreases to zero when the line of action of the muscle becomes parallel to the line of sight (51° of adduction). The horizontal components of the two oblique muscles are the same.

On the basis of a number of assumptions (some of which are highly unlikely in the case of the living human eye), Krewson (1950) has estimated that when the eye is in the straightforward position, about 54 to 55% of the energy of muscular contraction is used for elevation or depression in the case of the vertical rectus muscles and only 26% for torsion: in the case of the obliques, these figures become 37% and 52% (superior) and 38% and 55% (inferior), respectively.

D. DIAGRAMMATIC SUMMARY

Many of these relations are easy to visualize with a diagram proposed by Ewald Hering (1879). Figure 3 illustrates the path that would be traversed

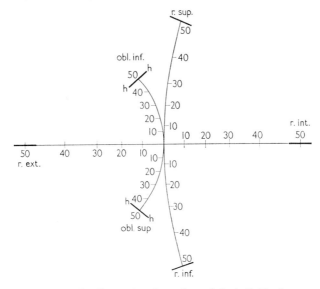

FIG. 3. Hering's schema for illustrating the actions of the individual eye muscles of the right eye.

on a frontal parallel plane by the line of sight if each muscle in turn was isolated and permitted to rotate the globe all by itself. The heavy marks at the end of each line represent the projection of a horizontal after-image of a light fixated in the primary position in order to illustrate the extent of torsion movements introduced by each muscle.

E. Combined Actions

While diagrams such as Fig. 3 are instructive in helping to understand the action of individual extra-ocular muscles, it would be misleading to expect that ductions of normal eyes occur by the activity of any single muscle alone. Sherrington (1893) showed many years ago that for conjugate movements, the medial rectus and lateral rectus of the same eye are reciprocally innervated. The demonstration of this phenomenon and its not inconsiderable clinical (as well as theoretical) implications, will be discussed at some length below. For the moment it means that when the eye looks nasally in a simple ballisti-form saccadic movement (cf. below) not only is the rotation effected by the contraction of the medial but by relaxation of the lateral rectus as well. Furthermore, the other four muscles, if they do not contract, at least actively maintain tone. In doing this the two vertical rectus muscles tend to prevent any torsion movement or vertical displacement, the two obliques also being antagonistic to one another in these two actions behave similarly while the abducting produced by the tonus of the obliques essentially neutralizes the adduction produced by the tonus of the two vertical rectus muscles. In this way, the movements of the globe are smoothly effected without any abrupt changes or irrelevant displacements having vertical or torsional com-ponents.

1. ELEVATION

In a simple elevation the superior rectus and inferior oblique work by active contraction with relaxation of their respective primary antagonists—the inferior rectus and the superior oblique. The horizontal and torsional com-ponents of these two antagonists more or less neutralize each other in the straightforward position. The medial and lateral rectus muscles neutralize one another in the horizontal plane while at the same time assisting in the elevation (once the globe is elevated) as they maintain normal tone. It has been proposed (Adler, 1959) that the superior rectus muscle is more strongly innervated than is the inferior oblique in such a movement in order to account for the fact that pure elevation from the primary position is not accompanied by any torsion at all. This explanation, however, has certain difficulties: if the right superior rectus is more strongly innervated than the right inferior oblique, one would also expect (according to Hering's † law) equally increased innervation to its yoked muscle of the other eye (the left inferior oblique). If this happened, elevation of the right eye would be associated with no torsion at all but yoked movement of the left eye would be associated with marked extorsion. This latter does not occur.

† A detailed discussion of this law of equal innervation to yoked muscles of the two eyes will be found in the Chapter on vergence movements.

2. OBLIQUE MOVEMENTS

Movement in oblique directions involves the active contraction of three muscles and the relaxation of their respective primary antagonists. For example, looking down and out is the primary action produced by contraction of the superior oblique. At the same time, the contraction of the lateral rectus moves the eye outward and (once a measure of depression has been achieved) further assists in the depression. The contraction of the inferior rectus assists in the depression but, at least at first, works against the abduction. This latter effect, however, becomes smaller and smaller as the globe is gradually abducted. It is to be anticipated that the contraction of these three muscles in this way would leave the eye intorted since the rolling action of the superior oblique would be enhanced while that of the inferior rectus would be reduced in the indicated tertiary position. It has already been pointed out, however, that the eye in the tertiary position (according to Listing's law) remains without cyclorotation with respect to the primary position. In some way this rolling action of the superior oblique must be counteracted. If it were by a differential contraction of the superior oblique as compared to the inferior rectus of this eye the requirements of Listing's law could be met but this would result in a marked cyclorotation for the other eye if it moved according to Hering's law of equal innervation to the yoked muscles. Just as is the case of pure elevation (or depression), the way such cyclorotations are avoided is not at all clear.

F. BINOCULAR MOVEMENTS

When the gaze is shifted the movements may be classified into two distinct classes depending upon whether or not the angle which the lines of sight of the two eyes make with each other remains constant. If it does, then the movement may be classified as a *version*; if it does not, one must call it a *vergence*.

When version movements occur the muscles of the two eyes work together. We shall see that this is also true for vergence but the muscles involved in the two situations differ. In version to the left the prime movers will be the lateral rectus of the left eye and the medial rectus of the right, while reciprocal inhibition will occur in the medial rectus of the left eye and the lateral rectus of the right. On the other hand, looking up and to the right is essentially the primary function of the inferior oblique of the right eye and the superior rectus of the left. While the movements in any direction of gaze are not, and cannot be, the function of any single muscle, the *prime movers* † in the various

† This diagram should not be confused with various diagrams which show the diagnostic positions of gaze. For example, to diagnose a limitation of movement produced by paralysis of the right inferior oblique, one rotates the eyes all the way to the left. Elevation of the right globe in this position can only be produced by the inferior oblique since the right superior rectus in this position has no ability to elevate the globe at all.

directions of gaze are of some clinical importance and so these relationships have been illustrated in Fig. 4.

Fɪɢ. 4. The relation of the prime movers in the various directions of gaze in the two eyes.

IV. Histology of the Extra-Ocular Muscles

A. Thick and Thin Fibres

The extra-ocular muscles contain muscle fibres that are extremely thin and may frequently be as fine as 0.009 or 0.011 mm in diameter. Not all the fibres in the eye muscles are as fine as this, however. Woollard (1931) has described three different sizes of muscle fibres, the thickest being two to three times that of the thinnest ones. Voss (1957), on the other hand, has suggested the ratio is 4 : 1. Woollard found the thickest fibres tend to occur in bundles of ten to fifteen. The most numerous fibres in these muscles were the medium thick fibres and these comprise the greater part of the muscle belly. The thinnest fibres are also very few in number and tend to be located towards the peripheral part of the muscle but some thin fibres can be seen throughout the muscle. The transition between the fibres of the medium to those of the thin group is gradual. Fixed contraction waves appear in both thick and thin fibres, and so the differences in fibre size are permanent features of the muscle fibre. The average cross-sectional area in the fibres of the superior rectus in five human eyes varied between $125\,\mu^2$ and $183.8\,\mu^2$. This may be as small as half the size of heart muscle fibres. There are about 0.5 to 0.92 nuclei in a square micron of cross-section of an eye muscle as compared to about the same number in heart muscle. On the other hand, the nuclei are only 7.3 to $7.5\,\mu^2$ in diameter while in heart muscle the figure varies from about 10 to $20\,\mu^2$. It has been suggested (Lockhart and Brandt, 1938) that the fibres of the extra-ocular muscles run the entire length of the muscle. Confirmatory evidence for this is lacking, however (Voss, 1957). Close to the tendons, almost all the fibres are small; in the belly the thin fibres are mostly to be found in the periphery while in the core of the muscle belly the fibres are much thicker.

B. ELASTIC FIBRES

The extra-ocular muscles are extremely rich in elastic tissue fibres which go to make up both the perimysium and the intermuscular septa separating individual muscle fibres. Schiefferdecker (1904) found the elastic fibres in the superior rectus to be extremely thick. They were so strong that he believed that it was just as correct to designate the superior rectus as an elastic band as it would be to call it a muscle. Schiefferdecker believed that this arrangement was responsible for a passive contraction of the muscle after it had been stretched by the active contraction of its antagonist. In this way the muscles would be under sufficient tension to have more efficient tone preliminary to action, and in the damping of movements produced by contraction of antagonist muscles. Both of these effects would be helpful in delicate regulation and smoothness of the movements of the globe.

C. RING BANDS

In the study of the histology of the extra-ocular muscles numerous authors have described ring bands (*Ringbinden*) of cross-striated muscle fibres that run around longitudinal muscle fibres. Some authors (Wohlfart, 1932, 1938; Cooper and Daniel, 1949) attribute them to a normal process of ageing. Voss (1957) found them only around thick muscle fibres in regions of the muscle where there are very few capillaries and believes that they are pathological changes.

D. RED AND WHITE FIBRES

The eye muscles have some fibres which are abundant in sarcoplasm (Irvine, 1936). This is a characteristic of *red* muscle fibres and indeed some histology textbooks (Jordan, 1947; Bremer, 1944) use the ocular muscles as a standard example of a muscle containing the most red muscle fibres. Red muscle fibres are thin and said to be slow acting. Some physiological textbooks (Amberson and Smith, 1948; Adler, 1959), however, describe the extrinsic ocular muscles as being made up *exclusively* of *white* muscle fibres. These are thicker, contain less sarcoplasm and are extremely fast acting. There can be little doubt that physiologically, as we shall see, the eye muscles behave in the way white muscle is supposed to (i.e., phasic responses, very rapid contraction time, etc.). Whether or not these physiological characteristics are indeed correlated with the anticipated histology is more or less academic. Modern histologists rarely use the red-white classification (Baker).

E. INNERVATION

The eye muscles are richly supplied with nerves. In human eye muscles one finds one nerve fibre for every two or three muscle fibres. Compare this

2*

to the ratio of one nerve to 50 muscle fibres in semitendinous muscles and to one nerve fibre for every 80 to 125 muscle fibres in the biceps femoris of the dog. Twenty-five years ago it was generally believed that the oculomotor, trochlea and abducens nerves were all purely motor. We know now, however, as a consequence of the histological studies of Daniel, 1946; Cooper and Daniel, 1949 and Wolter, 1954, 1955, among others, that the nerve fibre bundles that innervate the extra-ocular muscles contain many sensory as well as motor components. Histologically, one can differentiate the sensory from the motor nerves by the characteristics of the end organs, and these different forms of end organ are best seen by staining methods using silver, which has a particular affinity for nerve.

1. MOTOR FIBRES

Working in this way Wolter (1954, 1955) described three different kinds of centrifugal (i.e., motor) endings on the thick muscle fibres. The most obvious endings are the long varicose endings in the sarcoplasm. At the point of contact the ending is thickened into a sole plate. These are more or less typical motor end-plates. These motor plates contain in addition, small thin unmedullated nerve endings with loops in or outside the motor plate proper. This double innervation was described first by Boeke (1926) and he regarded them as representing innervation from both the skeletal and autonomic nervous systems. The typical motor ending has been described as a *terminaison en plaque*. A third kind of ending found on the thick muscle fibres is by a thin delicate network spread out upon the striated muscle fibre. These unmedullated nerve fibres appear to arise from the perivascular plexus rather than in the cranial nerve as do the other two types described. Wolter (1954) also found that the thin muscle fibres (of Woollard) had only innervation from the thin unmedullated nerve fibres and never from the *terminaisons en plaque*.

2. UNMYELINATED FIBRES

The thin delicate nerves with loop or bud-like endings described by Wolter have been seen by others in eye muscle. Woollard (1931) and Hines (1931) identified them with the *terminaisons en grappe* of Tschiriew (1879) and attributed to them a sensory function. Wolter, on the other hand, found evidence in the eye muscle of simple spiral endings and five forms of end-organs which do not end on muscle fibres at all—and hence are likely to be sensory in function. Wolter attributed an autonomic function to both types of unmedullated fibres that end on muscle fibres. Those that arise in the perivascular plexus he attributes to the sympathetic nervous system while those that descend with the medullated motor nerve he attributes to the parasympathetic nervous system. While these suggestions are unusual, there is evidence for this point of view. Working on superior oblique muscle of cats, Boeke

(1932) describes hypolemmal endings (an apparently reliable criterion of an efferent ending) from unmyelinated fibres with the knob-like form Wolter described. The fibres that made up these endings came from an unmyelinated bundle which remained intact after the section of IVth nerve although all of the myelinated fibres to the same muscle had degenerated. Unmyelinated nerve fibres have been traced from cervical segments of the sympathetic chain to the ocular muscles (Wolter) although stimulation of the cervical sympathetic ganglion does not routinely produce contraction of these muscles (Brecher and Mitchell, 1957). On the other hand, the ciliary ganglion has been destroyed and this results in degeneration among the muscle fibres of the extra-ocular muscles (inferior rectus, superior rectus and inferior oblique), (Kure *et al.*, 1927). It has also been found by Armaly (1959) that electrical stimulation of the ciliary ganglion can produce contraction of the extra-ocular muscles.

3. VERGENCE AND VERSION

Since Wolter did not find the rich nerve supply and the extremely fine muscle fibres of the eye muscle in other muscles, such as the levator, it occurred to Alpern and Wolter (1956) that the fine unmedullated nerve fibres that run along with the thick motor nerves to the muscles might well represent the final common path for certain kinds of eye movement. They suggested that the slow vergence movements of the eyes (cf. below) were produced by excitation of these fibres, while the thick medullated fibres formed the final common path for more rapid version movements. This rather unorthodox proposal has the advantage, as Adler has pointed out, that it emphasizes the essential difference in these two kinds of eye movements. The time characteristics of the two are, of course, quite different. Moreover, disorders of the central nervous system may produce paralysis of version movements while vergence movements in the identical directions are left intact. Conversely, vergences may be completely paralysed while versions are perfectly normal. This hypothesis also provides a basis for the understanding of the ability of an eye muscle to carry out a yoked movement together with a muscle of the other eye at one moment and immediately following, during the same change of fixation, carry out a second yoked movement with the latter muscle's antagonist (Figs. 14 and 22, Chapter V). The ability of the eyes to complete this rather amazing performance must involve a highly complex neuromuscular co-ordination system and it is possible that this rather unusual hypothesis is the most reasonable explanation.

4. SENSORY ENDINGS

In addition to efferent endings, a variety of sensory endings have also been described on human extra-ocular muscles. The *terminaisons en grappe* have already been mentioned. These are epilemmal grape-like endings. In many animal eye muscles they occur in rather extensive clusters and some (but by no means all) authors have attributed to them a sensory function (Hines, 1931). A large variety of nerve endings have been found in eye muscles on non-muscular tissue and it has therefore been assumed that such endings must serve a sensory function. Wolter (1955) describes at least five different varieties of these. Golgi tendon-organs have also been reported in the eye muscles of man although Golgi himself never demonstrated them despite some attempts. They appear in the anterior musculo-tendinous junction. They are found extensively distributed in the eye muscles of the cat (Huber, 1900) but apparently not in those of the rabbit (Hines, 1931).

a. Spindles

In 1946 Daniel, using silver techniques, demonstrated what appeared to be simple spiral sensory end-organs in the extra-ocular muscles of man. These results have been again confirmed histologically by Wolter (1954, 1955). Daniel (1946) described only simple and multiple spiral endings. In a simple spiral ending the nerve fibre, surrounded by its Schwann and myelin sheaths, makes from three to eight complete spiral turns around a single small muscle fibre and ends in finger-like processes in an end-plate resembling a motor end-plate or in some cases comes to a single fine point with no obvious relation to the nucleus. In the multiple spiral endings a thick medullated fibre approaching a muscle fibre (usually a large or medium sized one) divides into two or more fine fibrils on either side of the muscle fibre and encircles ". . . much as the thumb and fingers of a hand encircle a tube in grasping it" (Daniel, 1946).

In 1949, Cooper and Daniel used silver methods and found clear evidence of ordinary muscle spindles in the human extra-ocular muscles. This finding was almost immediately confirmed by Merrillees *et al.* (1950) and there seems little reason for doubting the generality of these findings in the case of human material. Surprisingly enough, human eye muscles are really quite richly supplied with these spindles, a single rectus muscle may contain as many as fifty. This supply is as ample as one finds even in the most richly innervated skeletal muscle. Most of these are concentrated near the origin of the eye muscle and this probably explains why some investigators (for example, Wolter, 1954, 1955) who studied only the belly of the muscle near the region where the motor nerve enters, failed to detect them. Merrillees *et al.*, however, also found them occasionally in the middle one-third of the muscle. The muscle spindles of the eye muscles contain a thin capsule which encloses within it several intrafusal muscle fibres (anywhere from one to fifteen, but about four on the average). These intrafusal fibres are somewhat thinner than the extrafusal (ordinary muscle) fibres. They vary in thickness between 5 and 30 μ being about 10 μ on average. The muscle spindles of the eye muscles are richly innervated probably with both sensory and motor nerves. These spindles may be anywhere from 50 to 1640 μ long but are about 0.9 mm. on the average, almost 30% of them exceed 1 mm. in length, however. Their diameter is between 20 and 100 μ.

5. FIBRE SIZES

Recently Donaldson (1960) has made a very careful count of the fibre sizes in the intracranial portion of the nerves to the eye muscles of the goat. He has found a bimodal frequency distribution in fibre size. One of these peaks occurs at 11–17 μ and these fibres undoubtedly represent the motor nerves to the extrafusal muscle fibres. A second peak occurred at 4 to 6 μ and Donaldson suggests that these fibres innervate the intrafusal muscle fibres. These small fibres constitute 30% of the total number of fibres in the nerve.[†] While the length of the nerve fibres was too short for Donaldson to measure conduction velocity, it seems likely, on the basis of physiological evidence to be discussed below, that some of these fibres are exactly similar to the gamma efferent fibres extensively studied in other skeletal muscle (Hunt and Kuffler, 1951; Eldred et al., 1953). Donaldson estimates that there are about 8 to 11 gamma efferent nerve fibres in the motor nerve to the inferior oblique muscle for each muscle spindle.

V. Neurology of Movements of the Eyes

A. RECIPROCAL INNERVATION

In certain types of eye movement the agonist and antagonist are reciprocally innervated. Electromyographic data verify this completely but the facts were quite well known long before the days of electrical recording of the activity of eye muscles. The experiment that most lucidly emphasized this fact was first described by Sherrington (1894). The cranial nerves III and IV of an experimental animal such as the monkey (which has frontally placed eyes) were cut on one—say, the left—side. Following degeneration of the motor nerves the operated eye diverged due to the unopposed action of the left lateral rectus. If now the region of left cerebral cortex that in normal animals produces conjugate deviation of both eyes to the right was stimulated, the left eye moved to the right but only so far as the mid-line. This

---

[†] It is possible that some of these small diameter fibres are the thin unmedullated fibres which innervate extrafusal muscle fibres as described by Boeke (1932) and Wolter (1954).

demonstrates that the inhibition of the lateral rectus is part of the rotation of the left eye to the right—a reciprocal innervation of the antagonistic muscles. Inhibition of the antagonist is characteristic not only of conjugate eye movements (i.e., saccades) but also of vergence movements as well. McCouch and Adler (1932) demonstrated it also in the nystagmus associated with caloric stimulation of the ear even when the globe was removed and the muscles attached to levers. However, it is not a feature of the muscles of the eyelid as Sherrington (1894) clearly demonstrated in one of his early preparations.

B. The Nuclei of the Motor Nerves of the Eye

The extra-ocular muscles are innervated by the IIIrd, IVth and VIth cranial nerves. There seems to be little doubt that fibres from the abducens nucleus innervate the homolateral lateral rectus while those from the trochlear nucleus innervate the contralateral superior oblique. The nucleus of N VI is a small spherical mass in the tegmental portion of the pons. It is the most caudal of the nuclei of the motor nerves to the eye. Rostral to this is the nucleus of the IVth nerve in the periaqueductal grey matter deep to the upper part of the inferior colliculus but dorsomedial to the medial longitudinal fasciculus, lateral and somewhat ventral to the aqueduct of Sylvius.

The oculomotor (IIIrd) nucleus lies in the grey substance ventral to the aqueduct. It is from 6 to 10 mm. in length, extending from the floor of the third ventricle caudally to the level of the trochlear nucleus and is intimately related to the medial longitudinal fasciculus, which lies against its ventral aspects.

There seems to be no very strong disagreement about the relations that have just been described. However, there is considerable amount of discrepancy among the descriptions of the rostral nuclei with reference to the relation of the various cell masses in the nucleus of the IIIrd cranial nerve to the respective extra-ocular muscles.

1. SUBDIVISION OF OCULOMOTOR NUCLEUS

Although the problem has been under serious consideration for over one hundred years, the controversy cannot be considered settled. The schema of Bernheimer, as modified by Brouwer (1918), was a cephalocaudal arrangement within which the nuclei were located in the following order: *a.* pupil sphincter, *b.* levator, *c.* superior rectus, *d.* medial rectus, *e.* inferior oblique, and *f.* inferior rectus. Brouwer also proposed that a mid-line nucleus (of Perlia) medial to the nucleus of the medial rectus of the two sides of the brain subserved convergence. While this description has not been confirmed by more recent studies on animal eyes, it is in harmony with clinical observations on patients in whom elevation of the gaze appears to be affected first in tumours in the anterior part of the brain-stem.†

Of the attempts to solve this problem by physiological methods, the experiments of Szentágothai (1942) on cats and dogs, Bender and Weinstein (1943) on monkeys, and Danis (1948) on cats may be pointed out. These investigators stimulated the brain-stem electrically using a stereotaxic apparatus in order to locate the position of the electrodes. They deduced the muscle of relevance from the eye movement which was observed. The results obtained by Szentágothai give the rostrocaudal arrangement illustrated in Fig. 5. The difference between this organization and that suggested by

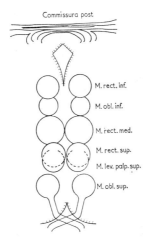

FIG. 5. Arrangement of the oculomotor nuclei according to the schema of Szentágothai (1942).

Brouwer is obvious. Bender and Weinstein (1943) published their results about this same time. They describe the following arrangement which they regard as being both dorsoventral and rostrocaudal: *a*. sphincter of the pupil, *b*. inferior rectus, *c*. ciliary muscle, *d*. inferior oblique, *e*. medial rectus, *f*. superior rectus, *g*. levator, and *h*. superior oblique (contralateral). Danis (1948) found no dorsoventral arrangement at all. His rostrocaudal arrangement does not differ too much from that illustrated in Fig. 5 except that he placed the portion innervating the inferior oblique behind that of the superior rectus. Danis regarded the transition from the nucleus of one muscle to the next to be quite gradual. While physiological measurements such as those

† Such evidence, however, should be viewed with some reservation since pressure differentials may well be distributed differently in different regions of the central nervous system and in this event the regions affected earliest by a tumour may not necessarily be those closest to it.

just described do not permit a decision as to whether or not such innervation is homolateral, contralateral or bilateral, Szentágothai, Bender and Weinstein, and Danis, all regarded the IIIrd nerve complex as completely homolateral.

Warwick (1953) approached this problem by sectioning the nerves to individual muscles and then studying the retrograde degeneration as revealed by chromatolysis of the cells in the oculomotor nucleus which then occurred. The results of this study on sixty-one monkeys are illustrated in Fig. 6. It is

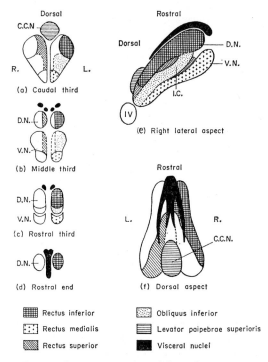

Dorsal

C.C.N

R.   L.

(a) Caudal third

D.N.

V.N.

(b) Middle third

D.N.

V.N.

(c) Rostral third

D.N.

(d) Rostral end

Rostral

Dorsal ————— D.N.

——— V.N.

I.C.

IV

(e) Right lateral aspect

Rostral

L.   R.

C.C.N.

(f) Dorsal aspect

▦ Rectus inferior   ⁚⁚ Obliquus inferior
⁛ Rectus medialis   ▤ Levator paipebrae superioris
▧ Rectus superior   ■ Visceral nuclei

Fig. 6. Diagrams showing the representation of the right extrinsic eye muscles in the oculomotor nucleus of the monkey according to Warwick (1953). Transverse sections shown in Fig. *a* to *d*. D.N. = dorsal nucleus; V.N. = ventral nucleus; C.C.N. = caudal central nucleus; I.C. = intermediate column; IV = trochlear nucleus.

evident that the results of this anatomical study differ in important ways from previous data. In the first place, there is both a dorsoventral and a rostrocaudal arrangement. The nuclei instead of being small circumscribed masses actually extend over large areas.

Crosby and Woodburne (1943) found little evidence at all for a mid-line nucleus (of Perlia) in the macaque mid-brain. Warwick (1955) verified this and also found only poor development of this feature in chimpanzee and man.

Where it did occur it did not represent internuncial neurons or neurons to the medial rectus but lower motor neurons for the superior rectus and inferior oblique. This does not support the idea that Perlia's nucleus is related to convergence as Brouwer believed.

In Warwick's schema the nucleus of the superior rectus is contralateral to the muscle that its nerve innervates, and the levator has only a single mid-line nucleus for both sides. It is the most caudal of all the nuclei in the oculo-motor complex. Its position is in sharp contradiction to the arrangement suggested by Brouwer in which the levator and superior rectus nuclei are at the rostral end of IIIrd nerve complex.

Summary

With the sharp disagreement between the various schemes used to describe these nuclei, it seems impossible for one who has not studied the problem experimentally to make any reasonable guess as to the most likely arrangement in normal man. Experiments involving electrical stimulation have the obvious disadvantage that the technique may result in the stimulation of fibres as well as cells. This perhaps is not a major source of error in the present instance because the areas outlined in Fig. 5 seem to be much less diffuse than are the areas in Fig. 6, which did not involve electrical stimulation at all. Chromatolysis seems to be a reliable technique, although in certain parts of the central nervous system (e.g., the lateral geniculate nucleus) trans-neuronal degeneration has been known to occur. Under these circumstances it is not possible to make any definitive statement of the pattern of the oculomotor nuclei. It seems likely that Warwick's work is most free of possible errors and most readily capable of extrapolation to normal man.

It is possible, but unlikely, that all of the above schemes are correct, and equally possible (and equally unlikely) that no pattern at all exists. It is apparent that the independent duplication of one or the other of the above experimental findings represents one of the more pressing problems in the neurology of eye movements. In such work it seems of value to assess eye muscle activity not (as has usually been the case in the physiological experi-ments) by extrapolation from observations of gross eye movements but by myographic study of small amounts of muscle activity. Perhaps such an approach will explain some of the major differences between results like those illustrated in Fig. 6 and those illustrated in Fig. 5.

C. The Supranuclear Relationships

In the reticular grey matter adjacent to the abducens nucleus, and inter-mingled with the abducens neurons, are small associative cells. These cells make up the parabducens nucleus. These cells send processes across the adjacent abducens nucleus forward to the nucleus of the medial rectus of the opposite side *via* the medial longitudinal fasciculus. It is not certain whether the crossing of these fibres occurs before or after they enter the medial longitudinal fasciculus. Both results have been described and the arrangement may well be different in different species. Stimulation of fibres that enter the parabducens and abducens nucleus is associated with rotation of both eye, horizontally toward the side of stimulation (Crosby, 1953). Consequently, such terms as the "centre of conjugate horizontal gaze," or "the pontine centre of conjugate lateral gaze" (Cogan, 1948) have frequently been used to describe the origin of such fibres. However, modern anatomists attempt to avoid such concepts (Crosby).

1. VESTIBULAR APPARATUS

Activity of the vestibular apparatus, as we shall see, has a profound influence upon the activity of the eye muscles. While the detailed morphological basis for these effects is still a matter of some dispute, it is apparent that, in the monkey, connexions are to be found between the medial and caudal two-thirds of the lateral vestibular nuclei through the contralateral medial longitudinal fasciculus to terminate in the abducens and parabducens nuclei (Crosby, 1953). Moreover, fibres to the nuclei of the IVth and IIIrd nerves ascend in the homolateral medial longitudinal fasciculus from the superior and rostral end of the lateral vestibular nuclei. Since stimulation of these portions of the vestibular complex produces (depending upon the exact location of the electrodes) elevation or depression of both eyes it seems quite likely that these fibres terminate bilaterally within the nuclei.

The superior vestibular nucleus sends fibres to the homolateral nuclei of the eye muscles by way of the homolateral medial longitudinal fasciculus. All of these pathways are thought to be excitatory (Szentágothai, 1952). Szentágothai and Scháb (1956) found, however, that the contraction of the eye muscles (left inferior rectus and right superior oblique) in response to stimulation of the right posterior crista acoustica with artificial endolymph currents could be inhibited by stimulation of the left nucleus of Darkschewitsch (i.e., the anterior periaqueductal grey matter of the mid-brain). These authors believe that inhibitory influences from the vestibular nuclei do not reach the final common path of the eye motor nerves directly but are relayed there by this anterior inhibitory region.†

Figure 7 summarizes this view. In the figure the primary vestibular neuron (1) stimulates the neuron (2), the axons from which pass in the medial longitudinal fasciculus to the final common path of the nerve to the superior

---

† Lesions in Darkschewitsch nucleus do not result in degeneration of terminal bouton synapses in the oculomotor nuclei and Szentágothai and Scháb believe, therefore, that this kind of a synapse must be purely excitatory.

rectus. At the same time the primary vestibular neurons stimulate vestibular neurons (3) of another type which reach Darkschewitsch nucleus (D. nu.) by paths other than the medial longitudinal fasciculus. The black arrows in this figure represent inhibition exerted by this nucleus on the neuron to the inferior rectus. The hatched arrows indicate other possible inhibitory influences which Darkschewitsch nucleus may exert on neurons which send fibres to the eye muscles.

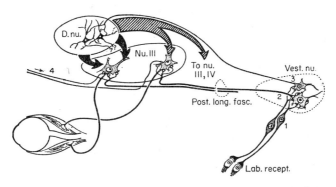

FIG. 7. The nerve pathways that serve as the basis of the reciprocal inhibition in the elementary vestibulo-ocular reflex arc according to Szentágothai and Scháb (1956).

2. CEREBELLUM

Lesions in the cerebellum are known to produce nystagmus. This nystagmus differs from that observed as a result of stimulation of the vestibular apparatus in that it appears only as the eyes are directed to positions other than the straightforward position. Undoubtedly impulses from the cerebellum reach eye muscles directly and/or indirectly. This occurs both by way of the cerebellar-vestibular connexions and by other pathways.

3. SUPERIOR COLLICULUS

In subprimates the superior colliculus plays an important part in movements of the eyes. In lightly anesthetized cats Apter (1946) applied strychnine to a localized (1 mm.^{2}) area of the right superior colliculus. If a light were then flashed into the eyes, both eyes moved to fixate a single point in the left visual field irrespective of the eye position at the beginning of the movement. These responses have been called "goal directed" by Hyde and Eliasson (1957). The position of the "goal" varied with the region of the superior colliculus stimulated and a map of the relation of the "goals" on the surface of the superior colliculus more or less coincided with the electrophysiological map of the visual field on the superior colliculus. Horizontal deviations result from discharge from one superior colliculus over the medial tectobulbar pathway to the contralateral abducens nucleus and thence to the homolateral medial rectus by way of the medial longitudinal fasciculus. While this pattern probably remains also for higher primates and man, it is overlaid and perhaps inhibited by activity from cortical areas in normal man.

4. TEGMENTUM AND MEDULLA

"Goal directed" responses were obtained in the encephale isolé (cat) by Hyde and Eliasson (1957) from electrical stimulation of rather extensive regions of the brain-stem. These include not only nuclei and fibre tracts already described, but more extensive regions in the tegmental reticular region as well.

5. INTERRELATIONSHIPS

Hyde (1960) has attempted to decide the relative functional dominance of some of these areas by stimulating simultaneously two areas each of which when stimulated alone produced eye movements directed to a different goal. Stimulation of superior colliculus and dorsal tegmentum of the mid-brain alone produced contralateral conjugate deviations; stimulation of the medial reticular substance produced a rotation of the eyes towards the side of the response. When two points (which when stimulated alone turned the eyes to different goals) were stimulated simultaneously, one of three reactions was observed: (a) the eyes assumed a position intermediate to the two different goals; (b) the eyes oscillated between the two goals; or (c) the eyes rotated toward the identical goal that they had turned to when one of the two areas was stimulated alone. If it can be assumed that the first two responses represented functional equivalence and the last functional dominance, then Hyde found the following hierarchy of dominance for conjugate eye deviations: (i) medial reticular substance of the medulla, (ii) dorsal mid-brain tegmentum, and (iii) superior colliculus. The implications of these findings are somewhat obscured by the fact that one cannot be certain whether she was stimulating cells or fibre tracts or both.

6. VERTICAL MOVEMENTS

While the relationships that have just been described give an idea of the complexity of the mid-brain nuclei influencing movements of the eyes, it would be a mistake to assume that the above description is exhaustive. A number of authors, for example, have suggested that mid-brain nuclei exert an extensive control over vertical eye movements. Szentágothai (1950) believed that the interstitial nucleus of Cajal and Darkschewitsch nucleus may be important in this respect. Figure 8 illustrates the schema suggested from his stimulation and degeneration experiments on anaesthetized cats and dogs. It illustrates a highly simplified diagram of the pathways associated with stimulation of the superior retina and the consequent reflex depression of the globe that follows. In this figure *a* and *c* represent frontal and occipital eye fields (see below), respectively; *d* and *b* represent the lateral geniculate nucleus and visual cortex along the afferent pathways (dotted line). In these animals the afferent pathways also terminate in the superior colliculus, *e* (Apter, 1946). Darkschewitsch nucleus, *f*, the oculomotor nuclei, *g*, and

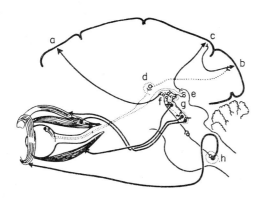

Fɪɢ. 8. Schematic diagram illustrating the nerve pathways associated with depression of the globe in consequence of stimulation of the superior retina, according to Szentá-gothai (1950).

the facial nucleus, *h*, all participate in the resulting movement (the latter by relaxation of the orbicularis below). The plus sign in the figure represents facilitation and the minus sign inhibition. Stimulation in the region of the nucleus of Darkschewitsch and the interstitial nucleus of Cajal was related to co-ordinated contraction of muscles which elevate and depress the globe and relaxation of the antagonists (including the lid muscles).

Szentágothai and Scháb (1956) showed, however, that lesions in Dark-schewitsch nucleus did not result, for example, in degeneration of terminal boutons in the oculomotor nuclei. There are many difficulties associated with extrapolating the results from experiments involving electrical stimulation of anesthetized subprimates to the physiological processes in living man and so one can only regard the diagram in Fig. 8 as being tentative.

Bender and Shanzer (1960) made small lesions in the pretectum or upper mid-brain. When these lesions were bilateral, paralysis of upward and downward gaze or isolated paralysis of upward gaze was obtained. Unilateral lesions in these areas did not produce paralysis of vertical gaze but normal vestibular nystagmus in the vertical plane was defective under these conditions.

D. Cerebral Cortex

The stimulation of the cerebral cortex with low intensity electrical currents produces conjugate eye movements. The kind of eye movements obtained depends, among other factors, upon the species studied, the parameters of stimulation and the degree of anesthesia. The most informative pattern was obtained in lightly anesthetized monkeys and is illustrated in Fig. 9, which is a diagram of the left hemisphere of the macaque. The eye movements elicited

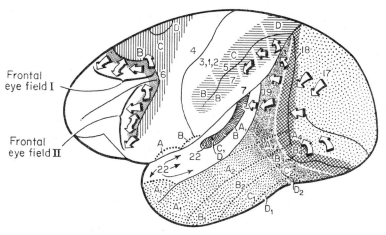

Fig. 9. Pattern of eye movements evoked by electrical stimulation of the left hemisphere of the macaque brain according to Crosby *et al.* (1959). Eye movements are indicated by the arrows; the direction of the conjugate movement is indicated by the direction the arrow points except that horizontal arrows indicate that an eye movement towards the other side was evoked upon electrical stimulation of this particular cortical area.

in studies of Crosby and Henderson (1948); Henderson (1949); Crosby *et al.* (1952); Henderson and Crosby (1952); and Crosby, (1953) and described in Crosby *et al.* (1959) are indicated by the arrows, which also illustrate the direction of eye movement elicited by electrical stimulation of these brain areas.

1. OCCIPITAL EYE FIELDS

There are two basic cortical areas for eye movements. The first of these is located in the occipital (area 17 and 18) and preoccipital (area 19) cortex. It is thought to be related to automatic eye movements such as pursuit (following) movements. The second, which is thought to be related to so-called voluntary eye movements, is in area 8 of the frontal cortex. In each case there is a pattern of movement related to a given small part of the cortex. In the occipital area this is related to the projection of the visual field on these same areas. Thus, the right half of the visual field projects to the left occipital cortex and stimulation of the left occipital cortex produces conjugate deviations of both eyes to the right. In a similar way, the inferior visual field is represented on the superior lip of the calcarine fissure (and vice versa) and stimulation of the superior part of the occipital eye fields is related to downward rotation of the eyes.

In the macaque brain the distinction between area 17 and area 18 is not very clear. In man, however, the distinction is definite enough, and, in this case, the motor fibres whose axons pass to the mid-brain have their cell bodies in area 18 only, although these cells are connected by internuncials to area 17. In a similar way, the preoccipital eye fields are connected to the occipital eye fields by internuncials but the pattern related to vertical eye movements in area 19 is reversed in comparison to the pattern in area 18. Crosby and Henderson found that stimulation of area 19 was still associated with conjugate deviations to the opposite side but the superior part of the preoccipital eye field was related to elevation of the eyes, the inferior part to their depression. Stimulation of the middle part of area 19, on the left side, was associated with a conjugate deviation of the eyes to the right and stimulation of areas intermediate to those mentioned results in a combined movement.

Wagman *et al.* (1958) have verified most of these observations. They did not observe the upwards movement caused by stimulation at the tip of the lunate fissure but there is some question as to whether or not they stimulated in this area. Moreover, they deny any reversal of patterns of eye movements between areas 18 and 19. This may be due to the fact that they used the lunate fissure as the line of demarcation between areas 18 and 19, whereas (cf. Fig. 9) 18 extends on either side of the lunate fissure. The reversal of eye movement pattern occurs farther forward in area 19 in a region in which Wagman *et al.* apparently did not stimulate (Crosby *et al.*, 1959).

a. Corticofugal Pathways

The pathways from the occipital eye fields to the tectum—the internal corticotectal tract—is divided into a preoccipital and occipital division depending upon whether the nuclei of origin of the relevant fibres are in area 19 or area 18, respectively. Fibres from the superior part of area 19 and the inferior part of the occipital eye-fields discharge to the rostral and medial portions of the superior colliculus. The lateral and caudal parts of this nucleus receive fibres from the ventral preoccipital area and the upper occipital areas. Those parts of the area 18 and area 19 which are concerned with horizontal movements perhaps also discharge to the colliculus, but this discharge is probably inhibitory, preventing reflex discharge of this region to conjugate horizontal deviations. The major descending fibres from areas in the occipital and preoccipital eye fields, which produce horizontal eye deviations on stimulation, by-pass the superior colliculus and end in the contralateral abducens nucleus. Here discharge sets off the usual arcs and these produce contraction of the contralateral lateral rectus muscle and the homolateral medial rectus muscle and conjugate gaze to the opposite side. It has been reported that stimulation of the appropriate preoccipital and occipital areas did not produce the change in horizontal gaze when the vestibular nuclei were destroyed bilaterally. Anatomical evidence for a connexion between the eye fields of the occipital cortex and the vestibular nuclei, however, is not well established.

2. FRONTAL EYE FIELDS

The pattern of responses obtained by stimulation of the left frontal eye field is also illustrated in Fig. 9. This pattern extends over the lateral surface of the frontal lobe beginning near the superior sagittal sinus ventralward along the front border of the arcuate fissure to a region dorsal to the lateral fissure. The dorsoventral extent of this area is divided into two parts by the principal fissure. The pattern below the principal fissure is a mirror image of that above it. The distinction between the two groups is not clear but it has been suggested that they represent the major area for conjugate deviation and a second or supplementary motor area, such as have also been described for other types of movement patterns.† Bilateral stimulation of the frontal eye fields in the region which, on unilateral stimulation evokes a movement up and to the other side, causes a movement straight up; bilateral stimulation in the region, which on unilateral stimulation causes the eyes to move in a conjugate deviation to the other side, causes the gaze to assume an "eyes front" position.

The arrangement in the macaque frontal cortex is somewhat different from that in man but the basic patterns still persist. The comparison of the two has been made by Lemmen et al. (1959), who were able to observe eye movements on stimulation of the frontal eye fields in man during surgery. Figure 10 shows two drawings of the left cerebral cortex from their paper, the upper representing the arrangement seen in man, the lower that found in macaque. The numbers represent the eye movements obtained: (1) conjugate movements up and to the opposite side (right); (2) conjugate movement to the right; (3) divergences; (4) conjugate movement down and to the right; (5) no response; (6), (7) and (8) represent hand, finger, thumb and lip movements; and, (9) represents the longitudinal sinus. The difference in the

† If the lateral rectus of the right and the medial rectus of the left eyes are cut, the eyes deviate to the left. It has been pointed out that Sherrington showed that stimulation of the left frontal eye field in this case caused the eyes to rotate to the right as far as the midline. Apparently, however, this is true only if the area below the principal fissure is stimulated. If the area above the principal fissure which normally produces horizontal conjugate deviations is stimulated, then no such movement of the eyes to the mid-line is obtained (Crosby, 1953). Apparently the reciprocal inhibition of eye muscles is functionally distinct in the two frontal eye fields.

topographical patterns demonstrated in man and monkey is probably related to the additional human cortical development in the rostral frontal lobe and in the speech areas in the inferior frontal gyrus.

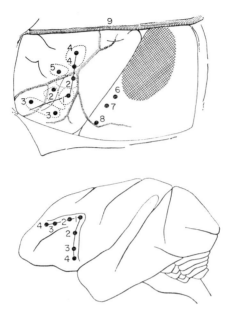

FIG. 10. Pattern of eye movements evoked by stimulation of the left frontal eye fields in man (above) compared to that found in macaque according to Lemmen *et al.* (1959).

a. Corticofugal Pathway

Fibres have been traced in the monkey brain from the region in the frontal eye fields producing horizontal conjugate deviations through the genu of the internal capsule into the base of the mid-brain. These fibres begin leaving the pyramidal system at oculomotor levels and gradually enter the medial lemniscus. They are joined by fibres from the pyramidal system at the level of the pons and the combined bundle passes across the mid-line to the contralateral abducens nucleus. From this, the lateral rectus on the same side as the relevant abducens nucleus and the medial rectus of the opposite side (by way of the parabducens nucleus and the medial longitudinal fasciculus) are again innervated. The pattern for horizontal conjugate deviation, which has already been described at mid-brain levels, is repeated. In this way, the right frontal cortex causes deviation of both eyes to the left. Crosby *et al.* (1952) demonstrated that fibres from the lower half of the apex of the frontal eye fields pass to the anterior third of the mid-brain tegmentum and discharge to the oculomotor nucleus of the opposite side. These fibres are presumably related to vertical conjugate eye movements. In Fig. 11 are illustrated some of the relations between the frontal, preoccipital and occipital eye fields and the mid-brain nuclei according to Crosby *et al.* (1959).

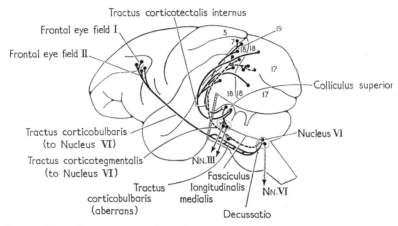

FIG. 11. The relation between frontal, preoccipital and occipital eye fields and the mid-brain nuclei for eye movements according to Crosby *et al.* (1959).

3. CORTICAL INTERCONNEXIONS

In addition to the relation of the eye fields of the cerebral cortex to the brain-stem oculomotor nuclei, these fields are in close relation to one another, although the physiological implications are still not well understood. Apparently, in man, area 17 is connected to area 18 in such a way that the lower part of 17 (superior contralateral visual field) discharges directly to the lower part of area 18 (eye movements up and to the opposite side), the superior part of area 17 is similarly related to the superior part of 18 and so on. Crosby and Henderson (1948) found that the pattern in area 19 is reversed from that of area 18 so that nerve fibres pass from superior 18 to inferior 19 and from inferior 18 to superior 19, in keeping with the reversed pattern. There are also internuncial neurons directly forward from 18 to 19 but these probably are inhibitory. There is no evidence of direct connexions between area 17 and area 19.

Moreover, the occipital eye fields discharge by fibre-pathways to the frontal eye fields. Interference with these pathways has been known to cause a homonymous hemianopsia. Crosby (1953) believes this is a pseudohemianopsia, i.e., that although vision in the affected visual field is not damaged, the ability to respond to the visual stimuli has been lost. Thus there is no way to transpose the visual sensation into meaningful responses. If the occipital and pre-occipital eye fields are destroyed, stimulation of the part of the frontal eye fields above the principal fissure associated with conjugate horizontal gaze still produces deviations to the opposite side but stimulation of the comparable area below the principal fissure produces no deviation to the opposite side.

Frontal eye fields send fibres to both the homolateral and contralateral occipital and preoccipital eye fields. Henderson and Crosby (1952) found that with these fibres the frontal eye fields appeared to exert a suppressor effect over the activity of the contralateral and homolateral preoccipital fields with respect to optokinetic responses in the horizontal plane. Unilateral ablation of the frontal eye fields still permitted regulation of the optokinetic responses in either direction by the intact frontal field. However, bilateral ablation of the frontal eye fields resulted in loss of this inhibitory influence and, under these conditions, optokinetic responses were maximal.

4. AREA 7

In addition to the occipital and preoccipital and frontal eye fields a pattern of eye movement responses has been obtained recently in area 7 of the parietal lobe. This pattern, found by Fleming and Crosby (1955), is also illustrated in Fig. 8. These areas, however, have a higher threshold and the movements obtained were in general less precise, less fine and not so discrete as those obtained in the other eye fields. They were often combined with movements of the shoulders, head and neck.

5. OTHER AREAS

Stimulation of other cortical areas may also produce eye movements. Convergence, accommodation and miosis were all found by Jampel (1958, 1959) to result from stimulation of a single localized area in the preoccipital eye fields in lightly anesthetized monkeys. These reactions are undoubtedly also important in the triad of the near "reflex" in man (cf. below). Accommodation was always accompanied by vergence changes and usually, also by miosis.

Areas in the precentral gyrus (motor cortex) produce eye movements in both the macaque and man. Crosby (1953) points out that these movements appear to have the characteristics of automatic associated movements of the cortical type rather than of so-called voluntary movements. They presumably accompany movements of the face and forelimbs.

Wagman et al. (1957) showed that in the macaque (encéphale isolé) centring and conjugate contralateral deviations of the eyes could be elicited by electrical stimulation of cortex and subcortex of "almost the entire cerebrum." As in all work in which only electrical stimulation is carried out, one can never be certain that one is dealing with merely motor fibres, or with sensory and/or association neurons, stimulation of which eventually gives rise to excitation of efferent fibre bundles (Wagman et al. 1958).

References

Adler, F. H. (1959). "Physiology of the Eye", 3rd edition, Chap. 10, pp. 312–489. C. V. Mosby Co., St. Louis.

Alpern, M., and Wolter, J. R. (1956). The relation of horizontal saccadic and vergence movements. *A.M.A. Arch. Ophthal.* **56**, 685–690.

Amberson, W. R., and Smith, D. C. (1948). "Outline of Physiology", 2nd edition, p. 128. The Williams and Wilkins Company, Baltimore.

Apter, J. T. (1946). Eye movements following strychninization of the superior colliculus of cats. *J. Neurophysiol.* **9**, 73–86.

Armaly, M. F. (1959). Studies on intraocular effects of the orbital parasympathetic pathway. *A.M.A. Arch. Ophthal.* **61**, 14–29.

Bender, M. B., and Shanzer, S. (1960). Effects of brainstem lesions on vertical gaze in monkeys. *Fed. Proc.* **19**, 288.

Bender, M. B., and Weinstein, E. A. (1943). Functional representation in the oculomotor and trochlear nuclei. *Arch. Neurol. Psychiat., Chicago*, **49**, 98–106.

Boeke, J. (1926). Die Beziehungen der Nervenfasern zu den Bindegewebselementen und Tastzellen. *Z. mikr.-anat. Forsch.* **4**, 448–509.

Boeke, J. (1932). Nerve endings, motor and sensory. *In* "Cytologic and Cellular Pathology of the Nervous System" (W. Penfield, ed.), Vol. I, pp. 243–315. Paul B. Hoeber, Inc., New York.

Brecher, G. A., and Mitchell, W. G. (1957). Studies on the role of sympathetic nervous stimulation in extraocular muscle movements. *Amer. J. Ophthal.* **41** (No. 4, Pt. 2), 144–150.

Bremer, J. L. (1944). "A Textbook of Histology Arranged Upon an Embryological Basis", 6th edition (rewritten by H. L. Weatherford), p. 163. The Blakiston Company, Philadelphia.

Brouwer, B. (1918). Klinisch-anatomische Untersuchung ueber den Oculomotoriuskern. *Z. ges. Neurol. Psychiat.* **40**, 152–193.

Cogan, D. G. (1948). "The Neurology of the Ocular Muscles". Charles C. Thomas, Springfield, Ill.

Cooper, S., and Daniel, P. M. (1949). Muscle spindles in human extrinsic eye muscles. *Brain* **72**, 1–24.

Cooper, S., Daniel, P. M., and Whitteridge, D. (1954). Afferent impulses from the muscle spindles of the extrinsic eye muscles and their course within the brainstem. *Trans. ophthal. Soc. U.K.* **74**, 435–440.

Crosby, E. C. (1953). Relations of brain centers to normal and abnormal eye movements in the horizontal plane. *J. comp. Neurol.* **99**, 437–479.

Crosby, E. C., and Henderson, J. W. (1948). The mammalian midbrain and isthmus regions. II. Fiber connections of the superior colliculus. B. Pathways concerned in automatic eye movements. *J. comp. Neurol.* **88**, 53–91.

Crosby, E. C., Humphrey, T., and Showers, M. J. (1959). Einige Anordnungen, Verbindungen und Funktionen der supplementaeren motorischen Rinden. *Med. Grundlagenforsch*, **2**, 103–124.

Crosby, E. C., and Woodburne, R. T. (1943). The nuclear pattern of the non-tectal portions of the midbrain and isthmus in primates. *J. comp. Neurol.* **78**, 441–482.

Crosby, E. C., Yoss, R. E., and Henderson, J. W. (1952). The mammalian midbrain and isthmus regions. Part II. The fiber connections. D. The pattern for eye movements on the frontal eye field and the discharge of specific portions of this field to and through midbrain levels. *J. comp. Neurol.* **97**, 357–383.

Daniel, P. (1946). Spiral nerve endings in the extrinsic eye muscles of man. *J. Anat., Lond.* **80**, 189–193.

Danis, P. C. (1948). The functional organization of the third-nerve nucleus in the cat. *Amer. J. Ophthal.* **31**, 1122–1131.

Donaldson, G. W. K. (1960). The diameter of the nerve fibres to the extrinsic eye muscles of the goat. *Quart. J. exp. Physiol.* **45**, 25–34.

Eldred, E., Granit, R., and Merton, P. A. (1953). Supraspinal control of the muscle spindles and its significance. *J. Physiol.* **122**, 498–523.

Fink, W. H. (1950). The anatomy of the extrinsic muscles of the eye. *In* "Strabismus Ophthalmic Symposium I" (J. H. Allen, ed.), pp. 17–62. C. V. Mosby Company, St. Louis.

Fleming, J. F. R., and Crosby, E. C. (1955). The parietal lobe as an additional motor area. The motor effects of electrical stimulation and ablation of cortical areas 5 and 7 in monkeys. *J. comp. Neurol.* **103**, 485–512.

Henderson, J. W. (1949). The anatomic basis for certain reflex and automatic eye movements. *Amer. J. Ophthal.* **32** (No. 6, Pt. 2), 232–238.

Henderson, J. W., and Crosby, E. C. (1952). An experimental study of optokinetic responses. *A.M.A. Arch Ophthal.* **47**, 43–54.

Hering, E. (1879). Der Raumsinn und die Bewegungen des Auges. *In* "Handbuch der Physiologie" (L. Hermann, ed.), Vol. III, Teil 1, pp. 343–601. F. C. W. Vogel, Leipzig.

Hines, M. (1931). Studies on the innervation of skeletal muscle. III. Innervation of the extrinsic eye muscles of the rabbit. *Amer. J. Anat.* **47**, 1–53.

Howe, L. (1907). "The Muscles of the Eye", Vol. 1. G. P. Putnam's Sons, New York.

Huber, G. C. (1900). Sensory nerve terminations in the tendons of the extrinsic eye-muscles of the cat. *J. comp. Neurol.* **10**, 152–158.

Hunt, C. C., and Kuffler, S. W. (1951). Further study of efferent small-nerve fibres to mammalian muscle spindles. Muscle spindle innervation and activity during contraction. *J. Physiol.* **113**, 283–297.

Hyde, J. E., and Eliasson, S. G. (1957). Brainstem induced eye movements in cats. *J. comp. Neurol.* **108**, 139–172.

Hyde, J. E. (1960). Patterns of competitive interaction for brainstem evoked eye movements in cats. *Amer. J. Ophthal.* **49**, 623.

Irvine, S. R. (1936). Histology of extra-ocular muscles. *Arch. Ophthal., N.Y.* **15**, 847–858.

Jampel, R. S. (1958). A study of convergence, divergence, pupillary reactions and accommodation from faradic stimulation of the Macaque brain. Ph.D. Thesis. University of Michigan.

Jampel, R. S. (1959). Representation of the near-response on the cerebral cortex of the Macaque. *Amer. J. Ophthal.* **48** (No. 5, Pt. 2), 573–582.

Jampel, R. S. (1960). Convergence, Divergence, Pupillary Reactions and Accommodation of the Eyes from Faradic Stimulation of the Macaque Brain. *J. comp. Neurol.* **115**, 371-400.

Jordan, H. E. (1947). "A Textbook of Histology", 8th edition, p. 103. D. Appleton-Century Company, Inc., New York.

Krewson, W. E. (1950). The action of the extraocular muscles. A method of vector-analysis with computations. *Trans. Amer. Ophthal. Soc.* **48**, 443–486.

Kuré, K., Sunaga, Y., Hatano, S., and Imagawa, T. (1927). Experimentelle und pathologische Studien ueber die progressive Muskelatrophie: V. Ueber die tropische Innervation der aeusseren Augenmuskeln. *Z. ges. exp. Med.* **54**, 366–381.

Lemmen, L. J., Davis, J. S., and Radnor, L. L. (1959). Observations on stimulation of the human frontal eye field. *J. comp. Neurol.* **112**, 163–168.

Lockhart, R. D., and Brandt, W. (1938). Length of striated muscle fibres. *J. Anat.* **72**, 470.

McCouch, G. P., and Adler, F. H. (1932). Extraocular reflexes. *Amer. J. Physiol.* **100**, 78–88.

Merrillees, N. C. R., Sunderland, S., and Hayhow, W. (1950). Neuromuscular spindles in the extraocular muscles in man. *Anat. Rec.* **108**, 23–30.

Schiefferdecker, (1904). Eine Eigentuemlichkeit im Baue der Augenmuskeln. *Dtsch. med. Wschr.* **30**, 725–726.

Sherrington, C. S. (1893). Further experimental note on the correlation of action of antagonistic muscles. *Proc. roy. Soc., Lond.* **53**, 407–420.

Sherrington, C. S. (1894). Experimental note on two movements of the eye. *J. Physiol.* **17**, 27–29.

Szentágothai, J. (1942). Die innere Gliederung des Oculomotoriuskernes. *Arch. Psychiat.* **115**, 127–135.

Szentágothai, J. (1950). Recherches expérimentales sur les voies oculogyres. *Semaine Hôp. Paris* **26**, 2989–2995.

Szentágothai, J. (1952). "Die Rolle der einzelnen Labyrinthrezeptoren bei der Orientation von Augen und Kopf im Raume". Akadémiai Kiadó, Budapest.

Szentágothai, J., and Scháb, R. (1956). A midbrain inhibitory mechanism of oculomotor activity. *Acta Physiol. Acad. Sc. Hung.* **9**, 89–98.

Tschiriew, S. (1879). Sur les terminaisons nerveuses dans les muscles striés. *Arch. de physiol. norm. et path.* Ser. 2, **6**, 89–116.

Voss, H. (1957). Beitraege zur mikroskopischen Anatomie der Augenmuskeln des Menschen; Faserdicke, Muskelspindeln, Ringbinden. *Anat. Anz.* **104**, 345–355.

Wagman, I. H., Werman, R., Feldman, D. S., Sugarman, L., and Krieger, H. P. (1957). The oculomotor effects of cortical and subcortical stimulation in the monkey. *J. Neuropath.* **16**, 269–277.

Wagman, I. H., Krieger, H. P., and Bender, M. B. (1958). Eye movements elicited by surface and depth stimulation of the occipital lobe of Macaque mulatta. *J. comp. Neurol.* **109**, 169–193.

Warwick, R. (1953). Representation of the extra-ocular muscles in the oculomotor nuclei of the monkey. *J. comp. Neurol.* **98**, 449–504.

Warwick, R. (1955). The so-called nucleus of convergence. *Brain* **78**, 92–114.

Whitteridge, D. (1960). Central control of eye movements. *In* "Handbook of Physiology": A Critical, Comprehensive Presentation of Physiological Knowledge and Concepts. Section 1. Neurophysiology (J. Field, H. W. Magoun, and V. E. Hall, eds.), Vol. II, pp. 1089–1109. American Physiological Society, Washington, D.C.

Wohlfart, G. (1932). Quergestreifte Ringbinden in normalen Augenmuskeln. *Jahrb. Morph. U. Mikrosk. Anat.* Abt. 2, **29**, 592–604.

Wohlfart, G. (1938). Zur Kenntnis der Altersveraenderungen der Augenmuskeln. *Z. mikr.-anat. Forsch.* **44**, 33–44.

Wolter, J. R. (1954). The morphology of the nervous system of the striated muscles of the human eye. *In* "Proceedings of the Seventeenth International Congress of Ophthalmology", September 10–17, 1954, Vol. III, pp. 1865–1873. University of Toronto Press, Toronto.

Wolter, J. R. (1955). Morphology of the sensory nerve apparatus in the striated muscle of the human eye. *A.M.A. Arch. Ophthal.* **53**, 201–217.

Woollard, H. H. (1931). The innervation of the ocular muscles. *J. Anat., Lond.* **65**, 215–223.

Chapter 5

Types of Movement

I. Methods of Measuring the Position of the Eye

It seems worthwhile to begin the discussion of the various types of eye movement by describing some of the more frequently used methods of estimating the position of the eye. A good deal of very important information about movements of the eyes can be obtained merely by watching them and, indeed, in clinical practice, this is almost the only method that one needs to employ. However, many laboratory situations require more precise estimates than can be obtained from careful observation. For such purposes more elaborate techniques must be employed. A discussion of these matters has become more timely because of the renewed interest in the study of eye movements by modern engineering psychologists.

A. SUBJECTIVE METHODS

Besides direct observation, the easiest methods of estimating eye position are all subjective. They have a number of advantages. Not the least attractive of these are simplicity and accuracy. One can, for example, place an after-image on the centre of the retina, presumably at the fovea, and by asking the person to indicate where in the visual field the after-image appears—or using a ruler to line it up—get an excellent idea of eye position. The use of this method by nineteenth-century physiologists in quantifying Listing's law has already been alluded to. The method has a number of other applications which have by no means been exhausted. For example, Bielschowsky (1943) recommended this technique for the accurate determination of the extent of binocular and monocular fields of fixation: one places an after-image on the fovea, seats the patient at the perimeter and moves a fixation target along its arc, until there is disparity between the object of regard and the foveal after-image. This suggestion is an excellent one. Since one may continue to see a target even when it is not centred precisely on the fovea, measurements of the field of fixation in this way are much more accurate (and considerably smaller) than those obtained by the more usual techniques. Another application of the same idea is to use the observer's entoptic perception of his own macula (Alpern, 1957) as an index of eye position. Entoptic macula perceptions, such as Haidinger's (1844) brush or Maxwell's (1856) spot, are usually rather indistinct and do not persist for any length of time (Ratliff, 1958) but arrangements can be made to see them long enough for reasonably exact measurements of position of the visual axis. In this way, for example, one can decide whether or not a patient has eccentric monocular fixation depending upon whether he sees the entoptic macula centred on, or peripheral to, the point of fixation.

B. OBJECTIVE METHODS

An extensive search has gone on for over fifty years for more objective indicators of eye position. It is true that subjective methods have limitations: the after-images are not seen, for example, during saccadic movements, hence, one could not use subjective methods to study the time characteristics of these movements very well. However, the search for objectivity has led to a number of invalid measurements being perpetuated in the literature of eye movements. Unfortunately, this tendency continues unabated down to our own day.

1. MIRROR METHOD

An excellent method for objective recording of eye position was suggested by Dodge (1921), according to which a band of light is reflected from a mirror mounted on a small wooden block pressed against the closed lid which rests over the centre of the corneal bulge and so pivoted that it tips from side to side as it remains tangential to the underlying corneal surface. The measurements are made of eye movements in the horizontal plane by recording the reflected image of a small source of light on photographic paper which moves in the vertical plane. Rotations of the mirror are associated with deflexions of the light-beam, and the angle of displacement of the latter is exactly twice the angle of rotation of the mirror. Unfortunately, a number of factors, such as lid consistency and thickness, and intercurrent movements, and the difference in scleral and corneal curvatures can lead to displacement artifacts, so that the technique is of more advantage for recording direction and time characteristics of the movements than it is for amplitude. The technique is only useful for the closed eye and does not allow for the recording of eye position when the eyes are seeing.

For this latter purpose ideally one could use a similar principle and record from a mirror attached to the eyeball directly. This could presumably be done by suturing the mirror directly to the bulbar conjunctiva, but so far as the author is aware, this has never been attempted for the purpose of studying the characteristics of eye movements.

a. Contact Lens

A more practical procedure, which has been extensively used, was developed by Ratliff and Riggs (1950). This consists in placing a small plane mirror in a button on the peripheral part of the corneal section of a contact lens. The contact lens is snugly fitted to the observer's eye. This method has been a relatively accurate method of recording eye position when the observer is attempting to hold his eye motionless in steady fixation. Ratliff and Riggs (1950), Ditchburn and Ginsborg (1953), Riggs *et al.* (1954), Cornsweet (1956) and Nachmias (1959), among others. It has less possibilities, however, when one attempts to use it for measuring large changes in eye position such as might be produced, for example, by a 20° saccadic movement. For such a large movement the assumption of the lens moving without slipping is not justified. The limits of rotation of the eye are such that conjunctival fornix may retard the rotation of the lens at its edge for the extreme directions of gaze. Even before this (in fact, according to some authorities, with a movement of more than a degree or so) enough slippage occurs to invalidate the method as an exact indicator of eye position.

The method of Dodge adapted to the contact lens can be used to record eye position in the horizontal, vertical and torsional directions by the suitable

3

arrangement of three mirrors and optical levers as Fender (1955a) was able to show. Simultaneous horizontal and vertical records can be obtained with a single mirror using a rather ingenious method suggested by Nachmias (1959).

Yarbus (1957a, b) has employed a modified version of this technique in which the mirror is attached not to a contact lens but to a suction cup which in turn is firmly maintained on the globe and does not permit any slipping at all. If one can extrapolate results from such experiments to those in which the eyes are free to move without such encumbrances, then this method may prove to be quite accurate.

2. PHOTOGRAPHIC METHODS

The most popular method of objectively estimating eye position is by photographing a light from a small source after it is specularly reflected from the convex surface of the cornea. The reflected image of the light source moves as the eye rotates, and these displacements can be recorded on photographic paper. This method was developed by Dodge (1903), Dodge and Cline (1901), and with various modifications it has been used extensively since. It has the advantage of simplicity, requiring a minimum of apparatus so that the field of view can be made relatively free of bulky equipment. The study of eye movements in everyday environment is facilitated in this way. One of the most common methods is in the ophthalmograph in which rotations in the horizontal plane are recorded on a film, which moves continuously in the vertical plane. Suitable modifications can be made to the optical apparatus so that simultaneous records in both horizontal and vertical planes are available. In a recent further modification of this technique (Mackworth and Mackworth, 1958), simultaneous photographs have been made of the corneal image and of the visual field with separate television cameras. The outputs of these two cameras are then mixed electronically and a motion picture record made of the composite pictures on the television screen. In this way a record is obtained of where, in the visual field, the eye is looking at any given moment.

3. LIMITATIONS

Unfortunately, while it was quite evident to Dodge, many contemporary investigators have not been fully informed as to the limitations of such a procedure. The desire in most (if not all of these) experiments has been to determine the position of the line of sight at any given moment. The film records the point of intersection of a line from the corneal image of the light source to the nodal point of the lens as the extension of this line strikes the photographic paper. Let us call this line the ophthalmograph axis. If the eye made rotations about a single centre of rotation then the line of sight and the ophthalmograph axis would be more or less parallel and the film would give a valid indication of eye position. However, we have already seen that normal changes of eye position are not as simple as a single rotation about a fixed centre of rotation. Under such conditions, the eyes undergo translational shifts and screw movements along with the rotation. The translational shifts and screw movements will invalidate the ophthalmograph (or other such photographic) records of eye position since under these conditions the line of sight no longer remains parallel to the ophthalmograph axis. Tani *et al.* (1956) showed that such shifts need be only very small in order to introduce an appreciable distortion in the record. Ditchburn and Ginsborg (1953) calculated that a lateral shift of only 0.01 mm. produces a recorded deflexion as great as that resulting from an angular movement of 8 minutes of arc. We as yet know very little as to the magnitudes of such shifts in normal eye rotations and so one cannot be certain as to the degree to which photographic records of eye position made in this way are invalid. Until such time that the relation of these shifts to rotations becomes better understood, one should be extremely cautious of making any precise analysis of eye movements in this way.

While the discussion has been directed to the problems of photographing the corneal image of a light spot, the same difficulty applies to measurements of eye position by photographing the entire anterior segment of the eye (Hyde, 1959). Recent photoelectric methods suggested by Smith and Warter (1960) and by Rashbass (1960) are subject to the same criticisms.

4. ELECTRICAL METHOD

Still another method that is frequently used to measure eye position is to take advantage of the fact that the external limiting membrane (Brindley, 1956), or the membrane of Bruch (Brown and Wiesel, 1958), or the pigment epithelium (Noell, 1953) is a highly resistant layer which separates the negatively charged choroid from the positively charged retina even under resting conditions. As a consequence of this fact, the flow of electrons through the only non-resistant part of the eye structure (i.e., the pupil) results in the resting eye (even in the dark) acting as a dipole with the cornea more positive than the back of the eye. This resting potential is almost always of sufficient magnitude (10 to 30 mV.) as to be measureable with reasonably sensitive electronic equipment (Marg, 1951).

To use this technique to record eye position, one merely places a pair of silver–silver chloride EEG electrodes on the inner and outer canthus of each eye (for horizontal movements) and/or above and below the eye (for vertical movements).† Any difference in potential between the two respective pairs of electrodes is "bucked out" when the eyes are in the straightforward position. Rotation of the eye from this position brings the more positive cornea nearer

† The technique is not useful for recording torsional movements of the eyes.

to one electrode than to the other. A difference in potential between the two electrodes can then be amplified and used as an index of change in eye position. The system is linear over a range of eye movements to at least 15° (Law and DeValois, 1957). This technique is useful for various kinds of studies, particularly when one takes care to calibrate voltages for known eye movements (Alpern and Ellen, 1956a, b; Alpern, 1957).

It is, of course, quite easy to differentiate the voltage any number of times and in this way to study, among other characteristics, the velocity and acceleration of the movements (Brockhurst and Lion, 1951; Powsner and Lion, 1950).

a. Difficulties in Application

This method, like the photographic ones, has recently gained wide popularity among human engineers as an absolute index of eye position (Ford *et al.*, 1959; Shackel, 1960). However, there are a number of difficulties associated with its use in this way that are not usually recognized in such applications.

Some of these difficulties are illustrated in Fig. 1 which demonstrates the record obtained from both horizontal and vertical leads when the eye makes a purely horizontal (15°) movement. As might be anticipated, eye-blinks occasionally will distort the record of eye position, but this difficulty can be overlooked in many laboratory operations although it limits the generality of the equipment for field applications. More important than this, however, are the electrical artifacts of drift and other sources of noise that handicap resolution (cf. Ford, 1959). These, however, can be overcome or modulated with considerable success with ingenious electronic instrumentation. More important than this, however, is the fact that the electrical record of eye positions in Fig. 1 indicates a change in vertical eye position even though the task was a pure horizontal movement. It is easy enough to show that these are not, in fact, associated with comparable vertical rotations of the globe. Gross inspection will show only a pure horizontal movement within a precision considerably smaller than that indicated by the vertical deflexion in the figure. This change in potential, produced between vertical leads during a pure horizontal movement (or between horizontal leads in a pure vertical movement), is almost an invariable finding in experiments of this kind although one finds no mention of it in usual discussions of electro-oculography (as the method is called). While individual differences may occur in this respect, this artifact was present in the not inconsiderable sample of observers studied at Michigan, and close inspection of published records of other investigators will invariably also reveal it. It is not due to a torsion of the eyeball, but one can sometimes reduce its amplitude almost to the noise level by tilting the head to an extreme position with respect to the body.

It is possible that such data indicate the fact that the position of the point of least electrical resistance between the charged membranes of the eye is not the centre of the pupil, as the method implicitly assumes. A more reasonable explanation, however, lies in the well demonstrated fact (cf. above) that the eyes in a normal change of fixation move with a screw motion. Thus a horizontal rotation of the globe results in its vertical displacement. This shift up or down of the entire globe would bring the positive cornea nearer one vertical electrode than the other with respect to the zero position

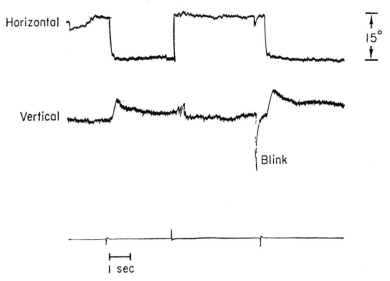

FIG. 1. Record of movement of the eye through 15° horizontally, record of artifact of vertical displacement. *Upper channel*: horizontal leads, up deflexion indicates movement to left; *middle channel*: vertical leads, up deflexion indicates movement down; *lower channel*: stimulus marker down deflexion indicates a light 15° to the right of the fixation light has been turned on at the moment the centre light is turned off. The subject is instructed to fixate each light in turn as it appears. Up deflexion: the light at the centre is turned on; that at the right is turned off.

of the eyes, even though the eyes had made only a pure horizontal rotation. If this interpretation of the "irrelevant" potential (as we have come to call it) is correct, then electro-oculography may, in fact, prove to be an accurate method of recording eye position in a purely horizontal or vertical plane. However, the two-dimensional analysis of eye rotation in this way, as several authors have tried to do (Law and DeValois, 1957; Ford *et al.*, 1959) would be inherently invalid.

Translational shifts in the plane of rotation would also induce an artifact in the electro-oculographic estimation of eye rotation. It is much more difficult to analyse the magnitude of such artifacts with these electrical methods than is the case with the optical ones, and so it is not certain whether or not such shifts, if they occur, produce any major distortion of the measurement of eye rotation.

A major difficulty with this method of estimation of eye position not illustrated in Fig. 1 is the fact that the resting potential of any given eye does not have a single constant value but varies widely, in accordance with the state of retinal stimulation. These changes in the resting potential are large enough to give markedly different values for the voltage generated by any given eye movement. Figure 2 illustrates the voltages generated by 60° eye

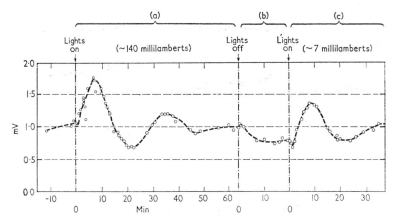

FIG. 2. Voltage generated from a 60° eye movement under various conditions of light-adaptation and dark-adaptation (Kris, 1958).

movements in various times and intensities of light- and dark-adaptation as measured by Kris (1958). It is to be emphasized that identical eye movements will generate voltages that may differ from one another as much as $1000 \mu V.$ with all other factors, except the adaptative state of the retina, remaining fixed. In the laboratory such fluctuations can (although many studies have not done so) be taken into consideration. This is done either by making careful adaptation control for some ninety minutes prior to the beginning of the experiment, or by obtaining frequent calibration records during the experiment. In the field, however, either or both of these precautions may be difficult to employ and its use is thus limited.

b. Limitations

Thus it is apparent that there is no well established method for the valid determination of large changes in eye position by objective methods. The mirror mounted on a contact lens is practical for the eye movements made when the observer is trying as best he can not to move his eye at all, but becomes rather questionable should the amplitude of movement exceed only a degree or so. The photographic methods are subject to major artifacts from even very small translational shifts and the electrical ones can be distorted by screw movements, by electrical noise, and by stimulation of the retina.

5. CATHODE-RAY METHOD

A number of techniques have recently been reported in the literature that will probably be able to overcome all of the obstacles enumerated above for validly and precisely measuring eye position objectively. The mirror attached to a suction cup that adheres firmly to the eye, which Yarbus (1957a, b) has developed, has already been referred to. Rashbass and Westheimer (1960) have suggested the following technique: a spot scanning the face of a cathode-ray tube is imaged on the eye and the reflexions are measured by suitably placed photo-multipliers. The amount of light received by the photomulti-pliers undergoes two changes: first, when the image of the spot passes over the limbus, and again, when it is specularly reflected by the cornea. Lateral head or eye movements produce parallel displacements of the two changes, whilst rotational eye movements displace them unequally. Their separation, measured electronically, can be suitably displayed, and in this way provides a measure of eye position. While this method yields a measurement which for large values appears to be non-linearly related to eye rotation, it does give data in which artifacts from lateral shifts of the eyes have been obviated.

Cornsweet (1958) focused a light on the retina and used it to scan the optic disc repeatedly. The light reflected from the fundus was then focused on a photomultiplier tube connected to the vertical deflexion plates of the os-cilloscope. The horizontal sweep was synchronized with the scanning spot. Each time the spot passed over a blood vessel in the optic disc, a vertical deflexion appeared on the oscilloscope. The distance between the beginning of the scan and this deflexion measured the optical position of the retina with respect to any stationary external stimulus. Changes in this distance repre-sented eye movements.

All of these techniques appear quite promising. It is, however, too soon to say which (if any of them) will be most useful in the study of the basic physiology of eye movements, as well as its application to field tracking (and other) problems.

II. Motor Aspects of Vision

The perception of objects in the visual field is a consequence of an amazingly complex series of processes that are still only very poorly understood. Even

MATHEW ALPERN

the simplest situation—when the eyes are steadily fixating an object directly ahead, as well as it can under conditions optimal for assuring steady fixation —is very complicated. It has been suspected for some time that under such conditions the eyes may, in fact, be constantly moving. Measurements of these effects began around the turn of the century but considerable doubt as to the facts persisted until relatively recently and it is only within the last few years that the full importance of the process is beginning to become clear.

Many features of these movements were described in some detail by Adler and Fliegelman (1934). More extensive data on certain phases of the phenomenon have been obtained since then by Lord and Wright (1948); Barlow (1952) and Ditchburn and Ginsborg (1952) in England; Ratliff and Riggs (1950) in America; and Iarbus (1957) in the Soviet Union, among many others. Three or four different kinds of movement have been recorded:

A. High-Frequency Tremor

These are very fine oscillatory movements of approximate median amplitude (peak to trough) of 17.5 seconds of arc with a range of from just perceptible to 2 minutes of arc. Ditchburn (1955) gives the range from 5 to 15 seconds for horizontal and vertical tremor and 45 seconds for torsional tremor.† Higgins and Stultz (1953) found an average of 1.2 minutes of arc but their method lacked the precision (limit of resolution 30 seconds of arc) of some of the others. The frequency of the tremor was found to be in the range 30 to 70 cycles/sec. (Ratliff and Riggs). Adler and Fliegelman found 50 to 100 cycles/sec. Higgins and Stultz also found 50 to 80 cycles/sec.; Ditchburn gives the range from 30 to 80 cycles/sec. Because of the variety of ways in which these measurements were made the close correspondence of the data makes it quite unlikely that such measurements are due to the natural frequency of the reflecting surface rather than to eye movements. Head movements are also not a possible explanation (Higgins and Stultz). The velocity of these eye movements at the maximum is about 20 min./sec.

B. Slow Drifts

These have a much wider amplitude than the tremor, being approximately 5 minutes of arc (Ratliff and Riggs; Ditchburn). Adler and Fliegelman give the range from 2′ 29″ to 4′ 58″. The duration of these movements is less than 0.2 second and the angular velocity about one minute of arc/sec.

† Adler and Fliegelman's original figure of 2′ 14″ is probably in error by a factor of two.

C. RAPID "FLICKS" OR SACCADES

These have an average extent of 5.6 minutes of arc but may range anywhere from 1 to 20 minutes (horizontal and vertical) but are rarely larger than 10 minutes. The torsional flick is about 2 minutes of arc. They have an angular velocity of 10°/sec. and are somewhat irregular in the frequency of occurrence. They may be as close as 0.2 second apart on the one hand or as far apart as 3 to 4 seconds on the other.

D. IRREGULAR MOVEMENTS

In addition to these three kinds of movement, Ratliff and Riggs (1950) describe a relatively large slow motion which has no characteristic frequency or extent. These movements differ somewhat from one subject to the next and even within subjects there is considerable variation from one record to the next. Although they cannot accurately be described, they have an approximate peak-to-trough amplitude ranging from 1–5 minutes of arc and a frequency of from 2–5 cycles/sec.

E. PHYSIOLOGICAL SIGNIFICANCE

The physiological significance of these movements is easiest to understand when considering the movement of the image of a point-object on the retina as a consequence of these saccades and the drifts. The excursion due to the tremor corresponds to a movement between 1 and 3 μ (Ditchburn, 1955) on the retina. O'Brien (1951) measured the centre-to-centre distance of human foveal cones as 2.02 to 2.32 μ. The total effect of the drifts and flicks operating together is to make the image of a point-object wander around a small region about 100 μ in diameter in the very centre of the retina. The locus of the mid-point of this region will vary with the colour of the target (Fender, 1955b). The characteristic movements of a small point within a 25 μ radius circle are illustrated in Fig. 3. On this particular occasion the whole movement was within the 25 μ (5 minutes) radius circle but longer records reveal movements within a circle twice this size. The experiments of Ditchburn (1955) and of Cornsweet (1956) lead to the following interpretation: during the normal fixation, the instability of the oculomotor system permits the eye to drift, and, consequently, the retinal image drifts across the retina. As the retinal image drifts farther and farther away from some particular region of the retina, it becomes more and more likely that a saccadic movement will occur, tending to return the retinal image to that particular region. Nachmias (1959) has recently tested this idea. He has measured the position of the eyes by recording both the vertical and horizontal components during steady fixation with a

3*

MATHEW ALPERN

method which obviates contamination from torsional movements. In keeping
with the Cornsweet hypothesis, he found that parallel to all but a very few
meridians, the drift and saccadic motion were predominantly in opposite
directions. On the other hand, he found that the 0.2 second drift-rate of the

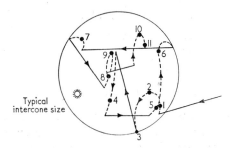

FIG. 3. Movement of the image of a point-object on the retina. The large circle is 10
minutes of arc in diameter, the dotted line represents slow drifts, the solid line rapid
flicks (or saccades). Numbered dots indicate order in which movements are made and
are spaced at equal time intervals of 0.2 second (Ditchburn, 1955).

eye was greater for near-vision accommodation than for far-vision accommodation but that the frequency of saccades was identical under the two situations. Nachmias points out that this is not anticipated by the probability-
deviation hypothesis just described, although it is exactly what one might
expect if the likelihood of a saccade occurrence increased simply with the
time since the last saccade.

1. VISUAL ACUITY

The presence of these fine oscillatory movements of the eyes during steady
fixation raises almost immediately the important question of their role in
visual perception. Weymouth et al. (1923) predicted that they were a major
factor in the ability of the eyes to detect spatial extents much smaller than
the diameter of a foveal cone. In general, they suggested that the high-
frequency tremor of the eyes served as the basis for an averaging mechanism
that "rectified" the blurred retinal image. Marshall and Talbot (1942) and
Jones and Higgins (1947, 1948) suggested that this tremor might be the
means by which the illumination on a given receptor was rapidly changed
from one level to another and in this way resulted in more effective stimulation
of certain receptor units. Such theories predict that the visual acuity would be
better under these "dynamic" conditions than under conditions in which the
eyeball was exactly steady during fixation. Ratliff (1952) tested this prediction by measuring visual acuity during various stages of the eye movements
which he was able to record at the same time by a mirror on the contact lens.
He found that drifts of the line of sight greater than 20 seconds of arc—an

angle presumably less than the diameter of a single foveal cone—were a hindrance rather than a help to monocular visual acuity. He also showed that relatively large amounts of the rapid tremor were a hindrance to monocular visual acuity.

a. Stabilized Image

In order to verify and extend these findings Riggs *et al.* (1953) devised a method of holding the image of the object of regard stationary on the retina. The technique is illustrated in Fig. 4. Light from the target is reflected off

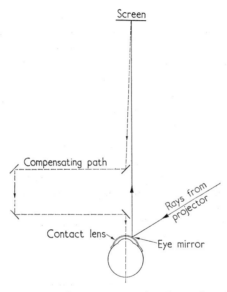

FIG. 4. Diagram of a method of counteracting the effects of small eye movements on vision. The viewing path is effectively double the distance from the eye to screen to compensate for the fact that when the eye rotates through an angle θ, the rays reflected from the mirror on the contact lens are rotated through 2θ. (Riggs *et al.*, 1953.)

the mirror onto the contact lens and then undergoes a series of reflexions before entering the eye. Under these conditions every motion of the image is exactly the same as a motion of the eye and the retinal image remains stationary or "stabilized." When visual acuity measurements were made with short exposures (0.01 to 0.1 second) they were found under these conditions to be higher than similar measurements obtained under normal viewing conditions. On the other hand, doubling the rate of oscillation of the image (by rotation, for example, of one of the mirrors in the optical system) then resulted in poorer visual acuity than normal. This finding verified Ratliff's (1952) results which suggested that the high frequency involuntary eye movements were not responsible for the high degree of foveal acuity of normal vision.

With the apparatus illustrated in Fig. 4, however, one striking result was obtained if the eye continued to look at the target for any length of time. Prolonged fixation of a target under these conditions resulted in the disappearance of objects from the field of view. Thus it seems that the involuntary eye movements of steady fixation are a necessary feature for normal vision. The disappearance occurs in about 5 seconds. It is greatest for low contrast images with minimal amounts of motion (Riggs and Tulunay, 1959). If a black bar of 8′ width and 2° length is seen, the black area soon appears to be invaded from the edges by patches of light and is finally completely obliterated so that the whole field appears uniformly illuminated. It should be emphasized that the black bars tend to become white rather than the white background to become darker (Ditchburn and Fender, 1955). Yarbus (1957b) studied coloured lights and found that these too tended to disappear when the retinal image became stabilized. The colour changed to a dark grey, but if the other eye (without a stabilized retinal image) were suddenly illuminated, the apparent colour of the empty field changed acquiring a tinge the same as the colour of the light that entered the other eye. While the characteristics of vision under image stabilization form an important chapter of physiology of vision, a thorough discussion of them is clearly beyond the scope of the present chapter. It will suffice to point out that the constant involuntary movements of the eyes under steady fixation are a necessary prerequisite for normal vision. Thus, in a very real and important way, vision is dependent upon and requires movement.

III. Reflex Eye Movements

A. Static Reflexes

Positions of the body and the head play a very essential part in positioning vertebrate eyes. Such control is also to be found even in the small compound eye of invertebrates. In certain decapods, in which the bilateral eyes are located on the ends of stalks, the angle of intersection of the major axis of the stalks of the two eyes changes as a function of the sine of the angle that the median body plane makes with the objective vertical plane (Fig. 5).

In the invertebrate, this function is governed by statocysts (Schöne, 1954). In the vertebrate, the otoliths (especially the maculas of the utricles) carry out perfectly analogous functions. If the head is tilted forward the eyes are reflexly deviated upward, whilst if the head is tilted backward the eyes deviate downward. The effect of this otolith-stimulated eye movement is to tend to maintain the eyes in the position that they held prior to the movement.

Indeed, all of the reflex eye movements operate in this way. If, for example, the head is tilted to one shoulder, the eyes rotate around the lines of sight. Such movements have been studied extensively in the lower mammals such as rabbits (Magnus, de Kleijn) and in fish (Benjamins, 1918). Korovina (1959) found these effects in new born kittens and rabbits immediately after birth.

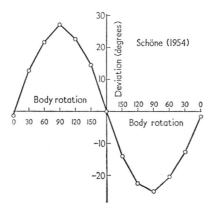

Fig. 5. The change in the angle of the eye-stalks in *Palaemonetes* as body is rotated, according to Schöne (1954). The ordinate gives the change in the angle (in degrees) that bisects the angle of intersection of the two eye-stalks. The abscissa gives the angle that the median body plane makes with the objective vertical.

In man similar phenomena occur but are much less pronounced. If the head is tilted to the right shoulder the right eye intorts, the left eye extorts. Once again these reflexes act to maintain the *status quo*, the vertical meridian of the cornea tending to remain vertical.

1. COMPENSATORY ROLLING

Woellner and Graybiel (1959) recently measured the degree of torsion associated with body inclination in a tilt-chair and when the body was exposed to a change in direction of force on a human centrifuge. These results are illustrated in Fig. 6. For equivalent directions of force the centrifuge produced more pronounced counter-rolling than the tilt-chair. In neither case, however, does the degree of counter-rolling compensate for the magnitude of the tilt. For a given direction of incidence force the two conditions are not precisely comparable since the lateral force acting on the head is greater in the centrifuge than in the tilt-chair. However, a single curve describes both sets of data provided one plots the magnitude of the counter-rolling of the eyes as a function of the magnitude of the lateral force directed against the head.

a. Utricle

The reflex movements of the eyes just described were classified as static reflexes by Magnus (1924). They are largely a consequence of stimulation of the macula of the utricle † in the otolith apparatus. This organ responds to stimulation by gravity and to linear acceleration. Thus it controls the static reflexes of head *position* and the dynamic reflexes in response to movements. The otoliths exert influence only on the four vertically acting extra-ocular

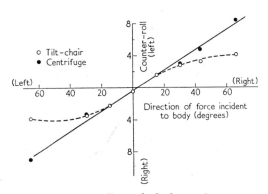

FIG. 6. Effect of force, acting laterally on the body, on the counter-rolling of the eyes, according to Woellner and Graybiel (1959). Compare these results to those in the invertebrate (see Fig. 5).

muscles and not on the medial and lateral rectus muscles at all. Thus, turning the head to the right or left is not associated with any *static* reflex deviation of the eyes. It is not possible, in fact, to stimulate the horizontal recti in this way. This is thought by some to be the reason why horizontal fusional movements are so easy to train in comparison with vertical or cyclo-fusional movements.

b. Neck Proprioceptors

de Kleijn (1921) showed that proprioceptors from the muscles of the neck played a role in reflex rotation of the eyes to tilt of the head (in rabbit). If the dorsal roots of the first and second cervical nerves were cut, de Kleijn found that the eye rotation following a 70° tilt of the head about a binaural axis was reduced by about 17° over the fully compensated eye rotation of the normal animal.

† There is no good evidence that the macula of the saccule, which is anatomically quite similar to that of the utricle (although in man the axes of the two are at right angles to each other), plays any role whatsoever in reflex deviations of the eyes.

B. STATO-KINETIC REFLEXES

In addition to the reflex mechanisms described above, stimulation of the semicircular canals also causes deviations of the eyes. The adequate stimulus for the semicircular canals is said to be angular acceleration. There is evidence, however, that head position, linear acceleration, electrical stimuli, sound (Ades et al. 1957), mechanical stimulation (with a pneumatic hammer), chemicals and temperature change (irrigation of the ear with warm or cold water), all can stimulate the semicircular canals (Wendt, 1951). All of these stimuli presumably also cause reflex deviation of the eyes. The eye reflexes caused by stimulation of the semicircular canals differ in character from those caused by stimulation of neck muscles and the utricular macula. The eye responses to stimulation of the semicircular canals were classified as stato-kinetic by Magnus perhaps because the adequate stimulus for the semicircular canals is angular acceleration, perhaps because the eyes themselves are constantly shifting in these reflexes.

1. NYSTAGMUS

The constant shifting of the gaze characteristic of stato-kinetic eye reflexes is classified as one form of *nystagmus*. A nystagmus is any rapid rhythmical to-and-fro movement of the globe. It is a consequence of a number of different kinds of reflex excitation of the extra-ocular muscles. In the stato-kinetic reflexes, the movements of the eyes are in a direction that tends to maintain fixation in much the same way as the eye movements of the static reflexes. Thus, angular acceleration of the head and body to the right causes a slow deviation of the eyes to the left. When the subject reaches the limit of his field of fixation, however, the eyes can no longer turn farther to the left. At this point a quick jerk of the eyes to the opposite (right) direction occurs and the slow phase then resumes with a second slow deviation to the left. This alternate slow and fast phase characterizes jerky eye movements, so that this kind of a nystagmus is called a jerky nystagmus. While the essence of the eye movement is the slow deviation that compensates for the rotation of the head (and body) it is the quick return movement that is most readily observed by an onlooker and thus common practice designates the direction of the nystagmus in terms of this quick phase of the movement.

a. Three-Neuron Arcs

These movements of the eyes are a consequence of stimulation of the semi-circular canals (whether by the adequate stimulus, or any one of the several inadequate stimuli already enumerated). It is commonly taught (Duke-Elder, 1932) that each labyrinth is associated with all the muscles of each eye. Szentágothai (1950b), however, found that the three-neuron arc connexions between each labyrinth are to only six extra-ocular muscles. Thus each labyrinth was found connected in this way to the contralateral lateral rectus, inferior oblique and inferior rectus and to the homolateral medial rectus, superior rectus and superior oblique. By stimulating single semi-circular canals with artificial endolymph currents, Szentágothai was able to show that the crista of each semicircular canal was related by three-neuron arcs to only two extra-ocular muscles. For example, the crista of the horizontal canal (crista ampullae lateralis) was found related to the homolateral medial and the contralateral lateral rectus; the crista of the superior (vertical) canal (crista ampullae superioris) was found related in this way to ipsilateral superior rectus and the contralateral inferior oblique and lastly the crista of the posterior canal (crista ampullae posterioris) was connected by three-neuron arcs with the homolateral superior oblique and the contralateral inferior rectus. Thus the crista of the right horizontal canal when stimulated causes contraction of the right medial rectus and the left lateral rectus, causing slow deviation of the eyes to the left in agreement with the slow phase of the nystagmus resulting from angular acceleration of the head to the right.† (The adequate stimulus for the right horizontal semicircular canal.)

b. Rotation Nystagmus

The horizontal canal is not perfectly horizontal. Its plane can be made normal to the earth's surface by tilting the head back through 60°, or parallel to the ground by tilting the head forward 30°. In the former position the horizontal canals can be stimulated by convection currents in the endolymph by irrigating the ear with hot (or cold) water; in the latter they are stimulated by angular acceleration as for example rotation in the Bárány chair. In similar ways the acceleration may be applied to the body when the head is tilted to one shoulder. One obtains in this way stimulation of the vertical canal. If the body is rotated about the line of sight then the posterior canal can be stimulated. This description is based on the assumption that rotation of the body affects the canal whose plane is nearest the plane of rotation. While this assumption is reasonable for clinical purposes, it can be demonstrated that rotation affects more than one canal (perhaps all of them to some extent) even when the canals are not in the "favourable" planes.

It is generally believed (e.g., Wendt, 1951) that inertia, acting on the endolymph and cupular mass, causes a shift of fluid that results in displacement of the cupula. This in turn stimulates the hair cells in the crista.

† Szentágothai also found that stimulation of a given canal produced other synergies than the three-neuron arcs to the two extra-ocular muscles just described. These latter, however, were much smaller and could be abolished by a bilateral section of the midbrain that just spared the median longitudinal fasciculus (a procedure that left the three-neuron arc reflexes intact).

When the body is exposed to a single acceleratory stimulus, by bringing the Bárány chair to a given speed (say, 180°/sec.) and this speed is maintained, the eye movements obtained last for several minutes and are somewhat more complex than is commonly described (Wendt, 1951). The slow phase of the nystagmus increases in speed until a little longer than the acceleration period and then shows a gradual decrease lasting from 25 to 50 seconds. As the eyes gradually drift to zero velocity they suddenly begin to drift in the opposite direction producing an inverse (or secondary) nystagmus. The speed of this latter increases for about 80 seconds until the slow phase is moving at about 5°/sec. Over a period from 3 to 10 minutes it now begins to decrease until the eyes return to the slow drift of the pre-stimulus condition. Upon deceleration to zero the entire process is repeated but this time in the opposite direction.†

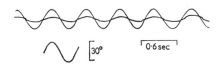

FIG. 7. Compensatory rolling of the eyes while the observer is swung to and fro about the line of sight according to Davies and Merton (1958). The large smooth trace shows body, the small jerky trace, eye position. The amplitude of this swing was 30°.

The eye movements just described are obtained when the eyes are closed, so that they are a consequence of purely vestibular excitation. If the eyes are open the sequence of events is altered considerably by visual reinforcement or inhibition. With a good fixation target during rotation a visually induced nystagmus lasts throughout the rotation regardless of the duration and predominates over the weaker opposing secondary vestibular nystagmus. The post-rotation nystagmus is also less vigorous than when the eyes are closed because of the opposition of fixation objects which now tend to keep the eyes motionless (Wendt, 1951).

Interesting compensatory eye movements are obtained when the subject is swung to and fro around the line of sight of one eye at a very slow rate, with the eyes open. Figure 7 shows a record obtained by Davies and Merton (1958) during a 30° swing with a frequency of 1.5 seconds. The large sine-wave trace shows body position, the smaller broken trace the rolling movement of the eye. It is seen that sudden jerky saccades are superimposed on the slow movement. The rolling movement of the eyes lags about 15° behind the swing of the body and has about 0.25 of the amplitude. (Thus in a 20° swing the

† The details of these eye movements are somewhat confused by the standard procedure of rotation in the Bárány chair of ten rotations in 20 seconds since the acceleration and deceleration are too close together.

relative movement of the eyes in the head was 15°.) These effects were absent in patients who had lost labyrinth function.

C. Opto-Kinetic Nystagmus

The rhythmical movements of the eyes in vestibular nystagmus are not essentially different from movements which occur when the visual field moves with constant velocity before an observer. One can obtain these movements by: (*a*) moving the field before the observer's eyes or (*b*) moving the observer with constant linear velocity in a fixed visual field. In the former case, a series of black and white stripes on a rotating drum is quite useful.

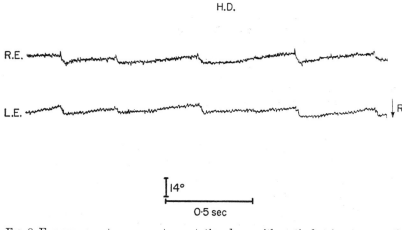

FIG. 8. Eye movement responses to a rotating drum with vertical stripes representing characteristic feature of opto-kinetic nystagmus. Drum rotated to the left.

Rotation of this drum will produce a conjugate jerky nystagmus with the quick phase opposite to the direction of rotation of the drum (opto-kinetic or optico-kinetic nystagmus). Figure 8 illustrates a record of the movements of the eyes under these conditions. If the observer moves and the field is stationary, the quick phase is in the direction of motion of the observer (railroad nystagmus). In either case the physiology is such that the eyes tend to maintain fixation on an object moving relative to the observer. At a certain point, not necessarily determined by the fixated object reaching the limits of the field of fixation, the eyes make a quick return movement and fix upon another moving object and the process is repeated. When motion of the visual field (or the motion of the observer) stops, there is an after-nystagmus which is in exactly the opposite direction and which persists for some time. The slow phase of the opto-kinetic nystagmus represents a pursuit movement of the eyes and its physiological characteristics, such as they are known, will be discussed in the section that follows. The rapid phase is quite like the rapid phase of the vestibular nystagmus. The physiology of its movement is not well understood.

D. Neural Mechanisms

Since the quick phases of the opto-kinetic and of the vestibular nystagmus are so similar and since, further, the latter persists in the absence of visual cortex, one tends to assume that intact cerebral cortex is not necessary for the quick phase of the opto-kinetic nystagmus. However, the quick phase cannot easily be demonstrated unless the slow phase is also present so the matter is difficult to prove. Smith (1937), in cat, and ter Braak (1936), in a variety of animals, demonstrated opto-kinetic nystagmus in animals deprived of visual cortex but Pasik *et al.* (1959) have not been able to confirm this in monkeys. Whatever the outcome of this dispute it is evident that the quick

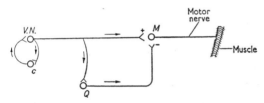

Fig. 9. Simple schema for illustrating the neurology of vestibular nystagmus according to Lorente do Nó (1933).

phase is probably not, as has been occasionally suggested, a consequence of stimulation by proprioception in the extra-ocular muscles at the limits of the field of fixation. McCouch and Adler (1932) found that imposing (or releasing) stretch on the eye muscles during the course of the nystagmus had little or no effect upon its rhythm.† Lorente do Nó (1933) suggested that stimulation of the peripheral labyrinth set into activity a machinery which gives rise to nystagmus in exactly the same way that stimulation of sensory nerves in the skin sets up the more or less rhythmic scratch reflex. He suggested that the rhythm of the nystagmus, i.e., its quick phase, required more neurons than were used in production of the slow components. He illustrated this argument with several hypothetical nerve networks that could produce such results. One of the simplest of these is illustrated in Fig. 9 (this figure should be compared with Fig. 7 of Chapter IV).

† When small inconsistent effects occurred they were far more pronounced on the slow than on the quick phase.

Peripheral stimulation eventually activates nerve cells in the vestibular nucleus ($V.N.$); these discharge in a reverberating circuit (c) in such a way that the nerve continues to fire over some time. Discharge of this cell then excites the final common path to the muscle M (and hence the slow phase of the nystagmus). At the same time, it also excites a system of neurons (Q) that sends a discontinuous series of inhibitory impulses to the motor nerve cell. When the excitatory and inhibitory impulses arrive together at M the motor neuron is not excited and the muscle relaxes (quick phase), when only excitation arrives at M slow phase contraction occurs. This scheme is, of course, very diagrammatic and only suggestive.

E. Other Types of Nystagmus

The nystagmus movements just described are those most frequently observed in the normal subject. There are, however, other types of such eye movements both in the normal eye and in disease. A discussion of this latter falls outside the scope of this review and reference is made to a standard text description of miner's nystagmus, spasmus nutans, amblyopic nystagmus and amaurotic nystagmus (Duke-Elder, 1949). Nystagmus also can occur as a consequence of neurological disorders, particularly those relating to the vestibular apparatus. Bechterew produced a nystagmus in dogs by cutting out one labyrinth, but this gradually disappeared in time. Cutting out the second ear resulted, then, in a second nystagmus, which also disappeared within a few days. Apparently some change in activity of the nerve centres counterbalances the effects of vestibular input from the first ear, and this compensation results in another imbalance when the second ear is removed (Wendt, 1951).

1. Voluntary Nystagmus

Normal observers can sometimes produce a nystagmus more or less on command. In a period of about six months we † have seen four of these people and typical results in one such case are illustrated in Fig. 10. When told to begin the nystagmus, a latent period of the usual order (250 msec.) is followed by an increase of convergence. The nystagmus begins before the vergence movement is completed and is superimposed on the vergence movement. Nystagmus movements are rhythmical but their time characteristics are different from those described in the "jerky" opto-kinetic or vestibular nystagmus. The movements in Fig. 10 have the same velocity in either direction and are thus called "pendular" nystagmus. While the synchrony of the two eyes varies somewhat, it is apparent that both eyes more or less

† This work was done in collaboration with R. S. Jampel, M.D.

tend to converge and diverge in synchrony. This is known as disjunctive as distinct from conjugate nystagmus in which the two eyes move to the left and then to the right in synchrony. Pendular nystagmus may also be conjugate, as for example in the pendular nystagmus associated with poor vision in some cases of typical total colour blindness (Alpern *et al.*, 1960). The rhythm in Fig. 10 is about 18 cycles/sec. and in the cases examined never varied outside of the range 18–20 cycles/sec. Some subjects believed they were able to change the rate at will but when asked to move the eyes as slowly as possible they interspersed the 18 cycles/sec. movements with periods of no

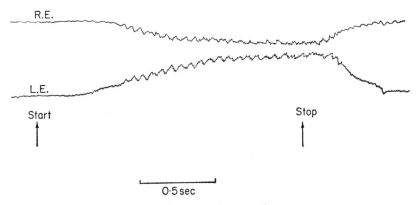

R.E.

L.E.

Start

Stop

0·5 sec

Fig. 10. Movements of the eyes during voluntary nystagmus.

movement, so that varying the speed of the nystagmus consisted merely in varying the duration of the intervals in which no 18 cycles/sec. nystagmus was present. Upon being told to stop the nystagmus, after a latent period of about 0.2 second the subject diverged the eyes to the former position and the movement stopped.

The so-called voluntary nystagmus could, in fact, be facilitated by placing a near target upon which to establish a convergence reference frame. Apparently the ability to learn this "trick" is fairly widely distributed in the population.

2. LATENT NYSTAGMUS

While nystagmus of disease is beyond the scope of this discussion, one exception can be made because of the light it may one day shed on the physiology of binocular fixation. This is the phenomenon of latent nystagmus, a more or less rare clinical entity in which when both eyes are fixating no nystagmus at all is present. Binocular nystagmus occurs when either of the eyes is occluded. Figure 11 illustrates the record from the left eye of a 19-year-old boy who had 20/25 vision in each eye when both were fixating.

In this condition the eyes are essentially stable (Fig. 11A) but, if the left eye alone fixates (Fig. 11B), a jerky conjugate nystagmus (quick phase to the left) of about 6° and about 3 to 3.5 shifts/sec. was obtained. If the occluder is placed over the left eye so that now the right eye fixates alone (Fig. 11C), the direction and form of the nystagmus change somewhat. One observes now only a 4° shift of slightly faster rate and with the quick phase to the right. Even the velocity of the quick phase is different in the two cases: in the former it is much slower than in the latter. The reasons for the phenomenon

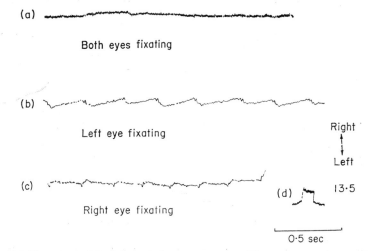

(a)

Both eyes fixating

(b)

Left eye fixating

Right

Left

(c)

Right eye fixating

(d) 13·5

0·5 sec

FIG. 11. Movement of the *left* eye in latent nystagmus. The patient, a 19-year-old boy, had quiet eyes when both eyes fixated (a), but a nystagmus when either the left (b) or the right (c) eye was fixating. The patient also had intermittent esotropia. His acuity with one eye alone fixating was 20/50, but with both eyes fixating the visual acuity was 20/25 in each eye.

and for the difference between the two eyes are not clearly understood (for detailed summary of the literature, cf. Duke-Elder, 1949). Smaller movements occur when the eye with the better acuity fixates. Various theories relating the movements to weakness of the lateral recti, disinhibition by the removal of the stimulus to unification and lack of co-ordination of supranuclear centres have little in the way of positive confirmation.

IV. The Saccadic Eye Movement

A very frequent type of eye movement is the simple saccade in which the eyes suddenly change fixation from one point in space to another. The electrophysiological characteristics of this movement will be described in some detail later on.

A. Temporal Characteristics

The latency of a saccadic movement, as measured by the time interval between the appearance of a light in the visual field (the subject having been instructed to fixate upon it) and the onset of the eye movement, varies (for practised subjects) from 0.12 to 0.18 second (Westheimer, 1954a). The movements of the two eyes themselves are very rapid and, within the errors of measurement, are exactly conjugated. The velocity of the movement is not constant throughout but builds up gradually to a maximum and then slowly subsides (Dodge and Cline, 1901; Tinker, 1942). For 20° movements, Westheimer (1954a) found the peak velocity to be almost half-way through the movement. Hyde (1959) on the other hand found the peak velocity to be achieved very early in the movement and the deceleration to be much more prolonged than the acceleration. For example, in a 60° saccade, only 49 msec. were spent (on the average) in bringing the eye from the starting position to the maximum velocity but 93 msec. were spent in completing the movement. The total duration of the movement was found to be linearly related to the amplitude—a 90° movement lasting 0.19 second while a 15° movement was completed in 0.045 second. Obviously these movements are extremely fast. Westheimer found the maximum velocity to increase as a function of the amplitude of the movement. Hyde verified this and found for movements of very large (90°) amplitude a maximum velocity as large as 830°/second (in the fastest subject). The velocity of the movement was apparently independent of "voluntary" control or of practice. Movements to the straightforward position were on the average about 58°/sec. (mean velocity, 30° movement) faster than movements from the straightforward position to some other position in the field.

B. Vision During Movement

It is commonly taught that the eyes are blind during a saccadic movement but this is difficult to verify. Ditchburn (1955) attempted to test this. He reflected a light off a mirror attached to a contact lens. The reflected light-beam fell upon the edge of a photocell so that movements caused signals in the cell. The cell output was fed through a high-pass filter into an amplifier whose response was poor at low frequencies. The output from the amplifier was displayed on the face of a cathode ray oscilloscope and the beam was displaced only when a saccade occurred. The displacements of the beam during a saccade were not noticed by the subject (looking directly at it) although they were clearly visible to a companion sitting beside him. Such experiments seem to verify the fact that the eyes are blind during such movements. However, the matter is more complex, since saccadic movements are so fast that the retinal stimulus from the target may have been sub-threshold during the movement. These data were obtained for the very fine eye movements. Hyde (1959) believes that it is possible that perception, to the extent of recognizing a peripherally located target, may be possible even before the eyes have come to a complete stop during a large saccade. Only a good deal of further experimentation will be able to show whether or not this is indeed the case. When an intermittent stimulus such as a neon lamp is observed in a dark room while the eyes change fixation, it is seen to continue to pulse even during the saccade. On the other hand, if an after-image is viewed during a vestibular nystagmus only the slow phase is seen entopically.

C. Version and Vergence

A considerable amount of information regarding the relation between vergence movements and saccadic movements was obtained in a recent experiment of Yarbus (1957a). In these experiments the position of the eyes was estimated by light reflected from mirrors attached firmly to the eyes

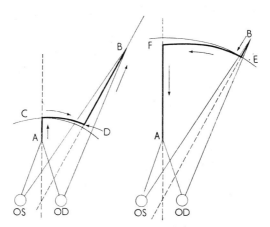

Fig. 12. Relation of vergence to saccadic movements in a shift of gaze between two objects at different directions and at different distances from the eyes. (According to Yarbus, 1957a). The left-hand figure shows the shift from near to distance; the right-hand figure the return.

(with suction cup devices) so that one can have a little more faith in the validity of the data than is the case with other photographic methods. The observer merely changed fixation from a point A in space to a point B, which was located at a different distance from the eyes as well as in a different direction. The schematic illustrations of the results of such experiments are presented in Fig. 12, the left-hand figure showing the divergence–saccade to the left associated with shifting the gaze from A to B; the right-hand figure showing the convergence–saccade to the right resulting from the movement in the opposite direction. The motion is divisible into the vergence and the version and each appears to be carried on more or less independently of the other. The vergence is carried on continuously throughout. The saccade appears only in the middle of the movement. The movement may be characterized as follows: (1) there is a brief period during which only a pure vergence movement is evident and this may last from 0.05 to 0.2 second; (2) a relatively short period follows during which both version and vergence movements occur together † and (3) there is a second period in which only the vergence movements occur. The complete independence of the two kinds of movement is strong evidence for two independent effector mechanisms.

This shift in the fixation point is sometimes also characterized by additional corrective movements, both in vergence and version, but the basic pattern is not essentially different from that illustrated in Fig. 12.

D. EYE MOVEMENTS IN READING

Eye movements in reading are characterized by a series of saccadic movements interspersed with fixation pauses (Tinker, 1936a, 1936b, 1938). The eyes move across the page fixating on one point and then making a saccadic movement to the next fixation point. It is commonly taught (see the discussion which begins at the bottom of page 87) that no perception occurs during the saccades. In this view, letters on either side of the fixation point are perceived during the fixation pauses. About 93 % of the total reading time is spent in these fixation pauses; only a little over 7 % of the time is spent in eye movements. These proportions vary to some extent depending upon the difficulty and interest of the material. A fixation pause may vary in duration from 217.8 ± 28.1 msec. for easy prose to 323.6 ± 83.8 msec. for completion items in an examination (Tinker, 1951). Apparently in good normal reading the two eyes are conjugated quite closely together (as is true of saccadic movements in general) and vertical deviations are minimal. There is occasionally a tendency for the eyes to return to a previously scanned part of the material. This is referred to as a regression. Good readers may show as few as 0.7 regressions per line and there will be almost 3 ems per fixation (25 ems per line). In appraising skill as a reader the fewer regressions, shorter pause duration, and increased pause frequency have been shown to correlate with academic achievement.

† Since the former is much more rapid than the latter, it effects a greater proportion of the eye displacement during this stage.

V. Pursuit Movements

Using a modified ophthalmograph, Westheimer (1954b) carried out the following experiment: A subject is instructed to look at a dark screen and then to follow a moving light spot when it appears. The spot appears in the central region and moves in the horizontal plane with constant velocity. After a reaction-time of 150 to 250 msec. (which is apparently longer for slower velocities) the eyes make a saccadic movement that brings the lines of sight onto the target. The eyes then start to move immediately with a velocity exactly that of the target (provided the latter is less than 25° to 30°/sec.). During the course of following the target there are often small saccadic movements of 1° (sometimes more) back and forth around the target without any change in the velocity of the following movements. These latter are extremely smooth and have a constant velocity in each eye. If the velocity of the target exceeds 30°/sec., following movements are observed that are considerably slower than this. The velocity of the following movement remains essentially the same throughout the movement even though there may be some discrepancy between the velocity of the target and that of the eyes. When changes in the latter do occur they are not always in a direction to correct for the discrepancy. The changes in velocity are always discrete. According to Rashbass (1959) the stimulus for the smooth eye movements is the movement of the target and not its position. His results indicate that ". . . the mechanism for smooth movement is aiming at achieving a stationary image on the retina irrespective of error in the position of fixation." Position errors larger than 0.1° are corrected by a saccade provided some 0.2 second has elapsed since the previous saccade. For sinusoidal tracking, however, in which the target path soon becomes familiar, the problem appears to be more complex. Fender and Nye (1961) used a stimulus condition in which eye movement could not influence the position of the retinal image. They found during simple harmonic tracking that the pursuit eye movements were determined by position error.

The reaction-time to a change in stimulus-velocity is about 150 msec. Sinusoidal tracking can, after considerable practice, become rather smooth and slow acceleration and deceleration of the eyes then occur (Stroud, 1951; Westheimer, 1954b). For a 30° movement Westheimer found the eyes could track reasonably accurately a 3 cycle/sec. sine motion. If the target moves faster than this the system breaks down even though the eyes are capable of making saccadic movements that are at least ten times as fast as the moving target.

A. Intermittent Exposure

If the moving target is only intermittently exposed, the following movement is not different from that in the continuously exposed condition except that the correlation between target and eye-velocity is somewhat poorer and many more saccades are used to reduce position error.

VI. Vergence Movements

A. Hering's Law of Equal Innervation

Corresponding muscles of each eye normally receive equal innervation so that for any shift of gaze the movements of the two eyes are yoked together. The nineteenth-century physiologist, Ewald Hering, described this principle in 1868 and it since has become known as Hering's law of equal innervation (Hering, 1868, pp. 2–14). Its operation is easy enough to demonstrate merely by covering one eye and watching it move behind the cover. When the uncovered eye makes a saccade up and to the right, the eye under cover moves in the same direction and the same amount. In fact, any saccadic or pursuit movement of the fixing eye is precisely duplicated in magnitude and direction by the eye under cover.

1. prism before one eye

It is commonly taught that Hering's law applies only to voluntary version movements but in fact it has a wider application. In Fig. 13A the two eyes are binocularly fixating an object O. In Fig. 13B a weak prism is placed base-out before the right eye. The effect of this prism is to deviate the retinal image of the object of regard to a peripheral retinal area γ degrees from the fovea of the right eye. It will be noted that since the prism is placed only in front of the right eye, the retinal image of O in the left eye is not displaced at all. In order to regain bifoveal fixation of O, therefore, only the right eye needs to move. However, the eyes are incapable of obtaining bifoveal fixation in this way. On the contrary, it is necessary for both eyes to move and the manner in which these movements are carried out is illustrated in Figs. 13C and 13D. First (Fig. 13C) both eyes make a version to the left. In this movement the medial rectus of the right, and the lateral rectus of the left, eye are yoked together and both of these muscles receive equal innervation so that they contract enough to move their respective eyes to the left by exactly the same amount $(\gamma/2°)$. As a result of this movement the image of O is no longer at the fovea in *either* of the two eyes. In the right eye it is at a point in the temporal retina at an angle of $\gamma/2°$ from fovea. In the left eye it is now also in the temporal retina at an angle of $\gamma/2°$ from the centre of the fovea. In order to regain bifoveal fixation it is necessary for both eyes to move again during this same single shift of gaze. This time, however, the movement is a vergence (Fig. 13D). The medial recti of both eyes become yoked together so that each eye moves toward the nose and again by an

amount $\gamma/2°$. This second movement positions the right eye so that its visual
axis intersects that of the other eye at O'. The left eye moves back to exactly
the same position that it had at the very beginning of the movement

a. Quantitative Verification

Many features of this phenomenon are easy enough to verify, simply by
observing the eye movements of a normal subject when a weak prism is
placed base-in or base-out before one of the two eyes during a binocular
fixation. However, an exact *quantitative* verification of this principle is more
difficult to achieve. Figure 14 illustrates one experimental attempt to do so

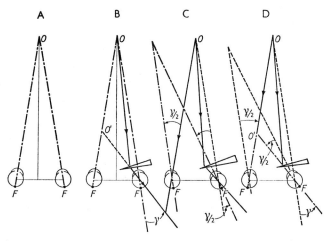

FIG. 13. Eye movements when a small amount of prism is placed base out before the
right eye while the two eyes are binocularly fixating the object at O. In A, the eyes fixate
prior to the addition of the prism. In B, the prism has been added and the retinal image
of the object in the right eye has been displaced temporally by an amount $\gamma°$. In C, the
eyes respond to this stimulus by beginning the movement. Both eyes make a saccade
$\gamma/2°$ to the left. In D, the movement is completed by a convergence of $\gamma/2°$.

(Alpern, 1957). The responses of the two eyes (using the method of electro-
oculography) were obtained when a prism (of deviation sufficiently large that
γ was equal to about 4°) was placed base-out before the right eye. Quite
obviously in a qualitative way all the predictions of Hering's law are easy to
verify in this example. Because of differences in velocity-characteristics it
can be seen that the shift of gaze is divided into a rapid version movement
(or saccade) and a much slower vergence movement. Furthermore, both eyes
show both types of movement. However, the amplitude of the maximum
displacement of the left eye is somewhat less than $\gamma/2°$. This could be due to
the fact that both types of movement begin at the same moment instead of
occurring in sequential steps like those illustrated in Fig. 13.

2. ASYMMETRICAL CONVERGENCE

The essential features of the operation of Hering's law can be duplicated in another kind of experiment. In this, the subject fixes binocularly a test target, such as a plumb-line, at a given distance. While fixation is maintained, a second plumb-line can be brought into view at a closer distance and carefully aligned along the line of sight of one (say, the left) eye. If the observer then is asked to shift his gaze from the first plumb-line to the second, it is

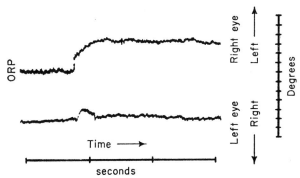

FIG. 14. Electro-oculographic record of eye position in an experiment exactly like that illustrated in Fig. 13 (Alpern, 1957). The value for γ was approximately 4°. Note the difference in velocity characteristics between the saccade and the vergence movements.

apparent that again only the right eye needs move in order to establish bifoveal fixation of the second plumb-line. In actual fact, it has been shown (Westheimer and Mitchell, 1956; Alpern and Ellen, 1956a) that once again both eyes move. The characteristics of the movements are (at least qualitatively) identical to those illustrated in Fig. 14, despite the fact that in this latter experiment a factor of accommodative vergence (cf. below) probably operates while in the former only fusional vergences are involved. Electro-myographic records of the activity of the muscles in the two eyes in the asymmetrical convergence experiment just described verify these observations (Tamler et al., 1958).[†] On the basis of a number of experiments of this kind, it seems likely that Hering's law remains valid for vergence as well as version movements.

B. DEFINITIONS

Vergence movements are movements of the eyes in which there is a change in the angle that the intersecting lines of sight of the two eyes form with each other. If attention is confined to the horizontal plane, the specifications of

[†] Of course, it is necessary to duplicate the experiment exactly. If one changes the experiment by slowly bringing the plumb-line in along the line of sight of one eye, then

these angular dimensions require but three reference points, the centres of rotation of each eye and the fixation point.† The case of symmetrical vergence (the simplest case for explanation purposes) is illustrated in Fig. 15. R and R′

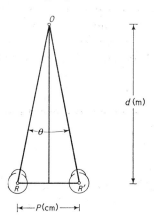

FIG. 15. Specification of the angle of (symmetrical) convergence in the horizontal plane.

represent the centres of rotation of the two eyes and O represents the point of fixation. It is desired to define the angle θ, which is twice the angle whose tangent is equal to one half the interocular separation $\left(\text{i.e., } \dfrac{RR'}{2}\right)$ divided by the distance d from the object of regard to the base-line.

1. PRISM-DIOPTRE

The measurement of an ophthalmic prism can be specified in terms of the size of the angle of deviation. Two different concepts describe this angle: (a) the centrad, which is a 100th part of the radian, and (b) the prism-dioptre which is the tangential deviation of one linear centimetre at one metre's distance. For angles smaller than 10° these two measurements are essentially identical (i.e., centrad = prism-dioptre) since for these small

the shift of gaze involves *following* rather than *saccadic* components. Under such conditions the eye, along the line of sight of which the plumb-line travels, does not reveal any overt change in electrical activity of the horizontal rectus muscles (Breinin, 1955; Blodi and Van Allen, 1957). The reasons for this discrepancy will become obvious in the discussion of the electrophysiological characteristics of pursuit and saccadic movements (cf. below).

† This definition is rigorous for defining both horizontal and vertical vergence movements, but is inexact for cyclovergence which can be described in terms of a change in angle that planes through the line of sight and the vertical corneal meridians make with each other.

angles, the angle (in radians) equals its tangent. It has been found clinically convenient to specify vergence in prism-dioptres, and so the term has developed a much wider use than merely the specification of the angle of deviation of an ophthalmic prism. Returning to the specification of the angle θ in Fig. 15, it is clear that if the interocular distance is measured in centimetres and d in metres, then the ratio of these two describes the angle θ in prism-dioptres (for all values of θ small enough so that the assumption $\tan \theta = \theta$ is valid (i.e., for $\theta \gtrless 10°$).

2. METRE-ANGLE

Nagel (1880) introduced the term metre-angle to represent the amount of vergence required for each eye to look at an object at one metre's distance. Numerically it is the reciprocal of the distance of the fixated object from the eyes in metres. Hence, when looking at an object, one metre away in the median plane, each eye converges one metre-angle and accommodates one dioptre. For an object at half a metre this would be equivalent to two metre-angles as well as two dioptres, etc. These statements would be precise only if the reference positions for vergence and accommodation were identical. Since we ordinarily specify vergence from the centre of rotation, and accommodation from the spectacle plane, the fixation of a single object does not, in fact, require exactly the same number of metre-angles of convergence as it does dioptres of accommodation. Furthermore, it is convenient to speak of the amount of vergence of both eyes (rather than of each eye) in metre-angles and usage has made this common practice. This latter has been designated as the *large*, as distinct from the small, metre-angle classically described by Nagel.

In Fig. 15 if we can assume small angles (in which the angle in radians is equal to its sine), the value for θ in prism-dioptres will be equal to the metre-angles of vergence (i.e., $1/d$ in metres) multiplied by the interocular distance in centimetres. This relationship is a convenient one to use in converting metre-angles to prism-dioptres. Obviously for individuals with different interocular separations, θ (in prism-dioptres) will have different values for an identical number of metre-angles. If the distance of the object is measured to the spectacle plane (as when one specifies accommodation) then it becomes essential to add the distance in metres from the spectacle plane to the centre of rotation to determine the value for d. Common practice permits the use of 0.027 metres as a value for the distance from the spectacle plane to the centre of rotation.

3. TYPES OF VERGENCE

In the usual method, vergence movements are classified according to direction and planes in which the movements are made. Accordingly we have horizontal, vertical and cyclovergence. In the horizontal plane there is convergence or divergence depending upon whether the lines of sight intersect before or behind the head, respectively. Vertical divergence may be either with the line of sight of the right eye moving above or below that of the left. This is designated as right sursumvergence (or left deorsumvergence) and right deorsumvergence (or left sursumvergence), respectively, since the matter is in any case only relative. Cyclovergence may be either encyclovergence or excyclovergence depending upon whether the vertical meridians of the two corneas would intersect above or below the eyes, respectively.

The classification of divergence and convergence is somewhat arbitrary and it should not necessarily be inferred that these functions are physiologically distinct.†

Another way in which vergences may be classified is according to the stimuli that may evoke them. The most common stimulus for a vergence movement is a disparity of egocentric localization of the centre of the visual fields of the two eyes. Vergence movements elicited in this way are known as fusional movements and the consequence of the fusional movement is usually a reduction (if not the elimination) in the disparity of stimulation in the two eyes. Fusional movements occur both in the horizontal and in the vertical planes, and it is now well established that cyclofusional movements also occur.

There are a number of different kinds of horizontal vergence movements. Maddox (1886) was the first to point this out. He suggested three different kinds of convergence:

(a) initial (he later [1907] adopted *tonic*) convergence

(b) accommodative convergence

(c) the fusion supplement.

a. Initial (Tonic) Vergence

Maddox phrased the question this way: "What is the starting point of convergence?" To answer this question he tried to decide what would be the position of the eyes if all of the extra-ocular muscles were devoid of all sources of innervation. This is the concept of the "anatomical position (of rest) of the eye" and, of course, cannot be operationally defined in any given observer. A variety of evidence from observations of eyes under deep anesthesia, in sleep, in complete ophthalmoplegia, and in fresh cadavers suggests, however, that Maddox's idea that, if the eye muscles were completely devoid of innervation,

† While it has been postulated from time to time that divergence and convergence are distinct functions controlled by separate "centres," such concepts lack sound foundation in modern neurological terms (Warwick, 1955), although they may have some clinical value.

the eyes would be divergent, is probably perfectly valid.† Initial (tonic) convergence represents the amount of convergence required to bring the eyes from this anatomical position of rest to the so-called physiological position of rest.

The factors influencing the magnitude of tonic convergence are but poorly understood. In many cases we can only talk about these matters in a qualitative way since much of our information comes from lower animals and there is every reason for believing that large inter-species differences exist.

The way in which the other sensory systems of the body as, for example, the otoliths and the vestibular apparatus and sensory receptors in the muscles of the head and neck, influence the tonicity of the extra-ocular muscles has already been described. The retina itself also contributes innervation to make up the basic tonus of the eye muscles. Consequently, when the eyes assume the position of physiological rest, the muscles do not become inactive. Electromyography of the eye muscles, under these conditions, shows that they exhibit a considerable amount of activity (Breinin, 1958).

b. Physiological Position of Rest

It is impossible to determine the absolute amount of tonic convergence present in any given observer, since one cannot know the anatomical position of rest. However, an indication of the extent of tonic convergence is obtained by the determination of the physiological position of rest. This is done by allowing the subject to align two targets—one seen by each eye—when all of the stimuli to fusion are obviated. The angle formed by the intersection of the lines of sight of the two eyes under these conditions is the magnitude of the distance-heterophoria. There are, for every observer, three different kinds of such measurements: a horizontal (heterophoria) angle, a vertical (heterophoria) angle, and an angle of tilt of the vertical (or any other) meridian of one eye with respect to that of the other (cyclophoria).‡

In healthy normal people these tests will usually measure very close to zero, i.e., the "normal" observer's lines of sight remain essentially parallel even in the absence of stimuli to fusional movements when he looks with relaxed accommodation at an infinitely distant object. The individual with an excess of tonic convergence will, under these same conditions, show a certain amount of esophoria. On the other hand, deficiency of tonic convergence will be demonstrated by a measurable exophoria by this same testing procedure.

† Not, however, for the waking state. When the lid is closed as in blinking, Ginsborg and Maurice (1959) obtained data suggesting that the eyes assumed a position slightly downward and 10° inward from the primary position.

‡ The various techniques of measurement of heterophoria (such as the Maddox rod, biprism and wing, the prism dissociation test, etc.) are properly described in clinical textbooks and will not be discussed here.

4

C. Fusional Movements

A person with good binocular vision has the amazing ability of orientating his eyes automatically in such a way that the visual fields of the two eyes have identical, or nearly identical, egocentric localizations. If two similar visual fields are presented, one to each eye, in such a way that their respective localizations are grossly different (say, by looking through a large vertical prism before one eye so that a large vertical disparity of homologous objects persists) the visual axes of the two eyes will remain in the position indicated by heterophoria measurements (plus, of course, the deviation of the prism). If now the disparity in the localizations of the two visual fields is gradually reduced (by reducing the strength of the prism), a point will be reached when, although considerable disparity still exists, the eyes suddenly and automatically make a movement in such a way that the egocentric localizations of the visual fields of the two eyes are immediately identical (or nearly so). The two eyes move in such a way that the visual axes are now pointing to the same object of regard. Such an eye movement is known as a fusional movement. The ability to make such movements immediately and effectively is the outstanding characteristic that differentiates people with good binocular vision from those having strabismus.

1. Demonstration of Fusional Movements

The easiest way to demonstrate fusional movements is to occlude one eye of an individual suffering from a rather large heterophoria. The eye under cover will deviate to the heterophoria position. This movement can be seen if one arranges to observe the eye movement behind the cover. It is easier, however, to observe the fusional movement that will occur when the cover is removed, as the lines of sight of the two eyes move so that both are redirected at the object of regard.† Fusional movements may be classified according to the axis of rotation about which the eye movement can be considered to occur. If this axis is a vertical axis through the centre of rotation of each eye, the movement is a horizontal fusional movement; if the axis is a line connecting the centres of rotation of the two eyes, the movement is a vertical fusional movement; if the axis of rotation is the line of sight of each eye, the movement is a cyclofusional movement. There is now abundant evidence that all three of these movements occur in people with good binocular vision. These types of fusional movement differ, of course, in the direction in which they occur, in their amplitudes, and in the nature of the disparity which is the adequate

† If the patient is strabismic—or if he has orthophoria for this observation distance—no movement may be observed. If the patient has strabismus, however, a movement of the unoccluded eye may be detected when the occluder is placed before the fixing eye. This latter movement, however, is a fixation movement not a fusional movement.

stimulus, but in many other ways they are very much alike. The stimulus for all of the fusional movements is basically a disparity in the egocentric localization of the visual field (or some part of it) in one eye compared to that of the other.†

2. STIMULUS FOR FUSION

Typically, just prior to a fusional movement the visual axes of the two eyes will not intersect in the plane of the object of regard. The consequence of the fusional movement is that the disparity in the egocentric localizations of the visual fields of the two eyes has disappeared and—what amounts to the same thing—the visual axes of the two eyes now (virtually) intersect at a single object of regard. If the disparity in the localizations of the two identical visual fields is larger, the observer will be aware of double vision—a diplopia —since the visual axes of the two eyes are pointing at different objects. It has been postulated that it is the diplopia that produces the effective stimulus for fusional movements. It is easy enough, however, to produce a fusional movement without any conscious diplopia merely by introducing a very weak prism in front of one eye while binocularly fixating a given object in the visual field. The eyes automatically move in response to the prism even though the subject is unaware of any diplopia. Experimental determinations of the threshold for a fusional movement—that is the determination of the minimum amount of disparity that will elicit the movement—has not yet been satisfactorily achieved but there is little doubt that the value is extremely small, perhaps smaller than the extent of Panum's fusional area.

a. Special Receptors

Tait (1949) postulated that special receptors are distributed in the region of the macula that function to elicit a fusional movement when there is a disparity in the stimulation of the retinas of the two eyes. The stimulation of these perimacular receptors by disparate retinal images, according to this theory, gives rise to the fusional movements required to bring the image of the object of regard upon the centre of the foveola of each eye. Such speculation accounts for some of the facts of fusional movements particularly the elicitation of a sudden fusional movement as the disparity in the localizations of the visual fields of the two eyes is gradually reduced. It is easy to see that the theory is not sophisticated enough, however, when consideration is given to the opposite situation: while fixating binocularly, a weak prism is placed before one of the two eyes. This, of course, elicits a fusional movement—

† The stimulus for stereopsis is a disparity in the oculocentric localization of a given object in the field of one eye with respect to its oculocentric localization in the field of the other eye. Other objects in the field—and in particular the object of regard—will typically have identical egocentric localizations in the two eyes.

according to the theory as a result of the disparate stimulation of perimacular receptors. If the prism is made sufficiently large no fusional movement will occur and the observer will experience diplopia. According to the theory, the image of the fixated object now falls outside the perimacular fusion receptor area and there are no receptors in the region of this image to evoke a fusional movement. Suppose, on the other hand, the power of the prism is only slowly and gradually increased. Records of eye movements under such conditions will reveal that the gradual increase in prism is associated with an eye movement (Tani *et al.*, 1956) so that the image of the object of regard continues to stimulate each fovea except immediately after the introduction of the increase in prism. Eventually, the prism becomes so strong that the observer is no longer able to make a sufficiently large fusional movement and a diplopia results. In this way one determines the amplitude of the fusional movement and such values can be obtained on any observer with good binocular vision. It is obvious, however, that the limitation of fusional movement in this situation is not related to the distribution of fusional receptors in the perimacular receptor zone. Prior to the addition of the final prism increment each fovea was stimulated by the object of regard and the addition of the final prism increment did not result in any greater disparity of retinal stimulation than did the addition of the first prism increment (which immediately elicited a prompt fusional movement).

Additional evidence against Tait's hypothesis can be found in the fact (to be discussed in detail later) that fusional movements are easy to elicit even when the visual axes of the two eyes are not directed at any object of regard at all. Disparity of egocentric localization of objects in the peripheral field of view suffices very well as a stimulus for fusional movements.

b. Stereopsis and Other Factors

It might be imagined that the stereoscopic impression of nearness (or distance) resulting from disparate stimulation of the two eyes might be responsible—i.e., the physiological stimulus—for horizontal fusional movement. Stewart (1951) tested this hypothesis by giving clues for the perception of depth that were in exact conflict with the disparity. He photographed the movements of the eyes in these circumstances and found invariably that they responded efficiently to the disparity, independently of conflicting stimuli for the perception of depth. Furthermore, there was no evidence that the various sources of stimulus for the perception of depth could give rise to fusional movements. This seems to suggest that the illusion of nearness (or distance) created by the disparity is not *per se* a stimulus for fusional movements. Apparently it is the disparity itself, rather than any stereoscopic effect resulting from the disparity, that is the important stimulus for fusional movements.

Rashbass and Westheimer (1961) have recently shown that both the amount of disparity and its rate of change affect the eye vergence response. Their experiments demonstrate that the rate of change of disparity influences the vergence in a way that anticipates the future course of the disparity. When the movement starts, the disparity begins to diminish. The differential of disparity with respect to time influences the response in a way which tends to reduce the rate at which the disparity is changing. This will reduce oscillations about the final position.

3. CHARACTERISTICS OF FUSIONAL MOVEMENTS

While the way in which disparity evokes a fusional movement is still very much of a mystery we have begun to learn a few things about the characteristics of the movements themselves. It has been known since the early pioneering efforts of Dodge (1903) and Judd (1907) that disjunctive movements of the eyes, that is the vergences, are very much slower than the conjugate movements (the versions). As a result of a number of recent studies (Stewart, 1950; Tani et al., 1956; Westheimer and Mitchell, 1956; and Alpern, 1957) it is clear that fusional movements are no exception to this rule. In fact, some of Stewart's early data suggested that the reaction-time of fusional movements was faster than, and the velocity of the movement slower than, any other kind of vergence. Subsequent work has not in general confirmed these results. In so far as reaction-time is concerned, 150 to 200 msec. seems to be the most reasonable value. This is certainly within the range of reaction-times for accommodative vergence (Alpern and Ellen, 1956a, b) and for conjugate movements as well (Westheimer, 1954a; Hyde, 1959). If differences exist between the reaction-times of these various kinds of eye movement, they are very small.

a. Effect of Amplitude on Velocity

Part of the confusion as to the velocity of fusional movements stems from the failure to realize that, just as with saccadic movements, the velocity of a vergence movement is a function of its amplitude. The greater the amplitude the faster the maximum velocity. Westheimer and Mitchell (1956) found a maximum velocity of about 21.43°/sec. for a lateral fusional movement of 5.5°, and this compares rather well with a maximum velocity of 20.2°/sec. found by Alpern and Ellen (1956a, b) for a 6.6° lateral vergence movement which had accommodative (and perhaps proximal) but no fusional components. Differences of this kind are well within the range of experimental error, and the most probable generalization that can be made is that vergence movements of comparable direction and amplitude all have the same velocity. The important point is that movements of this kind are very much slower than saccadic eye movements.

Rashbass and Westheimer (1961) found almost a linear relation between the velocity of the vergence movement (in the initial stages) and the amount of disparity. In some experiments the movement was not permitted to influence the disparity. In these, the vergence had a constant velocity very shortly after the reaction time. The velocity of such movements were related to the disparity in exactly the same way as the relation found when the movement was permitted to reduce the disparity in the usual way.

b. Type of Vergence

Increase of convergence in general has a somewhat higher velocity, and accelerates at a slightly more rapid rate, than decrease of convergence; and this appears to be true of fusional vergence (Stewart, 1951; Westheimer and Mitchell, 1956) as well as vergence movements without any fusional components (Alpern and Ellen, 1956a, b). It has been reported that the reaction-time for a decrease of positive fusional vergence may be larger than the reaction-time for an increase of positive fusional vergence, but this has not been confirmed for other kinds of horizontal vergence movements, and the discrepancies may be due to individual differences rather than to any basic difference in the physiology.

Many of these characteristics are evident in Figs. 16 and 17, which illustrate measurements of eye position in response to the sudden presentation of horizontally disparate stimuli of various amounts. The reaction time is about 160 msec. A constant velocity is soon developed and maintained for nearly 200 msec, after which the velocity falls off. The final level of eye vergence is reached in about 800 msec so that, in all, about 1 sec elapses between the onset of the stimulus and the stabilization of the response at the new level. The movement can, however, be modified during its course using information assimilated during the reaction time as well as during the movement itself. Of some interest is the fact that for higher degrees of stimulus the movement seems to occur in stages or steps. The meaning of this phenomenon is not altogether clear. It is open to a number of different interpretations, none of which can be unequivocally endorsed with the available data. Westheimer and Mitchell suggest the possibility that the two steps of the curve represent separate bursts of accommodative and fusional vergence. Another view is that the pause marks the end of the initial burst of convergence and that the fact that the images are still somewhat disparate brings about the initiation of another burst of convergence. That the latter interpretation may have some merit is suggested by measurements of cyclofusional movements (Ellerbrock, 1954). The amplitude of cyclofusional movements was measured by determining the eye position (by subjective methods) for various stimuli that were presented in equal discrete steps. The response of the eyes usually followed the change in stimulus only over a limited range and then gradually fell farther and farther behind. When this lag became quite large a burst of cyclofusional movement was induced, which caused the discrepancy between the eye position and the stimulus to disappear. Changing the stimulus caused the eye position to change but again the eye began to lag more and more behind the stimulus until it was sufficiently far behind to initiate another burst of cyclofusional movement and the cycle was repeated. Indeed the data show as many as ten such separate cycles.

4. FIXATION-DISPARITY

Perhaps the most unusual finding illustrated in Fig. 16 is the extent to which the record of eye position after one second has levelled off at a point much less than the amount of disparity of the targets. This was accompanied by no subjective diplopia. This failure of the visual axes to intersect in the plane of the stimulating target after the completion of a fusional movement is known as *fixation-disparity*. The finding itself is not surprising. It was discovered almost forty years ago (Lau) and has been confirmed independently by a number of investigators with a variety of subjective and objective measurements (Lau, 1921; Ames and Gliddon, 1928; Lewin and Sakuma,

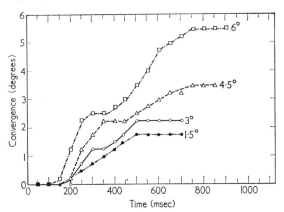

Fig. 16. Time characteristics of 1·5°, 3°, 4·5° and 6° increase in positive fusional convergence movements according to the measurements of Westheimer and Mitchell (1956) with a modified ophthalmograph. Stimulus change occurs at zero time.

1925; Ogle, 1950; Ogle and Prangen, 1951; and, Tani *et al.*, 1956). What is of some concern is the magnitude of fixation-disparity illustrated in the figure that is not associated with any evidence of diplopia. Such rather large discrepancies are frequently found when the positions of the eyes are recorded by objective methods. Tani *et al.* (1956) believe that this invalidates objective methods of recording eye position since some subjective methods show disparities of only a few minutes of arc instead of the degree or two often revealed by these objective measurements. Furthermore, these authors point out that strict interpretation of the theory of retinal correspondence requires that fixation-disparity larger than the extent of Panum's fusional areas be associated with diplopia. It has already been pointed out that the photographic method of estimating eye position does not differentiate between movements around a centre of rotation and shifts of the whole eye in the orbit. However, Verhoeff (1959) has questioned the validity of the subjective measurements of fixation-disparity. Electro-oculographic methods reveal almost the same degree of fixation-disparity as the optical methods and it is problematical whether the translational shifts of the eye in the orbit would cause an artifact that would give the same kind of distortion of the eye rotation by these two methods (Alpern, 1957). None the less the possibility exists. Rashbass and Westheimer (1961) have recently made a more exhaustive analysis of the characteristics of horizontal fusional vergences, by an objective method (Rashbass and Westheimer, 1960) which (*vide supra*) obviates artifacts from lateral displacements of the globe. Figure 17 shows a response of a step disparity stimulus of 2°. Their records do not reveal fixation disparities of more than a few minutes of arc. Whether the disparities in Fig. 16 are due

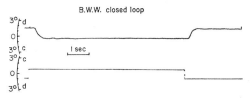

Fig. 17. Characteristics of a fusional vergence movement to a step disparity stimulus obtained by Rashbass and Westheimer (1961) using a technique which records rotations of the eyes independent of lateral shifts. The upper record is the movement, the lower the stimulus.

to artifacts of lateral eye displacement, or whether such other considerations as individual differences, size of the movement, target configuration and luminance (Ivanoff, 1953) are also important, can only be decided by further experiments.

5. REFLEX CHARACTER OF FUSIONAL MOVEMENTS

Hofmann and Bielschowsky (1900) found that an individual is incapable of initiating fusional movements on command, on the one hand, or of preventing their occurrence if adequate stimuli are present, on the other. For this reason, fusional movements were called "involuntary" or "reflex." Since nerve impulses from the two eyes remain essentially separated until they converge at the visual cortex, the nerve pathways for this "reflex" are much more complex than that of a simple patellar (or even of the more complicated pupillary light) reflex. Hofmann and Bielschowsky introduced the term psycho-optical reflex to designate the neuromotor system involved in the fusional movement.

a. Amplitude

The strength of the psycho-optical reflex—as measured by the amplitude of the fusional movements—depended upon a number of factors. First and foremost of these was the rate at which the disparity was introduced. Working on the vertical fusional movements, Ellerbrock (1949) has extended these observations. He found that if a 0.25° disparity were introduced, and the target fixated for only 0.2 minute, the amplitude of fusional movements was only about 1.3°. On the other hand, if the observer were permitted 5 minutes of fixation between each 0.25° change, the amplitude was measured as 3.7°. Experiments show that any factors that tend to make the disparate targets dissimilar will tend to reduce the amplitude of vertical divergence. For example, wearing a size-lens before one eye will reduce the amplitude of vertical fusional movements, and the effect is more pronounced the more complex the field of view. In a similar way, blurring the borders of the objects in the field of view of one eye, or reducing their luminance, or distorting them, will all produce a reduction in the amplitude of fusional movements.

If, however, factors such as these are held constant, Hofmann and Bielschowsky showed that the amplitude of fusional movements develops very gradually and increases during a series of successive tests up to a maximum value that cannot then be exceeded. They believed that even extensive practice could not increase the fusional amplitudes above this value. However, many orthoptists believe that the amplitude of positive fusional convergence can be increased through training. The extent to which the amplitudes of the other varieties of fusional vergence may be increased by practice is less certain.

Individual differences in the amplitudes of fusional movements are, of course, common and moreover the same individual may exhibit vastly smaller amplitudes than he normally does if he is tired or ill or if he is not paying careful attention to the testing procedure. Drugs such as ethanol will also depress the amplitudes of fusional movements (Colson, 1940) as well as the stability of the fusion process (Brecher *et al.*, 1955). Barbiturate intoxication produces similar effects (Westheimer and Rashbass, 1961).

6. FUSIONAL AFTER-EFFECTS

One of the most fascinating aspects about fusional movements is the fact that when binocular vision is interrupted the after-effects of any fusional movement may be quite prolonged. Thus, if the eyes are forced to make a fusional movement for some time and then suddenly the fusion-free position

4*

is determined, the lines of sight do not immediately return to the base-line phoria position they had prior to the induced fusional movement. Instead they will be deviated in the same direction as that of the fusional movement, and it will take quite some time before the measured phoria position is the same as that found prior to the beginning of the induced fusional movement. Exactly how long depends upon a number of factors including the extent of the fusional movement induced and the rate at which the stimulus for fusional movements was changed. Experiments with wearing a weak prism over one eye for prolonged periods of time indicate that rather marked effects of the fusional movement persist at least as long as one hour after the removal of the prism (provided binocular vision is then obviated). This rather slow return to the base-line phoria position can be somewhat accelerated by inducing a fusional movement in the opposite direction.

a. Interpretation

The reason for this effect is still not precisely clear. Presumably this represents some after-discharge to the extra-ocular muscles following the interruption of binocular vision, caused by incomplete fusional innervation which only very slowly disappears. It needs to be emphasized that the return to the base-line phoria position following the removal of the stimulus for fusional movements is a matter of minutes, hours or perhaps even longer (the upper limits of the curve have not been exhaustively probed). On the other hand, the immediate response of the eyes to a nominal fusional stimulus— as all other vergence movements, a "slow" ocular movement—is complete in a second or two. This difference is not merely the difference between velocity of, for example, convergence as opposed to divergence since the same effect occurs irrespective of the directions of the movements. It is rather a difference in the velocity of the response to the introduction of a fusional stimulus as compared to the response to its removal.

b. Practical Implications

Whatever the basis for this effect, it has a number of practical implications. The first of these is the obvious fact that prism-vergence testing will influence subsequent measurements of heterophoria. Most clinicians, therefore, always try to make all measurements of heterophoria prior to any measurements of prism-vergence. If this is not possible in any given case, one should be aware of the very real influence that the testing of vergence has on the phoria measurements (Ellerbrock and Fry, 1941). In general, prism-convergence testing will have a more pronounced effect on subsequent heterophoria determinations than will the testing of prism-divergence (Alpern, 1946). The reason for this is probably associated with the fact that the amplitude of convergence is usually larger than the amplitude of prism-divergence. On the other hand, the amplitudes of vertical divergence are invariably the same in the normal observer and there does not seem to be any real difference in the ability of the right deorsumvergence test as distinct from the left deorsumvergence test to influence heterophoria. Another, perhaps subtler, implication of the above phenomenon is that, in some clinical patients, heterophoria measurements may be unduly variable and unstable. This should be especially true in patients with considerable amounts of heterophoria who must use a large amount of fusional vergence to maintain clear single binocular vision in the everyday use of their eyes. The constant reliance upon the fusional vergence makes heterophoria determinations made immediately after the interruption of binocular vision much nearer to orthophoria than would be the case if the eyes were disassociated for some time prior to the phorometry. A number of clinicians have made use of this fact by prolonged occlusion of one eye prior to making measurements of heterophoria in cases in whom it was suspected that the phoria measured immediately after the interruption of binocular vision was erroneously small. Marlow (1921, 1927, 1930, 1933 and others); Bannon (1943); Swab (1930)—to name but a few— have used this method to uncover vertical heterophoria and have shown that the vertical heterophoria revealed after prolonged (the recommended duration varies according to different authorities from a few hours to several weeks) monocular occlusion will be clinically much more significant than that found under more usual testing procedures. Unfortunately a number of factors appear to complicate this procedure (Fink, 1927). First of all in a fairly large proportion (41%) of people with apparently normal eyes this procedure will reveal a hyperphoria of the occluded eye. Some authors (Abraham, 1931) feel that this is due to the fact that attempts at closing a lid are reflexly associated with an upward and outward movement of the occluded eye (Bell's phenomenon). There seems to be no obvious way of demonstrating that this is not an important factor, although recent experiments of Ginsborg and Maurice (1959), are not in accord with the basic assumption of this explanation. In addition there are well documented cases of patients who, when fusion is interrupted, will demonstrate an upward movement of the eye which is not fixating foveally, whichever one it may be (Schweigger, 1894; Stevens, 1895; Bielschowsky, 1931). With all of these difficulties it is apparent that the prolonged occlusion test can be a useful clinical tool when the above factors are kept in mind and steps are taken to avoid possible contaminating influences.

7. CYCLOFUSIONAL MOVEMENTS

These movements have been studied for almost one hundred years since Nagel (1861, 1868) rotated horizontal lines in the stereoscope in opposite directions before the two eyes while continuing to maintain single binocular vision. A number of authors (cf. Hering, 1868) have claimed that such movements did not occur and that the experiment merely demonstrated the limits of Panum's fusional areas. More recently measurements of the rotated positions of the eyes have been achieved by both objective—as well as subjective—methods and there can be little if any doubt of the ability of the eyes to make disjunctive rotations about their respective lines of sight in response to a disparate stimulation.

a. Experimental Studies

Figure 18 illustrates a typical testing situation (Ogle and Ellerbrock, 1946; Ellerbrock, 1954). A black vertical cord seen against a homogeneous white background is mounted on a ring in such a way that it may be rotated about an axis normal to the page. If one eye (the left) views the cord directly,

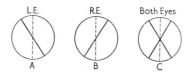

FIG. 18. Views to each eye of a black vertical cord mounted on a ring and seen against a white background when the ring is rotated counterclockwise. The left eye views the ring directly; the right eye sees it through a Dove prism which reverses the pattern.

and the other by looking at it through a Dove prism, rotation of the cord appears to the one eye as indicated in Fig. 18A, but to the other eye (the one looking through the prism) as in Fig. 18B. If the disparity in these two stimuli is not too large this target can be seen in one of two ways: (i) if the eyes make a cyclofusional movement equal to the magnitude of the disparity then a single vertical cord will be seen or; (ii) without making any cyclofusional movement at all, the crossed disparity of the bottom of the cord will cause it to appear nearer than its centre—the uncrossed disparity of the top of the cord will make it appear farther than its centre so that the cord does not appear vertical at all but tilted with its top farther away from, and its bottom closer to, the observer than its centre. Obviously these two conditions are not necessarily mutually exclusive so that the eyes can eliminate part of the disparity with the fusional movement, and whatever disparity remains will be translated into a fore-and-aft tilting of the position of the cord. One could measure the degree of cyclorotation of the eyes objectively by observing the change in position of distinctive markings of the iris with a telescope (Brecher, 1934) or by photographing the tilt of the line connecting two sutures placed for this purpose in the conjunctiva, one at the limbus near 9 o'clock, the other near the limbus at 3 o'clock (Graybiel and Woellner, 1959).

Subjectively the same result can be obtained by measuring the extent to which the cord appears to be tilted fore and aft and subtracting this from the amount of tilt predicted by the stimulus induced. The amount of tilt of the cord provides a direct measure of the amount the eyes have failed to respond to the stimulus. A variety of experiments have been done in this (or a similar) way. In one such case the targets were arranged so that the stimulus for cyclofusional movements induced by the vertical cord was exactly opposite—and thus antagonistic—to that induced by a horizontal cord. When both cords were present at the same time the vertical cord appeared to provide a much stronger stimulus for the fusional movement than did the horizontal cord. This was true even though the failure to correct for disparity of the vertical cord would still allow for stereoscopic perception of the single vertical cord in depth, while failure to correct disparity induced by the horizontal cord had no such "shock absorber." Not only is the disparity induced by vertical contours stronger, but the movement induced appears to be faster than those induced by horizontal contours (Ogle and Ellerbrock, 1946). Nevertheless, when the stimuli provided by the horizontal and vertical contours are conflicting, the horizontal contours appear to dampen down the magnitude of the response to the vertical.

Hofmann and Bielschowsky (1900) measured cyclofusional amplitudes by rotating two cards in the mirror haploscope. On the card for one eye was printed text with a horizontal line somewhat above the centre. The card for the other eye was similar except that the horizontal line for it was somewhat below the centre. The criterion for the amplitude was the extent to which the two horizontal lines appeared parallel. They found values as large as 16°. Ellerbrock (1954) using essentially the scheme illustrated in Fig. 18, found values as large as 33.9°. Factors such as target, contour, observer differences and rate of induction of disparity are undoubtedly relevant to this discrepancy.

b. Reaction-Time

Measurements of the sort described seem to indicate that there is a delay between the presentation of the disparity and the actual fusional movements, but accurate estimates as to the magnitude of this reaction-time are not available. Ogle and Ellerbrock (1946) report that the velocity of the movement is "slow" but quantitative data are not reported. Whether the velocity of these movements is the same as that of other types of fusional movement remains to be demonstrated. The movement in response to a cyclofusional disparity is carried out by both eyes even though the disparity is induced by changing the stimulus to only one eye. This fact merely reinforces the description of Hering's law of equal innervation to the yoked muscles of the two eyes—even for the case of disjunctive torsional movements.

The amplitude of cyclofusional movements was found by Herzau (1929) to be independent of the position of vertical divergence of the eyes as long as single binocular vision persisted.

8. VERTICAL FUSIONAL MOVEMENTS

Experiments to determine the position of the eyes during vertical fusional movement could be carried out by photography or by observing the position of landmarks on the iris by a telescope, but so far as the author is aware, no such objective measurements have ever been described. Estimates of eye position during vertical divergence testing have been made by subjective measurements (Burian, 1939; Ellerbrock, 1949). The observer is instructed to fixate a horizontal line visible in only one of the two eyes while a second horizontal line, visible only to the other, is moved along on a vertical track until the observer reports that the two lines are horizontally aligned. The actual position of the two lines relative to each other is read from a scale and is a measurement of the position of the lines of sight of the two eyes relative to one another in the vertical direction. This is essentially the same way that a vertical heterophoria measurement is made. However, with an ingenious arrangement of polarized targets and polaroid filters before the eyes (or by using a mirror haploscope) fusional stimuli may also be presented. The disparity of these latter targets may be varied as the independent variable. Measurements obtained in one of these ways are illustrated in Fig. 19. The vertical axis in this graph shows the measured value of the eye position in degrees, while the horizontal axis shows the disparity induced by displacing one of the 30′ white disks seen against a black background by one of the two eyes with respect to a similar disk seen by the other eye. These luminous disks served as a stimulus for the fusional movement and they were located at various angles above a monocular fixation point. It is clear that when they are in the centre of the visual field (curve labelled 0°) they are quite adequate stimuli to fusional movements. The record of the eye position changes in a linear way with the disparity until the amplitude of vertical divergence is exceeded in either direction. The curve has a unit slope which means that a unit change in disparity is associated with a unit change in the position of the eyes. In this case the amplitude of vertical divergence is roughly 4.25°. Hofmann and Bielschowsky found values as large as 5.5° with less exact methods. Depending upon the observer, the pattern of the fusional target, and other factors, measurements (by fairly precise methods) of the amplitude of vertical divergence as large as 7.5° to 8.4° have been reported (Ellerbrock, 1952).

The other curves in Fig. 19 are obtained by displacing (the indicated number of degrees) vertically, by the centre of the fusional targets, from the fixation point into the periphery. It is obvious that it is not necessary for the disparate targets to stimulate receptors in the macula at all, in order that they induce a fusional movement. The fusional movement can occur even though the observer is unaware of whether or not the stimuli were fused or of the extent of the movement. This emphasizes that hypothesized "attention" is not a necessary condition for such movements. Also, it is clear that while a centrally fixated fusional stimulus of only 0.5° can induce fusional movements as large as 4°, the displacement of the targets as far as 12° into the periphery can still

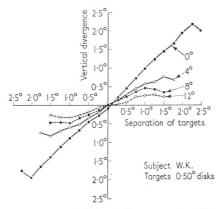

Fig. 19. The amplitude of vertical fusional divergence for different amounts of eccentric localized fusional targets according to the measurements of Ellerbrock (1949).

be associated with a fusional movement when a disparity between the targets persists. To be sure, the amplitude of the movement and the rate of change of eye movement with change in the disparity, is small in this latter condition. Nevertheless, the fact that any movement at all occurs in the latter case demonstrates that the theory of a perimacular receptor zone, as the basic sensory modality for fusional movements, is unsatisfactory.

a. Peripheral and Central Disparity

In general, disparity in the centre as well as in the peripheral field will be associated with larger amplitudes of fusional movement than if the disparity is only in one place or the other alone, provided the disparity of each is in the same direction. On the other hand, if the disparity in the centre is opposite to that in the peripheral field, then these stimuli for two opposing fusional movements will oppose each other. Other things being equal, the central stimulus in this situation should prove stronger than the one in the peripheral field but it is possible to arrange matters in such a way (by using very sharp contours and very many of them in the periphery) that the *peripheral* stimulus will predominate over the central one. This ability of fusional stimuli to summate or to subtract exists only within certain limits.

b. Horizontal Disparity

While almost all of the experimental studies of fusional movements induced by peripheral disparate stimuli have been done in the vertical direction, there is every reason for expecting that similar phenomena occur in the horizontal direction as well. In this latter case the procedure for investigation is complicated by the fact that horizontal disparities of isolated parts of the field can induce stereoscopic vision as well as accommodation changes (and the associated changes in accommodative vergence). This has tended to encourage the study of vertical fusional movements at the expense of definitive studies of the above aspects of horizontal fusional movements.

c. Fusional Movements in Strabismus

It is possible to arrange matters to demonstrate rudimentary fusional movements in certain individuals with strabismus (Alpern and Hofstetter, 1948). This occurs only with peripheral disparate stimuli usually in patients who show a sensorial disturbance when the two foveae are stimulated simultaneously (Burian, 1941).

9. HORIZONTAL FUSIONAL MOVEMENTS

Changes in disparity in the horizontal direction can induce changes in accommodation. This is a complication that needs to be kept in mind in the investigation of horizontal fusional movements. Ames and Gliddon (1928), as a matter of fact, held that there was no such thing as relative (i.e., fusional) convergence or divergence. It is very easy to demonstrate that such movements do in fact exist, even with the very equipment that Ames and Gliddon used in their experiments. For this purpose one need merely place a weak prism base-out (or base-in) before the eyes while instructing the subject to maintain clear single vision and make simultaneous measurement of the accommodation. More conveniently the prisms may be placed in the lens cell of the haploscope. The subject views the target through half-silvered mirrors observing it from the light transmitted through the mirror and a subjective optometer—to measure the accommodation—by the light reflected at the mirror surface (Morgan and Olmstead, 1939). Alternately the haploscope may have completely silvered mirrors, in which event no prisms are necessary and one merely rotates the haploscope arms to change the stimulus to convergence (Fry, 1937; 1939). In this latter case one (or each) arm of the haploscope also will have a beam splitter which reflects the light from the subjective optometer onto the observer's line of sight. Regardless of the specific techniques employed the results are invariably the same. Typical results of such experiments are illustrated in Fig. 20. The ordinate shows the measured accommodation values while the abscissa shows the independent variable, that is, the amount of stimulus to convergence (or divergence).

It should be emphasized that throughout the curve the observer continues to see the target singly.†

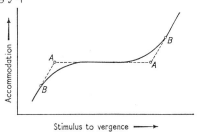

Fig. 20. The variation in accommodation as the vergence stimulus is varied throughout the range of single vision with the stimulus to accommodation held fixed.

The important point of this experiment is that the eyes respond to a change in the stimulus to horizontal vergence by continuing to see the target singly and without necessarily any change in the accommodation. This means that within limits changes in horizontal disparity produce changes in eye position without change in accommodation.

a. Accommodation

If the disparity is changed beyond these limits then the eyes begin to change their state of accommodation. If the disparity is "crossed" (i.e., a stimulus for an increase in convergence) then the refracting power of the eyes will normally increase. If the disparity is "uncrossed" or even in some cases if there is a further decrease in the amount of "crossed" disparity (i.e., a stimulus for; in the first case, an increase in divergence and, in the second, a decrease of convergence) the refractive power will normally decrease.‡

b. Stimulus for Fusion

Results like those illustrated in Fig. 20 emphasize that the definition of the stimulus for fusional movements (a disparity in the egocentric localization

† While it is true that the experiments are usually done without any objective evidence that the eyes moved in the experiment to the extent indicated by the vergence-stimulus, the assumption is usually made that this is the case. When one attempts to verify this assumption (Alpern, 1957; Westheimer and Mitchell, 1956; Tani *et al.*, 1956; Stewart, 1950 and 1951; and, Peckham, 1936) one is confronted with the problem of lack of precise methods of estimating objectively the magnitude of large eye movements. There is none the less complete agreement among all investigators that the eyes make substantial movements under these conditions and the controversy exists only as to whether the visual axes of the two eyes may fail to intersect in the plane of the target by only a few minutes of arc or whether this disparity may be as large as, say, 1° or 2°.

‡ Exceptions to this can occur. Some observers do not obtain accommodation changes from disparity. In such cases the limits of fusional movements are characterized by diplopia.

of the two eyes) is too general when applied to movements in the horizontal plane. In this latter case one can say: *The stimulus for fusional movements in the horizontal plane is a disparity in the egocentric localizations of the visual fields of the two eyes which is associated with a disjunctive movement of the eyes independent of change in their refractive power.*

c. Blurring of Image

Measurements like those illustrated in Fig. 20 have considerable clinical value, even though clinicians seldom have the time or facilities to carry them out on any given patient. However, one can measure positive and negative horizontal vergence while introducing prisms base-out, or base-in, respectively, equally before the two eyes, while the patient continues to read a row of fine print. When the patient reports a blur of these letters (which does not clear), the amount of prism represents a measure of the fusional vergence, when proper consideration is given to the amount of horizontal heterophoria under the identical testing conditions.† However, the eyes have a depth of focus of about 0.44 dioptres (Campbell, 1957). Thus, when the limit of fusional amplitude has been achieved the patient then brings about a change of accommodation (and the associated change in accommodation-vergence) and in this way overcomes the disparity. However, a certain amount of additional prism must be introduced before the observer's accommodation has been changed sufficiently that he reports a blur. Thus, in Fig. 20, the limits of fusional vergence are indicated on the diagram by A but the blur will be reported only after the accommodation change exceeds the depth of focus limit indicated at B. Hence such measurements are likely to be too large by an amount equal to the change in vergence associated with the accommodative change $(A–B)$. This is approximately 44% of the AC/A (cf. below). If the observer does not use changes in accommodation (and the related change in accommodation-vergence) to overcome the disparity (many do not) he will report a diplopia as soon as the limits of fusional vergence have been reached, and the clinical measurement will be more valid because this depth of focus factor no longer enters.

d. Amplitudes

Table I summarizes a large number of clinical measurements of horizontal fusional amplitudes obtained by different investigators and at different testing

---

† A patient with $6\varDelta$ of exophoria, a base-out to blur measurement of $9\varDelta$, and a base-in to blur measurement of $8\varDelta$, would have $15\varDelta$ (i.e., $9\varDelta + 6\varDelta$) of positive fusional vergence and $2\varDelta$ negative fusional vergence (i.e., $8\varDelta - 6\varDelta$). The range of fusional vergence would be $17\varDelta$ (i.e., $9 + 8 = 15 + 2$).

distance on normal young adult observers. In the table the values for vergence represent the amount of relative vergence, which is the amount of prism introduced until the limit of fusional vergence has been reached. No correction has been made for the amount of horizontal heterophoria. Also, included in the table are the results of measurement of horizontal heterophoria at a number of different testing distances (the negative sign indicating exophoria).

TABLE I

CLINICAL MEASUREMENTS OF THE RANGE OF FUSIONAL VERGENCE AND OF PHORIA
(PRISM-DIOPTRES)

Author	6 m. + Relative Vergence	6 m. − Relative Vergence	6 m. Phoria	40 cm. Phoria	40 cm. + Relative Vergence	40 cm. − Relative Vergence	33.33 cm. Phoria
Kirsch (1943)		8.5	− 1.25				
Haines (1941)	8.7 ± 2.1	9.2 ± 1.5	0 ± 1.0	− 4.8 ± 3.2	14.9 ± 3.2	16.3 ± 2.9	
Weymouth *et al.* (1925)				− 5 ± 7	18 ± 6	21 ± 10	
Shepard (1941)				− 5 ± 5	10 ± 4	13 ± 6	
Betts and Austin (1941)				− 3 ± 2	18 ± 5	18 ± 6	
Morgan (1944a, b)				− 3 ± 5	13 ± 4	17 ± 5	
Scobee and Green (1946)			1.11 ± 2.3				− 5.33 ± 5.33

Clinical prism testing is frequently carried on until the patient reports a diplopia instead of merely a blur of the test-target. If no blur occurs at all prior to the report of the diplopia then the prism required to elicit diplopia represents a valid measurement of the amount of fusional vergence under the given testing conditions. On the other hand, if the blur response occurs prior to the diplopia then the prism required to elicit diplopia represents a combination of the fusional vergence and whatever accommodative vergence was employed in this particular testing situation.

The magnitude of the range of fusional vergence seems to be quite independent of the amount of the accommodation-stimulus that exists in a given test situation. This fact has some importance for the relation of heterophoria and vergence and can best be elaborated after a discussion of accommodation-convergence.

e. Divergence

In Table I it is apparent that the eyes may overcome a certain amount of prism placed base-in, even when fixation is maintained at a distant object and all accommodation is relaxed. The limit of this movement is, of course, associated with a diplopia—never a blur unless the test is done improperly. The fact that such measurements can be made implies that the lines of sight of the two eyes are capable of diverging beyond a position of parallelism.

Photographic records of the position of the eyes under these conditions occasionally (but not invariably) will verify this fact, although there is the suggestion (Stewart, 1950) that fixation disparity may be unusually large under these conditions. ·

10. PUPILLARY CHANGES

Schubert and Burian (1936) reported that the pupils tend to dilate when fusion is disrupted and to constrict when the fusion is resumed but efforts to repeat this work under carefully controlled conditions have so far been unsuccessful (Marg and Morgan, 1950a). On the other hand, it is true that changes in horizontal fusional vergence (in which no change in accommodation occurs) in some subjects will be associated with a change in pupil-size (Knoll, 1949; Marg and Morgan, 1949, 1950b). About one-half of the subjects so far examined for this effect demonstrate it. The pupil becomes smaller with increasing positive fusional vergence, larger with decreasing positive fusional vergence. The rate of change, on the average, even for those subjects who show the effect at all is very small: amounting to only 0.05 mm. of pupil-size change for each prism dioptre of fusional vergence. The results of experiments of this kind serve to emphasize the importance of factors other than fusional movements (such as accommodation and its associated accommodation-convergence) in the constriction of the pupil that occurs when one fixates a near object.

D. ACCOMMODATION-VERGENCE

It has been known since the early part of the last century that the functions of accommodation and vergence are closely related. Johannes Mueller (1842) described the experiment in which, with one eye closed, he changed fixation from a distant to a near object both of which were on the same sighting line. Figure 21 illustrates a record of the change in the position of the two eyes in this experiment (Alpern and Ellen, 1956a, b). It is clear that under these conditions the fixating eye makes no detectable movement at all. On the other hand, the eye under the cover makes a clear inward vergence movement upon accommodating, and an outward vergence movement when the accommodation is relaxed.

1. MUELLER'S EXPERIMENT

In Fig. 22 the identical experiment has been carried out except that the cover has been removed from the left eye and both eyes fixate the targets. In this case, the change of fixation from the far to the near object is invariably associated with an "irrelevant" movement of the right eye. This movement is made up of two components and each of these components is a movement yoked with a movement of the other eye. The first component is a yoked saccadic (version) of both eyes to the right, the second component is a vergence movement of the left eye to the right and the right eye (to the left) back to its starting point. Note the similarity of the movements in Fig. 22 to those in Fig. 14. In each case the results follow the prediction of Hering's law.

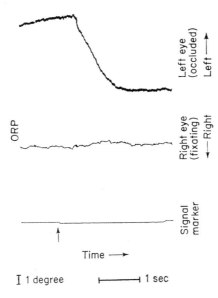

FIG. 21. Record of the eye position when fixation of the right eye is changed from a far to a near object (along its line of sight) when the left eye is occluded. Note that only the occluded eye moves.

For this reason, it is all the more surprising that when the left eye is occluded (Fig. 21) it (and only it) moves, and the movement is a pure vergence without any saccadic component at all. The reason for the differences in the behaviour of the eyes in these two experiments is not well understood. It undoubtedly is a reflexion of basic differences in the innervation patterns to the ocular muscles in these two situations.

The movement of the occluded eye in Fig. 21 is an example of what has been called *accommodation-vergence*.

2. BINOCULAR VIEWING

While it has been frequently denied, it is easy to show that changes in accommodation are associated with changes in accommodation-vergence in binocular (as well as monocular) viewing conditions by use of the fixation-disparity procedure (Ogle and Prangen, 1951; Martens and Ogle, 1959; Hebbard, 1960). Thus, the addition of minus lenses before both eyes, while it produces no change in the overt position of the eyes (and none should be anticipated since it would interfere with single binocular vision), causes a measurable shift in fixation disparity. Moreover, if one measures the amount of prism-vergence that produces a comparable shift of fixation-disparity, one

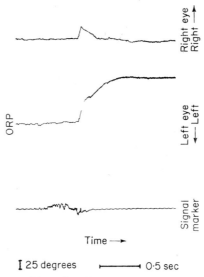

Time ⟶

I 25 degrees   ⊢————⊣ 0·5 sec

FIG. 22. Record of eye position when fixation is changed from a far to a near object along the line of sight of the right eye with binocular fixation. Note both eyes move. Compare with Fig. 21 and Fig. 14. (Data from Alpern and Ellen, 1956a.)

finds that this vergence closely parallels the amount of accommodation-vergence that the eye would show if it were occluded and its fellow provided with the same accommodation-stimulus. Thus, there are excellent reasons for supposing that the slow vergence movements of both eyes in Fig. 22 represent accommodation-vergence, and that this kind of a movement is as operative when accommodation occurs in the normal (binocular) use of the eyes as when one of the two eyes is occluded. Such a conclusion is important, since a great deal of the available information regarding accommodation-vergence has been obtained under monocular viewing conditions.

3. THE RELATIONSHIP BETWEEN ACCOMMODATION AND ACCOMMODATION-VERGENCE

Considerable speculation has gone on for a long time regarding the relation of the inward rotation (i.e., convergence) of the eye to the changes in its refracting power. Helmholtz in particular suggested that since these functions normally go hand in hand they become in their mutual relationship a manifestation of a built-up association. Tait (1933, 1951a, b) has developed and extended these views. He regarded the association as a learned reflex built up only after simultaneous co-operation of both functions in looking at near distances for some time. Similar views have been advanced by Scobee (1947) and by others.

a. Learned Association

It is not easy to arrive at a crucial experimental test of this notion. Tait (1933) showed that, in the absence of a stimulus for fusional movements, changes in accommodation produce changes in accommodation-vergence, as we have already seen, and also that, in the absence of any change in the stimulus for exact focusing, convergence changes produce changes in accommodation (i.e., convergent accommodation). The positive correlation that he found between convergence-accommodation and accommodation-vergence was taken as verification of the hypothesis of a "learned association." It is easy to show, however (Fry, 1940, 1941), that Tait's method of measuring convergent accommodation was unsatisfactory and that changes in the stimulus for exact focusing were in operation throughout his testing procedure.† More exact recent experiments of Fincham (1955); Fincham and Walton (1957); Balsam and Fry (1959); Morgan (1954); and, Heinemann et al. (1959) clearly show that when the testing procedure is adequately arranged, convergent accommodation can be demonstrated. However, it now seems quite evident that there is little if any correlation between convergent accommodation and accommodation-vergence, since the most powerful factor yet shown to influence convergent accommodation is age, which has no obvious effect at all on accommodation-vergence.

b. Myopia and Hyperopia

If the relationship between accommodation and accommodation-vergence were learned it might be expected that marked differences would exist in this relationship in myopia as a class as compared to hyperopia as a class. Donders (1864) and Maddox (1907), among others, believed such differences existed but more exact recent measurements (Morgan, 1944a and Hofstetter,

---

† Morgan (1944a) has shown that what Tait in fact was measuring was negative relative accommodation and this was verified by Fry. It can easily be demonstrated that a correlation between negative relative accommodation, and accommodation-vergence is precisely what one might expect on the basis of the nature of the zone of single binocular vision independent of any theory of the relation of accommodation and vergence. Morgan (1944b) found a smaller correlation coefficient than did Tait but this is probably due to the difference in testing distance.

1945) fail to show any relation at all between error of refraction and accommodation-vergence. Moreover, according to the learned association theory, one would not anticipate that people who have been devoid of normal single binocular vision throughout the majority—if not all—of their life, would have the same pattern of relation between accommodation and accommodation-vergence that is found in a random sample of the population of more fortunate (i.e., normal) people. This, however, is exactly what has been found (Hofstetter, 1946). Furthermore, analysis of variance of this relationship in 30 pairs of identical twins showed a greater variance between families than between members of the same family (Hofstetter, 1948). Finally, there is a lack of any substantiated evidence that the relationship between accommodation and accommodation-vergence can be modified by practice despite repeated attempts with every conceivable training device to do so.†

c. Cortical Stimulation

If the relationship between the accommodation and accommodation-vergence is not learned, how does it come about? It is not, of course, possible to give a definitive answer to this question, perhaps because it does not lend itself to ready empirical solution with controlled experiments on animal eyes. Vergence is a phenomenon largely associated with the extensive overlapping visual fields of the higher primates and man, hence almost all of the available data describing its characteristics have been obtained from (human) psychophysical experiments. Recently Jampel (1958, 1959) applied weak faradic currents to various parts of the occipital and frontal cerebral cortex in monkeys (*macaca mulatta*), while looking for horizontal vergence movements. Localized regions in the preoccipital cortex could be found in which faradic stimulation was associated with an increase in accommodation, convergence and constriction of the pupil. He found that when the eye increased accommodation, a vergence movement and pupillary constriction were associated with the change in refraction.

Such purely physiological data can serve as a foundation for a model that is quite useful in explaining the available data on the relationship of accommodation and accommodation-vergence in man. One has merely to assume that the excitation of some such region in the central nervous system occurs

† With conventional training devices it is not possible to exercise accommodation and accommodation-convergence reciprocally, since fusional vergence acts as a differential "shock absorber." If one could mechanically restrain accommodation-vergence while changing accommodation it might be possible to develop a method of changing the relationship between these two functions. However, measurements that show temporary changes due to the effects of drugs (even though the drug may be applied continually for several years) always return to the initial relationship once the effect of the drug wears off.

each time the eye (or eyes) receives a stimulus to accommodate.† Whenever this region is so excited simultaneous innervations occur to the extra-ocular muscles for the vergence movement and to the intra-ocular muscles for an accommodative change. It is necessary, however, to suppose that unit changes in innervation to accommodation are associated with a fixed change in the innervation to accommodation-vergence. This is to say that these respective innervations are linearly related to each other and that they are simultaneously evoked by a change in the accommodation-stimulus (Alpern *et al.*, 1959). There is every reason to suppose that the ratio of vergence innervation to ciliary body innervation evoked by central excitation is a unique characteristic of each individual and is not capable of modification by such factors as age, practice, drugs topically applied to the eye, surgery ‡ of the extra-ocular muscles, and the presence of normal single binocular vision, etc.

4. THE RELATIONSHIP OF CHANGES IN PUPIL-SIZE TO ACCOMMODATION AND VERGENCE

When the normal observer changes fixation from far to near his two eyes accommodate, their lines of sight converge, and their pupils constrict. This is the "near reflex" of the pupil. The virtually simultaneous coincidence of these three events (Allen, 1949a, b) greatly facilitates the task of precise clear single binocular vision of near objects. The narrowing of the pupil is related to clear vision, in this phenomenon, since small pupils greatly enhance the depth of focus of the eye (Campbell, 1957). One of the time honoured questions about this effect has been : Are the changes in pupil-size caused by the changes in accommodation or by the changes in convergence? The question has several interesting features. In the first place, it seems to assume that whatever changes occur in pupil-size are more or less secondary to the more primary changes in accommodation or in vergence. Perhaps this is due to the fact that the increased depth of field seemed to most investigators to be a much more subtle (and thus less important) effect than the more dramatic changes in refraction and in eye position. Obviously, there is no justification for such an assumption. It is easy to imagine a situation (e.g., in presbyopia or aphakia) in which changes in pupil-size would be the only possible mechanism for clear vision and hence much more important than any changes in innervation to accommodation. A second aspect of the above question is that it does not lend itself to crucial experimental testing. Changes in pupil-size occur when accommodation changes and the stimulus to vergence is

† The important theoretical question as to what constitutes an effective stimulus to accommodation will not be elaborated upon here, as it is discussed in some detail in the chapter on accommodation.

‡ Surgical procedures can, however, influence the magnitude of the AC/A (see below) by changing the relationship between muscle contraction and eye rotation.

held fixed, or *vice versa*, i.e., when convergence is changed with the stimulus to accommodation held fixed. A much more meaningful question can be raised in terms of the classifications of vergence described by Maddox and viewed in the light of the theoretical interpretation of the relationship between accommodation and accommodation-vergence described above: To which of the types of vergence changes described by Maddox are the changes in size of the pupil in the near reflex more closely related? Experimental attacks on this question have been carried out recently (Knoll, 1949; Marg and Morgan, 1949, 1950b). Whilst a definitive solution has not been reached, it is now possible to make more exact quantitative statements. It has been found that each time the eye accommodated (and, therefore, according to the above theoretical model, each time the eye brought accommodation-vergence into play) the pupil constricted, and the magnitude of these changes in pupil-size were quite marked. On the other hand, in only about 50% of the people so far examined have changes in fusional vergence been associated with changes in pupil-size. When this latter effect does occur, it is quite small (only 0.05 mm. pupil change per prism dioptre of vergence-change, on the average). If other types of vergence play any role at all in the near reflex, conclusive experimental demonstration of the fact has not been achieved.

These findings suggest that it does not seem unreasonable to expand the model of the relation of accommodation and accommodation-vergence described above. Changes in the stimulus to accommodation are associated with central excitation, which is associated in turn with simultaneous innervation to accommodation, accommodation-vergence, and to pupil-size changes, and that the ratios of these innervations are linearly related to each other. Evidence is lacking as to whether or not the ratio of innervation to pupil-size, to that of the other two processes, is modifiable by practice effect, age, drugs, and so on. However, in the light of what we can predict about the ratio of accommodation-vergence innervations, and accommodation innervations, it is likely that such modifications, if they occur at all, must be extremely small. Innervation to fusional vergence may very well arise following excitation of an adjacent part of the central nervous system and it seems likely that, in this case, innervation to changes in pupil-size will only occur in some subjects. All of this physiological model building, speculative as it may seem at first glance, is in precise accord with Jampel's (1958, 1959) experimental data on the macaque visual cortex.

5. THE AC/A RATIO

It now becomes necessary to discuss what is known quantitatively of the relationship between accommodation and accommodation-vergence. It would be desirable to quantify the ratio of the innervations to accommodation-vergence and accommodation described above. To do this, however, would require techniques not readily achievable in the relatively near future. Alpern *et al.* (1959) have shown, however, that this ratio can be reduced to measured quantities provided certain precautions are taken. They showed a linear relation between accommodation-stimulus, accommodation-response, and accommodation-vergence over an intermediate range of stimulus values. At very high and very low stimulus values a clear departure from linearity appeared. However, if one takes the precaution to make all measurements in the range in which the relation between the stimulus to accommodation and the accommodation-response is linear, then it is easy to quantify the relationship between accommodation and accommodation-vergence. The amount of accommodation-vergence associated with a unit change in the refraction of the eye expresses this quantification. This is what they called the *response AC/A ratio*. They also showed that when the above precautions are kept in mind the response AC/A ratio is mathematically identical to the ratio of innervation to accommodation-vergence to that of accommodation, according to the above theoretical model.

a. Practical Measurement

It is not clinically practical to measure the response AC/A ratio. One needs some way of measuring changes in refraction of the eye when the accommodation-stimulus is changed. To obviate this difficulty it was suggested that one should measure the amount of change in accommodation-vergence per unit change in the accommodation-*stimulus*. This is a practical measurement but since it is one step removed from the ciliary innervation it is not a measurement of the same process as is the response AC/A. Nevertheless, for many purposes it is quite adequate and if one keeps in mind the precautions of requiring accurate focus on the fixation target, it has been found that the stimulus AC/A is usually only a little bit smaller than the response AC/A. Indeed, a fair estimate of the latter can be had by multiplying the former by 1.08. While the response AC/A is clearly the preferable quantity to be used in exact research, many of the investigations that have been made have depended upon only stimulus AC/A, and this must be kept in mind when one makes an evaluation of the data.

Perhaps the best way of measuring the AC/A is haploscopically with the observer viewing, and actively reading a line of fine print with one eye. Simultaneous measurements are made of the heterophoria and of the accommodation status (with a subjective, or objective, optometer) at a number of different accommodation-stimulus levels, all of them within the range in which the accommodation response is a linear function of the accommodation. Figure 23 illustrates data (more or less typical for such an experiment) obtained in this way. It is apparent that the phoria increases as the eye accommodates. Although the data are somewhat scattered it is clear that the relationship is adequately described by a line whose slope is about 0.568. The phoria at zero accommodation would be expected to be zero, which is only slightly different from what might be found for the mean of a fairly large sample of the normal population. The reciprocal of the slope of the line is about 1.76° of phoria change for each dioptre change in the amount that the eye accommodates. This is, of course, the response AC/A.

The stimulus AC/A has been measured in a number of different ways (Ogle and Prangen, 1951; Morgan, 1944b; Cridland, 1949). The most popular of these is to make a phoria measurement at infinity (with the spectacle lens

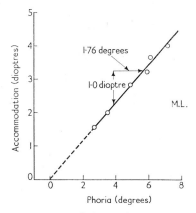

Fig. 23. Haploscopic measurements of the accommodation associated with various phoria values when the stimulus to accommodation was varied by adding + and − trial lenses before the two eyes. The AC/A is 1.76°/dioptre.

prescription in place) and also at a near distance. Actually this method is somewhat complicated by the fact that viewing at different distances sometimes involves factors other than changes in accommodation (such as changes in size, "awareness of nearness"), which increase the complexity of the interpretation of the results. Some of these factors will be discussed in more detail below. To compute the stimulus AC/A from such measurements one usually assumes that the only variable is the amount of accommodation even though the assumption is rarely warranted.

b. Calculation

The calculation involves the estimation of the amount of accommodation-vergence in the change of focus from far to near and dividing this value by the amount of dioptric change associated with the two different distances. The best way of explaining this latter calculation is by reference to Fig. 24. In this figure the right is the fixing eye and the distance heterophoria is represented by ψ; the near heterophoria by ρ. The angle γ represents the amount of assumed accommodation-vergence that one desires to calculate. It represents the amount of vergence that comes into play to bring the eyes from the distant phoria position to the near phoria position. It should be remembered that the near heterophoria value is measured, not in terms of the angle through which the lines of sight converge from a parallel position, but the angle ρ that the lines of sight make from their angle θ, which they form while comfortably reading at the near distance with single binocular vision.

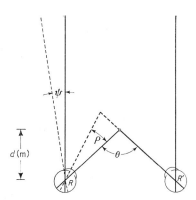

Fig. 24. Calculation of the stimulus AC/A from the distance (ψ) and near (ρ) lateral heterophoria. The accommodative vergence is assumed to be all the vergence required to bring the eyes from the distance to the near phoria position (i.e., $\theta + \rho - \psi$). The AC/A is this value divided by the difference in the stimulus to accommodation afforded by the change in the target distance. Thus when the distance phoria measurement is made at optical infinity ∞: AC/A $= d(\theta + \rho - \psi)$, where d is measured in metres and all angles are measured in prism-dioptres.

It has already been pointed out (cf. Fig. 15) that an estimate of this latter value (in prism-dioptres) can be made by multiplying the interocular separation (P in centimetres) by the reciprocal of the testing distance (d) in metres, i.e., $\theta = P/d$. It should be clear that the amount of convergence brought into play to bring the eyes from the distant phoria to the near phoria position is:

$$\gamma = \theta + \rho - \psi \quad . \quad . \quad . \quad . \quad (1)$$

In these equations the phorias are assigned a minus sign if they are exophoria and a plus sign if they are esophoria. Equation (1) shows how to compute the accommodation-vergence from the clinical measurements of the distant and near phoria. Clearly the stimulus AC/A is obtained by dividing γ by the dioptre equivalent of the near testing-distance, and this is equivalent to multiplying γ by the near testing distance (d) in metres. Thus:

$$\text{AC/A} = P + d\,(\rho - \psi) \text{ (prism-dioptres/dioptre)} \quad . \quad . \quad (2)$$

It is necessary to keep in mind, of course, that Equation 2 only applies for values of θ smaller than 10°, and that it is assumed that the only stimulus for the change of vergence is the change in accommodation. If the measurements are made on ametropic patients without correcting glasses, then the accommodation change may be less (or more) than estimated in Equation 2 and the computation will lead to an error. That is, any factor that tends to make the amount of accommodation brought into play different from $(1/d)$, such as enhanced depth of focus or inexact focusing on either the distant or near targets, can lead to an incorrect result. This is why it is always desirable —if the near phoria is to be used for this purpose—to measure the near phoria while the observer is actively accommodating on a target. Therefore, small discrete targets (such as test letters) are required for this near heterophoria measurements rather than a gross target such as a muscle light.

c. Near and Far Phorias

The computation of the AC/A using Equation (2) is fairly easy, but a considerable degree of insight may be had just by evaluating the relation of the far phoria to the near phoria and many clinicians are satisfied with this type of analysis. Thus, if the distant and near heterophoria are identical then the AC/A is exactly equal to the interocular separation. Parks (1958) recommends a difference of the far and near (i.e., 33.33 cm.) heterophoria of greater than 10 Δ as indicative of an abnormal AC/A. This rule, largely defined for young children (with their corresponding reduced interocular separation), is probably valid, also, for adults with abnormally high AC/A ratios. In the case of adults with abnormally small AC/A ratios a difference of 15 Δ between the far and near phoria would probably be a more realistic borderline between abnormal and normal. Excessively high esophoria at near compared to that at far suggests a high AC/A—an excessively high exophoria at near compared to that at far suggests a low AC/A.

Since none of these measurements involve normal single binocular vision it is possible to analyse measurements of heterotropia in exactly this same way, and the interpretation in this latter case is much the same.

d. Gradient Measurement

Another way of measuring the stimulus AC/A that involves very little computation, and is thus sometimes very handy, is the measurement of the gradient. This is the determination of the phoria at a near distance with and without + 1.00 dioptre lenses placed before the two eyes. The difference between these two heterophoria measurements represents the amount of accommodation-vergence relaxed by reducing the accommodation-stimulus one dioptre. It probably is a more realistic estimate of the response AC/A since factors such as target size and target distance are relatively constant. Measurements of the gradient made in this way on a random sampling of the population of 800 subjects by Morgan (1944b) revealed a mean gradient of 4.0 Δ/dioptre with a standard deviation of $\pm$ 2.0Δ/dioptre (Fig. 25).

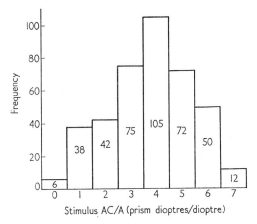

FIG. 25. Frequency distribution of gradient measurements on 200 subjects over the age of 45 years. Each measurement was made twice. (The data are from Morgan and Peters, 1951.)

e. Fixation–Disparity

Still another way of determining the stimulus AC/A is with the fixation-disparity technique developed by Ogle (1950); Ogle and Prangen (1951); Ogle *et al.* (1949); Ogle and Martens (1957) and elsewhere. The basic principle of the method is illustrated in Fig. 26. The two eyes of an observer (he must be

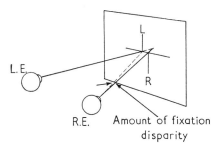

FIG. 26. Principle of measurement of fixation disparity as described by Ogle and colleagues.

capable of normal single binocular vision) look at a test-target that appears virtually identical to each of them. The exception to this is a small region in the centre in which the right eye sees only a vertical line below, while the left eye sees only a vertical line above the centre. The position of one of these two lines is varied. In the test the subject reports when the lower line is moved until it appears to be directly below the upper one. In the figure it is seen that, contrary to what might be expected, the visual axes of the two eyes do not intersect in the plane of the target but slightly behind it. The small actual separation of the lines, when they appear aligned, represents the amount of fixation-disparity and can be expressed in minutes of arc. A number of factors

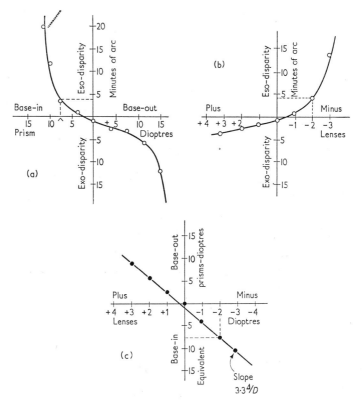

Fig. 27. Fixation disparity for various prism-vergences (a) and for various lenses placed before the eyes (b). The data in these two figures can then be used to compute a line showing the relation between accommodation and vergence. (The measurements are from Martens and Ogle, 1959.)

influence the amount of fixation-disparity including the distance of the target, the heterophoria of the observer, and prisms or lenses placed before the subject's eyes. Figure 27 illustrates the influence of these latter two factors. It is seen that the magnitude of the fixation-disparity changes in a regular manner during the prism-vergence test, and that this is also the case when the stimulus to accommodation is changed. One can derive from these two sets of data the accommodation-stimulus value that will be associated with the same fixation-disparity at a given prism-vergence value. When these latter values are plotted on a third graph (Fig. 27c) they show (in 92 % of the cases so far examined) a linear relationship between stimulus to accommodation and vergence. Since the slope of the line in Fig. 27c more or less corresponds to the more usual measurements of stimulus AC/A in the subject, one is inclined to regard this technique as a valid way of studying stimulus AC/A. However, a detailed quantitative correlation of the stimulus AC/A, as measured in this way, and other measurements of AC/A has yet to be reported on a reasonable population sample.

In a preliminary study in this direction carried out by Hebbard (1960) it became apparent that the matter was more complex than this. One of Hebbard's subjects was a part of that 8 % of the population who show a non-linear relationship between accommodation-vergence and accommodation-stimulus with the fixation-disparity method. However, the usual measurements of the relationship between accommodation and accommodation-vergence showed this latter to be perfectly linear in this same subject. Hebbard showed that fixation-disparity was not a function alone of fusional vergence (induced by prisms and/or lenses) and that other factors therefore influenced the stimulus AC/A as measured by fixation-disparity methods also. Thus, one cannot regard the fixation-disparity technique as completely satisfactory if one is interested in studying the relationship of the innervation to accommodation-vergence to the innervation to accommodation.

f. Distribution of AC/A

The distribution of the response AC/A in a random sample of the population has not been systematically investigated. Measurements of stimulus AC/A in a population of presbyopic patients are illustrated in Fig. 25. These measurements are not very different from those found in a sample of non-presbyopes. Figure 28 shows measurements using the fixation-disparity method. The mean of the population of 100 is 3.39 Δ/dioptre which is almost halfway between the value of 3.12 $\pm$ 1.64 reported by Emmes (1949) and the value of 4 $\pm$ 2 reported by Morgan (1944a, b). Both of these authors used the gradient method. Clearly a negative AC/A, that is one in which the lines of sight diverge as the stimulus to accommodation increases, or one higher than 7 Δ/dioptre is outside the range of these population samples.

g. Interocular Separation

The frequency distributions in Figs. 25 and 28 are quite different from the distribution one would obtain by sampling the interocular separation of a random sample of the normal population. This latter sample would have a mean value of about 6.2 cm. Now if the interocular separation of any given observer were exactly equal to his stimulus AC/A then the difference between

5

his distance and near lateral heterophoria would be zero. Many authors have called such an arrangement "perfect" since the observer could then look from distant objects to any required near ones without needing to exert a change in the amount of fusional vergence employed. The difference between the frequency distribution of AC/A ratios and that of the interocular separation shows that the "average normal observer" is far from "perfect." Only a very small group of the normal population (about 12%) will have a stimulus AC/A of about the same size as their interocular separation.

Most normal people have AC/A ratios just a little larger than half the interocular separation.

h. Constancy

Considerable evidence is beginning to accumulate suggesting that, while individuals differ quite remarkably in the magnitude of the AC/A, it is a fairly constant characteristic of any given individual. Fixation disparity measurements of AC/A on a single observer over a six-week period have shown a mean AC/A of 3.62 Δ/dioptre with a standard deviation of only 0.25 Δ/dioptre. Haploscopic measurements of the response AC/A repeated 30 times have yielded standard deviations of 0.13°/dioptre and 0.19°/dioptre in the case of two different observers. Measurements employing only distance and near heterophoria data are somewhat more variable but even here the day-to-day variability is smaller than a single prism-dioptre.

i. Age

In order to study the effect of age on the AC/A it would be most desirable to have a longitudinal study of response AC/A ratios on a representative sample of the population over a major part of the life-span of those individuals making up the sample—particularly between the ages of 10 and 50 years. No data of this sort have been reported. (See, however, Fry, 1959.)

On the other hand it is possible to study the mean and frequency distribution of AC/A in population samples made up of individuals of various ages. Studies of this kind have not been reported for the response AC/A, but Figs. 25 and 28 illustrate two frequency distributions of stimulus AC/A. Figure 25 shows a distribution of the measurements (by the gradient method) on presbyopic subjects (people older than 45 years of age) made by Morgan and Peters (1951); Fig. 26 shows the distribution using fixation-disparity measurements on 104 patients in the Mayo Clinic who varied in age from 14 to 72 years. It is obvious that, despite the differences in the method and in the age ranges in the samples, these two populations do not have very different stimulus AC/A ratios.

It is possible, of course, to break a given population into separate age groups and to measure the mean AC/A in each age group. Two such studies have been carried out with the stimulus AC/A. In the first of these, carried out in collaboration with Dr. Monroe J. Hirsch (unpublished data), the analysis was made of 1202 clinical cases by calculating the stimulus AC/A according to Eq. 2. Only those cases were included who did not need any additional

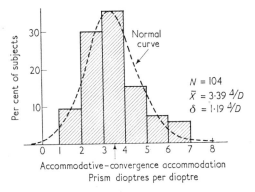

FIG. 28. Distribution of stimulus AC/A in the population as measured by fixation disparity methods. (Data from Ogle and Martens, 1957.)

plus lens in order to read the near (i.e., 40 cm.) target. The cases were grouped into five year intervals and each group contained approximately the same number of people. The results of this study are illustrated in Fig. 29 by the open circles. The trend, if any, is towards a slight decrease in the stimulus

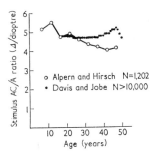

FIG. 29. Stimulus AC/A as a function of age as obtained by two different methods. (Alpern and Larson, 1960.)

AC/A with age. This is what Tait (1951a, b) reported for accommodation-vergence in much more broadly grouped age classes. Figure 29 (dots) shows similar data reported by Davis and Jobe (1957) from Ortho-Rater measurements on a much larger sample. The number of people in their older groups was much smaller than in the younger ones, and there is evidence that, in the cases over 40, considerable inability to read the near (i.e., 33.33 cm.)

target existed; and this makes any interpretation of the Ortho-Rater data in the 40-to-50 age range rather difficult. While differences in the two studies are apparent they both strongly suggest that, if the decline in the amplitude of accommodation with increasing age is associated with any change at all in the stimulus AC/A, this change must be quite small and (at least in the age range below 40) in the direction of a *decrease* in the AC/A.

j. Drugs

While little information on the effects of various drugs on the AC/A is available, several research and clinical studies have been made and these have generally had a theoretical as well as a practical importance.

Most of the information of this kind is available on the topical application of drugs that influence the peripheral accommodation system. Foremost

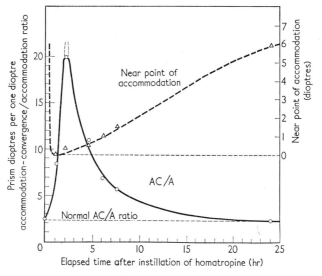

Fig. 30. Effect of topical homatropine on the near point of accommodation and on the stimulus AC/A according to Christoferson and Ogle (1956).

among these are parasympatheticolytic agents—such as atropine, homatropine, etc.—which produce cycloplegia. The onset of the cycloplegia following topical application is usually quite rapid, so that data on the effects of partial cycloplegia can be obtained best by studying the AC/A as the effects of the drug gradually begin to wear off. Flieringa and van der Hoeve (1924) made measurements of this sort; their results clearly show that the AC/A gets larger and larger as the effect of cycloplegia becomes more and more pronounced. Morgan (1954) made measurements of the response AC/A under these conditions on his own eye and found that the AC/A increased from a normal value of 4.2 Δ/dioptres to 34.3 Δ/dioptres under cycloplegia. As the cycloplegia began to wear off the AC/A gradually decreased and returned to its normal value. Very similar results have also been reported by Van Hoven (1959) and by Christoferson and Ogle (1956) who used the fixation disparity apparatus. Figure 30 illustrates the results from one of their experiments. Such experiments have been repeated a number of times also in our own laboratory and the results are always the same. There can be little doubt as to the interpretations. Drugs that block the action of acetylcholine at the myoneural junction of the ciliary muscle cause a reduction in the amount of accommodation evoked by a given innervation to the ciliary muscle. In order to produce a unit change in accommodation it is necessary to provide a greater

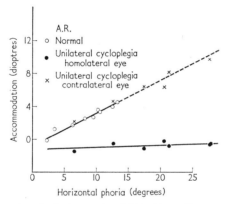

FIG. 31. Influence of cycloplegia on the AC/A. (According to the measurements of Alpern and Larson, 1960.)

than normal amount of innervation to accommodation. Since there is a linear relation between the innervation to accommodation and the innervation to accommodation-vergence (according to the theory outlined above), a greater than normal amount of innervation to accommodation-vergence will also be provided. The drug has no effect on the vergence function directly. However, a unit change in accommodation is associated with a greater than normal change in accommodation-vergence and the AC/A ratio is in this way increased.

In order to prove this interpretation, Alpern and Larson (1960) produced a unilateral cycloplegia and made measurements on the accommodation of each eye while the cycloplegic eye fixated. The results are illustrated in Fig. 31 in which the open circles represent the measurements under normal viewing conditions, the closed circles those under the influence of cycloplegia.

It is seen that the AC/A increased from 2.65 ± 0.28°/dioptre to 28.6°/dioptre under the influence of cycloplegia. In the same figure the x's are data obtained on the non-fixing eye, which also was not under the influence of the drug. Because Hering's law of equal innervation to the yoked ocular muscles of the two eyes applies to the ciliary muscle with the same validity that it does to the extra-ocular muscles, the increased innervation to the ciliary muscle of the paralysed (fixing) eye is associated with a marked increase in refracting power of the non-paralysed occluded eye. Moreover, the relationship between the amount of vergence and the change in refraction of *this* eye is precisely that obtained under normal viewing conditions.

Clinical experience in the use of atropine in the treatment of accommodative esotropia also bears this interpretation out. If only a partial cycloplegia is achieved and the child exerts some efforts to see objects clearly, then the strabismus may well be increased by the topical application of the drug. On the other hand, if extensive application of the drug is continued in sufficient dosage and over a long enough period of time, the child may soon learn that any effort to accommodate with this condition of cycloplegia is futile. He no longer makes any attempt to see clearly. Since under these conditions no innervation is sent to the ciliary muscle to accommodate, no innervation will be sent to accommodation-vergence either and the strabismus may therefore disappear.

Drugs that enhance the action of acetylcholine might at first glance be expected to act in just the opposite way. In this latter respect, however, the data are not nearly as clear cut. Sabin and Ogle (1958) studied the effect of topical application of 2% pilocarpine on the AC/A using the fixation-disparity method. The mean stimulus AC/A of their ten subjects was 4.0 ± 1.3 Δ/dioptre prior to the installation of the pilocarpine and 3.3 ± 1.0 Δ/dioptre following the application of this drug. They did not feel that such a small difference was significant. A statistical analysis of their data, however, readily shows that a difference as large as they found could occur by chance one time in much more than one hundred.† This means that a drug like pilocarpine, which presumably mimics the action of acetylcholine on the ciliary muscle, is associated with a reduction in the stimulus AC/A. A similar result would be anticipated for strong concentrations of physostigmine. Unfortunately Sabin and Ogle studied only two cases with this drug and the size of the dose is not given. One of these two observers did indeed show a decrease in AC/A—the second showing no change at all. On the basis of these findings it is reasonable to anticipate that if one gives sufficiently strong doses

† With this small sample, student's t-test may be employed provided the variances of the two groups do not differ significantly from each other. In this case F = 1.68 justifies the assumption of homogeneity of variances. Calculation shows $t = 5.6$ for 9 degrees of freedom (p = 0.01 whenever $t = 3.25$).

topical application of eserine, just like pilocarpine, will result in a significant decrease in the AC/A. As early as 1907 Maddox described such an effect of eserine on accommodation-vergence.

Di*iso*propyl fluorophosphate (DFP) also acts in a similar way. Curiously enough the effect is much more pronounced for long application of low doses (0.025%) than in single doses of high concentration (0.1%). Sloan *et al.* (1960) found in fifteen cases of continued application of the low dose over extended periods (varying from 9 days to 2 years), that the stimulus AC/A decreased in all but one case. The magnitude of the decrement seems to vary with the amount of original AC/A. (The single case which showed no decrease at all also had the lowest stimulus AC/A.)

Thus it seems quite clear that cholinergic drugs produce a decrease in AC/A. Clinical experience indeed verifies this. Application of pilocarpine, eserine, DFP and other cholinergic drugs to the eye frequently results in a reduction of the angle of strabismus (at near) in accommodation-esotropia. Parks (1958) found that 0.05% DFP (one drop in each eye once each day) caused abnormally high AC/A ratios to fall within normal limits in almost every case on which it was tried. While it may seem somewhat paradoxical that either a cholinergic drug or a choline blocking substance results in the same effect in accommodative esotropia the reasons are, of course, quite different in the two cases. Anticholinesterase agents prolong the action of acetylcholine at the motor nerve ending by inhibition of the cholinesterase enzyme. Thus, a given amount of innervation to the ciliary body causes a greater than normal accommodation change. Furthermore, the miosis enhances the amount of the depth of field and further reduces the amount of accommodation innervation required by fixation at a given near distance. As a consequence of such factors as these, an observer with topical anticholinesterase soon learns that a given accommodation-stimulus requires less than normal accommodation innervation in order to obtain clear focus. The reduction in the innervation to the ciliary body is associated with a corresponding reduction in the innervation to accommodation-vergence—because of the linear relation between these two innervations. The effects may persist for some time even after the DFP treatment has been stopped but the AC/A gradually returns to its former value (Sloan *et al.*, 1960).

It is clear that the effects described above are a consequence of the peripheral action of these drugs; but it is also possible that certain changes in AC/A can come about by action of drugs on the central nervous system. One possible example of this is the effects of systemic ethanol. A number of studies have been carried out on these effects. Powell (1938); Colson (1940); and, Brecher *et al.* (1955) showed that the increase of blood-alcohol was associated with a marked increase in tonic convergence—i.e., an increase of esophoria measured at 6 metres. Heterophoria measurements at 82 cm. showed only a

slight increase in esophoria as the blood-alcohol level increased, while heterophoria measurements at 33 cm. showed an increase in *exophoria* with increase of the blood-alcohol. This could mean that increase of the blood-alcohol
was associated with a progressive decrease in the stimulus AC/A as well as an
increase in tonic convergence. They also found that the near point of convergence was reduced and it may well be that this is merely another manifestation of the reduction in the AC/A. The same results were obtained by Powell
(1938). His data are illustrated in Fig. 32 in which the measured mean

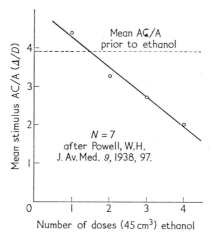

Fig. 32. Effect of alcohol on stimulus AC/A. (Data computed from the experiments of
Powell, 1938.)

stimulus AC/A is plotted against the number of doses of ethanol. These measurements were made 1 hour following the dose (and immediately prior to the
next one). It is possible, of course, that effects of this kind merely reflect a
change in the ability of the eyes to respond to accommodation-stimuli,
rather than any real change in response AC/A. It is of some interest that the
fusional mechanisms are also presumably affected by this drug. Exactly
similar results were obtained in barbiturate intoxication by Westheimer and
Rashbass (1961). In these experiments there was no evidence of any decrement in measurements of accommodation by three different methods, indicating that the drug must have acted on the central nervous system.

E. Other Stimuli for Vergence Movements

It has been known for a long time that vergence movements can also be
evoked by stimuli other than those already described. For example, a
heterophoria measurement made with a stereoscopic device can frequently

show more esophoria than those made in the usual way even though the accommodation-stimulus is the same in the two cases. Such effects have gone under various names: proximal convergence, instrument convergence, and psychic convergence, to name only a few. Vergence movements of this kind are much less predictable than other kinds, and it is far from definite precisely how they come about. The results from one individual to another are extremely variable—some people even showing a reverse effect. On the other hand, the effect may be quite large in certain observers. The suggestion has been made that one can quantify the proximal convergence-distance relationship by a ratio similar to the AC/A ratio—i.e., the amount of change in proximal convergence associated with a unit change (in dioptres) in the reciprocal of the actual measuring distance (Knoll, 1959). Such notions seem ill-advised since what evidence is available seems to indicate that the relationship between the change in vergence (at a fixed value of accommodation) and the reciprocal of the testing distance in dioptres is seldom, if ever, linear (Alpern, 1955).

1. AWARENESS OF NEARNESS

It has been suggested that so-called proximal effects are a manifestation of a facilitation of fusional convergence induced by an "awareness of nearness" of the target (Hofstetter, 1951). This is based on the finding that "proximal" convergence is larger when the limit of positive fusional vergence is used as the criterion, than when the limit of negative fusional vergence is used. Moreover, it is a frequent observation in prism-vergence testing that, as the strength of a base-out prism before the eyes is gradually increased the test-target is perceived as smaller and moves in toward the observer (the so-called *silo-effect*). It might be imagined that this would induce "proximal" convergence.† The changes in perceived size and distance are quite analogous to changes in the size of a projected after-image as the surface on to which it is observed is brought closer to the eye (Emmert, 1881).

2. RELATION TO SIZE CONSTANCY

Despite these facts, the evidence suggests that the above interpretation is inadequate. Strabismic observers—who do not show any evidence of being able to make ordinary fusional movements at all—still show a pronounced "proximal" convergence and the phenomenon is, if anything, even more pronounced in the case of such observers than in those with good binocular vision (Alpern, 1955). Ittelson and Ames (1950) have shown that changes in size produce changes in vergence, and it is easy to show that these effects can occur independently of any changes in accommodation of the eyes (Alpern,

---

† This effect was first described by Wheatstone (1852). If negative fusional vergence is being tested then the target appears larger and moves away from the observer. The term *silo* derives from the initials: *s*maller, *in*; *l*arger, *out*.

5*

1958). Unlike the silo-effect this latter phenomenon is manifest even when the stimuli for any fusional movement at all have been obviated. In this latter case, the increase in vergence is associated with an increase in physical size of the object and presumably an increase in size of the retinal image. In other experiments, the size of the retinal image remains fixed and the increase of vergence is associated with a decrease in perceived (as distinct from retinal image) size (Heinemann et al., 1959). In order to classify all these effects together, let us assume (the assumption is easy enough to test) in the Ittelson and Ames experiment that the increase of retinal image-size is associated with a reduction in the perceived size over what would be expected if the laws of size-constancy did not operate. It is this reduction of the perceived size of objects, whose retinal images are large and whose positions in space are very near the observer, that is now proposed as the effective stimulus for increase of "proximal" convergence. Conversely, the increase of the perceived size of objects whose retinal images are very small and whose positions in space are very far from the observer, is the effective stimulus for a decrease in proximal convergence.

3. INDUCED BY VERGENCE CHANGES

While change in size is an effective stimulus for producing a change in vergence, it is now also quite clear that, conversely, changes in convergence are effective stimuli for producing changes in perceived size. Again, unlike the silo-effect, this occurs, whether one eye only, or both observe the target (Heinemann et al., 1959). Thus a reciprocal relationship appears evident: size change may induce vergence movement and vergence change may induce a size change and either effect can occur in monocular vision. It does not seem too unreasonable to propose that this reciprocity comes about as a result of the continued association of these two processes concurrently in the everyday use of the eyes over a long period of time. Hence increased convergence is so continuously associated with reduction of perceived size in the operation of size-constancy that by the time these size-constancy changes are firmly established (Leibowitz and Hartman, 1959), the presence of either process by itself is an effective stimulus for the production of the other.

F. APPRAISAL OF THE CHARACTERISTICS OF BINOCULAR VISION

1. TYPES OF DYSFUNCTION

The classification of vergence movements developed by Maddox (1886) is quite helpful in understanding some of the motor aspects of binocular vision in any given observer. Duane (1897) suggested that one could classify people in the following way: (a) convergence insufficiency; (b) convergence excess; (c) divergence insufficiency; and, (d) divergence excess. Subsequent writers have modified the original meaning of these terms more or less arbitrarily and so the same terms have come to mean different things to different people. Usually, however, the following symptoms are considered: convergence insufficiency, little or no heterophoria at distance with a large exophoria at near and a reduced near point of convergence; convergence excess, little or no heterophoria for distance with a large esophoria for near and an increased—or normal—near point of convergence; divergence insufficiency, esophoria for distance and approximate orthophoria for near; and, divergence excess, exophoria for distance with orthophoria at near. In convergence insufficiency the tonic convergence is normal, but the AC/A ratio is low. In convergence excess the tonic convergence is again normal but the AC/A is very high. In divergence insufficiency there is a low tonic convergence associated with a normal or low AC/A; low tonic convergence is also a feature of divergence excess but in this case the AC/A ratio is high.

2. ACCOMMODATION AND CONVERGENCE

Considerable insight into the operation of the motor aspects of binocular vision can be obtained from studying the accommodation associated with various amounts of convergence and at various stimulus levels to accommodation. The easiest way of doing this is to measure the accommodation-response at a fixed stimulus to accommodation as the vergence-stimulus is varied in both a positive and negative direction over the range in which the observer is capable of single binocular vision. The data obtained can be

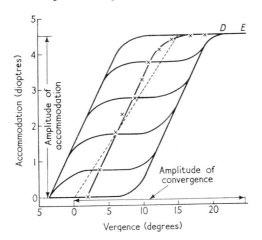

FIG. 33. The zone of clear single binocular vision. The dotted line represents the amount of convergence and accommodation required for symmetrical convergence on a target. The line marked with X's represents phoria values at various accommodation levels.

fitted by a sigmoid curve like that already described in Fig. 20. A curve of this shape can be obtained at each stimulus level of accommodation throughout the range in which the eye can accommodate (Fig. 33). In this way one can outline the zone of clear single binocular vision. This is a graph that contains within its borders all possible accommodation and convergence values with which an observer is capable of seeing both clearly and singly. Experimental determinations of this sort have been carried out by the classical physiologists of eye movements such as Donders (1864); Pereles (1889); Nagel (1880); Landolt (1886); Percival (1892); and, Howe (1907). It is only fairly recently (Fry, 1937, 1939; Fincham and Walton, 1957), however, that precise instruments that make accurate

measurements of the accommodative state of the eye have been employed. The results †
of experiments of this sort are illustrated in Fig. 33. The zone is, roughly, a parallelogram in shape, with sloping vertical sides. The slope of these sides is identical to the slope
of the line showing the change in the phoria with increasing accommodation (cf. Fig. 23)
which is drawn in Fig. 33 with the x's. This is the justification for the statement already
made (when discussing the data in Fig. 20) that when the limits of the amplitude of
fusional vergence are achieved, accommodative vergence may be brought into play.
In this way the subject postpones the onset of diplopia. The width of the zone represents
the total amplitude of horizontal fusional movements. The height of the zone represents
the amplitude of accommodation. The dotted line drawn in the figure represents the so-
called Donders's line—i.e., the amount of convergence and accommodation required for
symmetrical convergence on a target that is brought in along the middle towards the
eyes.‡ The curves in Fig. 33 are more or less typical with the exception that the distance
heterophoria is considerably more esophoric than what is usually found. The separation
between Donders's line and the phoria(x's) line shows, at any given accommodation level,
the amount of fusional vergence required for binocular fixation at the given target-dis-
tance. Some subjects do not bring any accommodation into play at the limits of fusional
vergence, and for these observers the target breaks into two without blurring. In this
case, the shape of the curve at any given stimulus level of accommodation is a straight
horizontal line and not sigmoid, but the form of the zone is no different from that illustrated in Fig. 33. The upper right-hand part of the graph shows a projection, DE, beyond
the limits of the parallelogram to the near point of convergence, E. Some authors have
more or less arbitrarily assumed that this represents fusional vergence somehow enhanced
or facilitated as the near point of convergence is approached. It is easy enough to show,
however, that designation of accommodation-vergence for this part of the graph is much
more accurate. (Alpern, 1950b; Alpern $et\,al.$, 1959). It is true, of course, that the amplitude
of accommodation is reached (because of the sclerosis of the fibres of the lens) so that
changes in innervation to accommodation at this level are not associated with further
changes in accommodation. However, these changes in innervation to accommodation are
as much associated with changes in vergence at this level as they were at lower accommo-
dation-levels. Consequently, the relationship between accommodation response and

† A comprehensive summary of the literature on this problem and some interesting
experimental data can be found in the monograph by Hofstetter (1945).
‡ The line is curved, and not straight because the accommodation of the eyes is specified
at the spectacle plane while the vergence is specified at the centre of rotation. The dotted
curve in Fig. 33 is also drawn with the assumption that the eyes have no spectacle lenses
in front of them. The form of the curve will, of course, be changed if spectacle lenses are
worn; plus-lenses shifting the curve farther to the right, minus-lenses shifting it farther
to the left at near distances. The exact equation, considering these factors, can be derived
from the geometry of Fig. 15 and the first-order theory of spectacle lenses (Alpern,
1950a). It has the form:

$$\theta = \frac{P}{h - u + Fuh} \tag{3}$$

In this equation P, as before, is the separation of the centres of rotation of the two eyes
in centimetres; F is the power of the (thin) lens in dioptres; u is the distance of the target
from the spectacle plane, and h is the distance from the lens to the centre of rotation of
the eyes. Both of these latter quantities must be measured in metres. θ is measured in
centrads (or prism-dioptres). The equation is valid when $\theta \leq 10°$.

vergence now departs from linearity even though the relationships of innervation to accommodation, and of innervation to vergence, remain the same. Thus, the projection DE in the limit of positive vergence remains parallel (and at the extreme, collinear) with the phoria line even though neither of these is any longer a straight line at the higher levels of accommodation.

It has already been pointed out that the AC/A—and therefore the slope of the zone— does not change with age. The net result of this is that the progressive decrease in the amplitude of accommodation with age is merely associated with a reduction in the height of the zone. There is also some evidence, that there may be, in oddities, a corresponding increase in the projection DE at the upper right-hand limit. These results have important implications for the theory of presbyopia but it is easier to discuss this in the chapter on the mechanism of accommodation.

a. Area of Comfort

A study of the features of the zone give an insight into the binocular visual character-istics of any given observer. If, for example, the Donders's line falls outside the zone then, wherever this occurs, binocular vision is no longer possible. Certain authors have taken advantage of this fact to attempt to outline areas within the zone that would permit comfortable binocular vision. It should be emphasized that these criteria have been developed from more or less arbitrary estimates, rather than from empirical data. Never theless, a considerable amount of usefulness can be attributed to them from the fact that they have accumulated a certain degree of clinical "validity."

Percival (1892) recommended that the "area of comfort" could be outlined by the region in the middle third of the zone of clear single vision. If, at any given fixation distance, the Donders's line falls within the middle third of the range between the positive and negative fusional vergence limits the patient should be comfortable. On the other hand, if the Donders's line at this distance falls outside the middle third of the range between the positive and negative fusional vergence limits, then the patient would be uncomfortable. Percival then recommended the use of lenses, prisms, and orthoptics in this latter case in order to bring the zone of comfort within the point of intersection of the Donders's line. Percival made these recommendations for accommodation stimuli less than 3 D (and convergence stimuli smaller than 3 metre-angles) but recent usage has advanced the same notion for all fixation distances.

b. Demand and Reserve

Another rule for the same purpose was recommended by Sheard (1930). He pointed out that Percival gave no consideration to the relationship of the phoria to the zone of single vision. He regarded the phoria as a measure of the "demand" of single vision and the measurement of fusional vergence in the opposite direction to the phoria (i.e., the dis-tance from the Donders's line to the limit of fusional vergence) as a measure of the amount of "reserve." For comfortable vision he recommended that the "reserve" be equal to or greater than twice the "demand." Lenses and prisms were indicated when these criteria were not met. In this way the phoria point (through the glasses) was shifted so that the residual "demand" was equal to one-half the resultant "reserve." A critical clinical comparison of these two rules for treatment of discomfort has yet to be completed. In most practical situations they lead to similar recommendations so that the distinction in many cases is purely academic. In some cases, however, quite different treatment procedures evolve from the application of the two rules and it would be important to know which of the two had greater value.

c. Zone of Single Vision

Clinically, the determination of the characteristic outline of the zone of single vision becomes impractical. However, a rough idea of its shape can be approximated from only a very few tests. The determination of the phoria at distance and near gives a measurement of the stimulus AC/A ratio, and thus an indication of the slope of the zone. The determination of the limit of positive and negative fusional vergence at distance and near, the near points of accommodation and convergence, suffices for an approximate estimate of the shape of the zone. In individual cases in which measurements are ambiguous, further measurements can be made, at a near distance, of the limits of positive and negative fusional vergence, and of the heterophoria with various plus- and minus-lenses.

While these rules have been developed for appraisal of the binocular vision characteristics in the horizontal plane, many investigators have also recommended their use in analysing the need for and the amount of vertical prism to be prescribed as well. An evaluation of the relative merits of the rules for this purpose would also be desirable.

G. DEVELOPMENT OF BINOCULAR VISION

At birth the fovea is still not fully developed and still contains both ganglion cells and bipolar cells. The foveal cones are short and not fully developed. This fact may explain the absence of sustained fixation in the newborn. Conjugate eye movements and opto-kinetic nystagmus are present at, or near, the time of birth. Co-ordinated compensatory eye movements, in which the eyes move in the opposite direction of head movements, occur during the first week and are effective by the end of the first month. (Gesell *et al.*, 1949). Four months after birth the bipolar and ganglion cells of the fovea have disappeared, the foveal cones are more fully developed and there are several layers of cones at the fovea. Henle's fibre layer makes its appearance. By this time sustained foveal fixation of objects becomes well established, and the child is able to shift his gaze from one object of interest to another with facility. Alternation of fixation of objects leads to binocular convergence which may appear as early as the second month. At first this appears as a series of short jerks, but as age increases the movement becomes increasingly smooth. If the movement is maintained for too long or too near a distance a temporary strabismus may set in. Gesell *et al.* (1949) point out that even in early infancy the movements of fixation, accommodation, and convergence develop in close correlation. Co-ordination of eye and hand is achieved by the end of the twenty-eighth week. By the end of the first year there is a general increase in the mobility of the eyes and in the awareness of depth and movement.

References

Abraham, S. V. (1931). Bell's phenomenon and the fallacy of the occlusion test. *Amer. J. Ophthal.* 14, 656–664.

Ades, H. W., Graybiel, A., Morrill, S. N., Tolhurst, G. C., and Niven, J. I. (1957). Nystagmus elicited by high intensity sound. U.S. Naval School of Aviation Medicine Res. Rept., Proj. No. NM 13 01 99, Subtask 2, Report No. 6.

Adler, F. H., and Fliegelman, M. (1934). Influence of fixation on the visual acuity. *Arch. Ophthal., N.Y.* 12, 475–483.

Allen, M. J. (1949a). An investigation of the time characteristics of accommodation and convergence of the eyes. Ph.D. Thesis. Ohio State University.

Allen, M. J. (1949b). An objective high speed photographic technique for simultaneously recording changes in accommodation and convergence. *Amer. J. Optom.* 26, 279–289.

Alpern, M. (1946). The after effect of lateral duction testing on subsequent phoria measurements. *Amer. J. Optom.* 23, 442–447.

Alpern, M. (1950a). Further comment on accommodation and convergence with contact lenses. *Amer. J. Optom.* 27, 238–241.

Alpern, M. (1950b). The zone of clear single vision at the upper levels of accommodation and convergence. *Amer. J. Optom.* 27, 491–513.

Alpern, M. (1955). Testing distance effect on phoria measurement at various accommodation levels. *A.M.A. Arch. Ophthal.* 54, 906–915.

Alpern, M. (1957). The position of the eyes during prism vergence. *A.M.A. Arch. Ophthal.* 57, 345–353.

Alpern, M. (1958). Vergence and accommodation. I. Can change in size induce vergence movements? *A.M.A. Arch. Ophthal.* 60, 355–357.

Alpern, M., and Ellen, P. (1956a). A quantitative analysis of the horizontal movements of the eyes in the experiment of Johannes Mueller. I. Method and results. *Amer. J. Ophthal.* 42 (No. 4, Pt. 2), 289–296.

Alpern, M., and Ellen, P. (1956b). A quantitative analysis of the horizontal movements of the eyes in the experiment of Johannes Mueller. II. Effect of variation in target separation. *Amer. J. Ophthal.* 42 (No. 4, Pt. 2), 296–303.

Alpern, M., and Hirsch, M. J. Age and the AC/A. Unpublished.

Alpern, M., and Hofstetter, H. W. (1948). The effect of prism on esotropia—a case report. *Amer. J. Optom.* 25, 80–91.

Alpern, M., Falls, H. F., and Lee, G. B. (1960). The enigma of typical total monochromacy. *Amer. J. Ophthal.* (in press).

Alpern, M., Kincaid, W. M., and Lubeck, M. J. (1959). Vergence and accommodation: III. Proposed definitions of the AC/A ratios. *Amer. J. Ophthal.* 48 (No. 1, Pt. 2), 143–148.

Alpern, M., and Larson, B. F. (1960). Vergence and accommodation: IV. Effect of luminance quantity of the AC/A. *Amer. J. Ophthal.* 49, 1140–1149.

Ames, A., Jr., and Gliddon, G. H. (1928). Ocular measurements. *Trans. Ophthal. Amer. med. Ass.* pp. 102–175.

Balsam, M. H., and Fry, G. A. (1959). Convergence accommodation. *Amer. J. Optom.* 36, 567–575.

Bannon, R. E. (1943). Diagnostic and therapeutic use of monocular occlusion. *Amer. J. Optom.* 20, 345–358.

Barlow, H. B. (1952). Eye movements during fixation. *J. Physiol.* 116, 290–306.

Benjamins, C. E. (1918). Contribution à la connaissance des réflexes toniques des muscles de l'oeil. *Arch. néerl. Physiol.* 2, 536–544.

Betts, E. A., and Austin, A. S. (1941). Seeing problems of school children. *Optom. Wkly.* **32**, 369–371.

Bielschowsky, A. (1931). Die einseitigen und gegensinnigen ("disseziierton") Vertikalbewegungen der Augen. *v. Graefes Arch. Ophthal.* **125**, 493–553.

Bielschowsky, A. (1943). "Lectures on Motor Anomalies". Dartmouth College Press, Hanover, N.H.

Blodi, F. C., and Van Allen, M. W. (1957). Electromyography of extraocular muscles in fusional movement: I. Electric phenomena at the breakpoint of fusion. *Amer. J. Ophthal.* **44** (No. 4, Pt. 2), 136–144.

Brecher, G. A. (1934). Die optokinetische Ausloesung von Augenrollung und rotatorischem Nystagmus. *Pflüg. Arch. ges. Physiol.* **234**, 13–28.

Brecher, G. A., Hartman, A. P., and Leonard, D. D. (1955). Effect of alcohol on binocular vision. *Amer. J. Ophthal.* **39** (No. 2, Pt. 2), 44–52.

Breinin, G. M. (1955). The nature of vergence revealed by electromyography. *A.M.A. Arch. Ophthal.* **54**, 407–409.

Breinin, G. M. (1958). Analytic studies of the electromyogram of human extraocular muscle. *Amer. J. Ophthal.* **46** (No. 3, Pt. 2), 123–142.

Brindley, G. S. (1956). The passive electrical properties of the frog's retina, choroid and sclera for radial fields and currents. *J. Physiol.* **134**, 339–352.

Brockhurst, R. J., and Lion, K. S. (1951). Analysis of ocular movements by means of an electrical method. *A.M.A. Arch. Ophthal.* **46**, 311–314.

Brown, K. T., and Wiesel, T. N. (1958). Intraretinal recording in the unopened cat eye. *Amer. J. Ophthal.* **46** (No. 3, Pt. 2), 91–98.

Burian, H. M. (1939). Fusional movements: role of peripheral retinal stimuli. *Arch. Ophthal., N.Y.* **21**, 486–491.

Burian, H. M. (1941). Fusional movements in permanent strabismus. A study of the role of the central and peripheral retinal regions in the act of binocular vision in squint. *Arch. Ophthal., N.Y.* **26**, 626–652.

Campbell, F. W. (1957). The depth of field of the human eye. *Optica Acta, Paris* **4**, 157–164.

Christoferson, K. W., and Ogle, K. N. (1956). The effect of homatropine on the accommodation-convergence association. *A.M.A. Arch. Ophthal.* **55**, 779–791.

Colson, Z. W. (1940). The effect of alcohol on vision. An experimental investigation. *J. Amer. med. Ass.* **115**, 1525–1527.

Cornsweet, T. N. (1956). Determination of the stimuli for involuntary drifts and saccadic eye movements. *J. opt. Soc. Amer.* **46**, 987–993.

Cornsweet, T. N. (1958). A new technique for the measurement of small eye movements. *J. opt. Soc. Amer.* **48**, 808–811.

Cridland, N. (1949). The relation between accommodation and non-fusional convergence. *Trans. ophthal. Soc. U.K.* **69**, 567–574.

Davies, T., and Merton, P. A. (1958). Recording compensatory rolling of the eyes. *J. Physiol.* **140**, 27–28P.

Davis, C. J., and Jobe, F. W. (1957). Further studies on the A.C.A. ratio as measured on the ortho-rater. *Amer. J. Optom.* **34**, 16–25.

de Kleijn, A. (1921). Tonische Labyrinth und Halsreflexe auf die Augen. *Pflüg. Arch. ges. Physiol.* **186**, 82–97.

Ditchburn, R. W. (1955). Eye movements in relation to retinal action. *Optica Acta* **1**, 171–176.

Ditchburn, R. W., and Fender, D. H. (1955). The stabilized retinal image. *Optica Acta* **2**, 128–133.

Ditchburn, R. W., and Ginsborg, B. L. (1952). Vision with a stabilized retinal image. *Nature, Lond.* **170**, 36–37.

Ditchburn, R. W., and Ginsborg, B. L. (1953). Involuntary eye movements during fixation. *J. Physiol.* **119**, 1–17.

Dodge, R. (1903). Five types of eye movement in the horizontal meridian plane of the field of regard. *Amer. J. Physiol.* **8**, 307–329.

Dodge, R. (1921). A mirror-recorder for photographing the compensatory movements of closed eyes. *J. exp. Psychol.* **4**, 165–174.

Dodge, R., and Cline, T. S. (1901). The angle velocity of eye movements. *Psychol. Rev.* **8**, 145–157.

Donders, F. C. (1864). "On the Anomalies of Accommodation and Refraction of the Eye; With a Preliminary Essay on Physiological Dioptrics". (Translated by W. D. Moore.) The New Sydenham Society, London.

Duane, A. (1897). A new classification of the motor anomalies of the eye, based upon physiological principles. *Ann. Ophthal.* **6**, 84–122.

Duke-Elder, W. S. (1932). "Textbook of Ophthalmology", Vol. I. C. V. Mosby Company, St. Louis.

Duke-Elder, W. S. (1949). "Textbook of Ophthalmology", Vol. IV. C. V. Mosby Company, St. Louis.

Ellerbrock, V. J. (1949). Experimental investigation of vertical fusional movements. *Amer. J. Optom.* **26**, 327–337; 388–399.

Ellerbrock, V. J. (1952). The effect of aniseikonia on the amplitude of vertical divergence. *Amer. J. Optom.* **29**, 403–415.

Ellerbrock, V. J. (1954). Inducement of cyclofusional movements. *Amer. J. Optom.* **31**, 553–566.

Ellerbrock, V. J., and Fry, G. A. (1941). The after-effect induced by vertical divergence. *Amer. J. Optom.* **18**, 450–454.

Emmert, E. (1881). Groessenverhaeltnisse der Nachbilder. *Klin. Mbl. Augenheilk.* **19**, 443–454.

Emmes, A. B. (1949). A statistical analysis of the accommodative-convergence gradient. *Amer. J. Optom.* **26**, 474–482.

Fender, D. H. (1955a). Torsional motions of the eyeball. *Brit. J. Ophthal.* **39**, 65–72.

Fender, D. H. (1955b). Variation of fixation direction with colour of fixation target. *Brit. J. Ophthal.* **39**, 294–297.

Fender, D. H. and Nye, P. W. (1961). An Investigation of the mechanisms of eye movement control. *Kybernetik.* **1**, 81–88.

Fincham, E. F. (1955). The proportion of ciliary muscular force required for accommodation. *J. Physiol.* **128**, 99–112.

Fincham, E. F., and Walton, J. (1957). The reciprocal actions of accommodation and convergence. *J. Physiol.* **137**, 488–508.

Fink, W. H. (1927). Significance of latent ocular muscle imbalance. *Amer. J. Ophthal.* **10**, 168–170.

Flieringa, H. J., and van der Hoeve, J. (1924). Arbeiten aus dem Gebiete der Akkommodation. *v. Graefes Arch. Ophthal.* **114**, 1–46.

Ford, A. (1959). Significance of terminal transients in electro-oculographic recordings. *A.M.A. Arch. Ophthal.* **61**, 899–906.

Ford, A., White, C. T., and Lichtenstein, M. (1959). Analysis of eye movements during free search. *J. Opt. Soc. Amer.* **49**, 287–292.

Fry, G. A. (1937). An experimental analysis of the accommodation-convergence relationship. *Amer. J. Optom.* **14**, 402–414. (*Trans. Amer. Acad. Optom.* **11**, 64–76.)

Fry, G. A. (1939). Further experiments on the accommodation-convergence relationship. *Amer. J. Optom.* **16**, 325–336. (*Trans. Amer. Acad. Optom.* **12**, 65–73.)

Fry, G. A. (1940). Skiametric measurement of convergent accommodation. *Optom. Wkly.* **31**, 353–356.

Fry, G. A. (1941). An analysis of the relationships between phoria, blur, break and recovery findings at the near point *Amer. J. Optom.* **18**, 393–402.

Fry, G. A. (1959). The effect of age on the AC/A ratio. *Amer. J. Optom.* **36**, 299–303.

Gesell, A., Ilg, F. L., and Bullis, G. E. (1949). "Vision: Its Development in Infant and Child". Paul B. Hoeber, Inc., New York.

Ginsborg, B. L., and Maurice, D. M. (1959). Involuntary movements of the eye during fixation and blinking. *Brit. J. Ophthal.* **43**, 435–437.

Graybiel, A., and Woellner, R. C. (1959). A new and objective method for measuring ocular torsion. *Amer. J. Ophthal.* **47**, 349–352.

Haidinger, W. (1844). Ueber das directe Erkennen des polarischen Lichts und der Lage der Polarisationsebene. *Annal. der Physik u. chemie.* Ser. 2, **63**, 29–39.

Haines, H. F. (1941). Normal values of visual functions and their application in case analysis. *Amer. J. Optom.* **18**, 1–8; 58–73; 167–173.

Hebbard, F. W. (1960). Foveal fixation disparity measurements and their use in determining the relationship between accommodative convergence and accommodation. *Amer. J. Optom.* **37**, 3–26.

Heinemann, E. G., Tulving, E., and Nachmias, J. (1959). The effect of oculomotor adjustments on apparent size. *Amer. J. Psychol.* **72**, 32–45.

Hering, E. (1868). "Die Lehre vom Binocularen Sehen", pp. 92–102. W. Engelmann, Leipzig.

Herzau, W. (1929). Ueber das Verhaeltnis von erzwungener Vertikaldivergenz und Rollung bei der Fusion. *v. Graefes Arch. Ophthal.* **122**, 59–74.

Higgins, G. C., and Stultz, K. F. (1953). Frequency and amplitude of ocular tremor. *J. opt. Soc. Amer.* **43**, 1136–1140.

Hirsch, M. J. (1943). A study of forty-eight cases of convergence insufficiency at the near point. *Amer. J. Optom.* **20**, 52–58.

Hofmann, F. B., and Bielschowsky, A. (1900). Ueber die Willkuer entzogenen Fusionsbewegungen der Augen. *Pflüg. Arch. ges. Physiol.* **80**, 1–40.

Hofstetter, H. W. (1945). The zone of clear single binocular vision. *Amer. J. Optom.* **22**, 301–333; 361–384.

Hoftstetter, H. W. (1946). Accommodative convergence in squinters. *Amer. J. Optom.* **23**, 417–437.

Hofstetter, H. W. (1948). Accommodative convergence in identical twins. *Amer. J. Optom.* **25**, 480–491.

Hofstetter, H. W. (1951). The relationship of proximal convergence to fusional and accommodation convergence. *Amer. J. Optom.* **28**, 300–308.

Howe, L. (1907). "The Muscles of the Eye", Vol. I. G. P. Putnam's Sons, New York.

Hyde, J. E. (1959). Some characteristics of voluntary human ocular movements in the horizontal plane. *Amer. J. Ophthal.* **48**, 85–94.

Iarbus, A. L. (1957). A new method of studying the activity of various parts of the retina. *Biophysics* **2**, 165–167.

Ittelson, W. H., and Ames, A., Jr. (1950). Accommodation, convergence and their relation to apparent distance. *J. Psychol.* **30**, 43–62.

Ivanoff, A. (1953). Convergence des yeux aux faibles luminances. *In* "Coloquio sobre Problemas Opticos de la Visión", Vol. II, pp. 1–3. C. Bermejo, Madrid.

Jampel, R. S. (1958). A study of convergence, divergence, pupillary reactions and accommodation from faradic stimulation of the Macaque brain. Ph.D. Thesis. University of Michigan.

Jampel, R. S. (1959). Representation of the near-response on the cerebral cortex of the Macaque. *Amer. J. Ophthal.* **48** (No. 5, Pt. 2), 573–582.

Jones, L. A., and Higgins, G. C. (1947). Photographic granularity and graininess. III. Some characteristics of the visual system of importance in the evaluation of graininess and granularity. *J. opt. Soc. Amer.* **37**, 217–263.

Jones, L. A., and Higgins, G. C. (1948). Photographic granularity and graininess. IV. Visual acuity thresholds; dynamic versus static assumptions. *J. opt. Soc. Amer.* **38**, 398–405.

Judd, C. H. (1907). Photographic records of convergence and divergence. *Psychol. Rev., Monog. Suppl.* **8**, 370–423.

Knoll, H. A. (1949). Pupillary changes associated with accommodation and convergence. *Amer. J. Optom.* **26**, 346–357.

Knoll, H. A. (1959). Proximal factors in convergence. A theoretical consideration. *Amer. J. Optom.* **36**, 378–381.

Korovina, M. V. (1959). Electrical changes in the various eye muscles produced by impulses from the vestibular apparatus and from the neck muscles in animals of different ages. *Sechenov J. Physiol.* **45**, No. 1, 29–35.

Kris, C. (1958). Corneo-fundal potential variations during light and dark adaptation. *Nature, Lond.* **182**, 1027–1028.

Landolt, E. (1886). "The Refraction and Accommodation of the Eye and Their Anomalies". (Translated by C. M. Culver), pp. 195–218. J. B. Lippincott Company, Philadelphia.

Lau, E. (1921). Neue Untersuchungen ueber das Tiefen- und Ebenensehen. *Z. Psychol. Physiol. Sinnesorg.* Abt. **2, 53**, 1–35.

Law, T., and DeValois, R. L. (1957). Periorbital potentials recorded during small eye movements. *Pap. Mich. Acad. Sci.* **43**, 171–180 (meeting 1957).

Leibowitz, H., and Hartman, T. (1959). Magnitude of the moon illusion as a function of the age of the observer. *Science* **130**, 569–570.

Lewin, K., and Sakuma, K. (1925). Die Sehrichtung monokularer und binokularer Objekte bei Bewegung und das Zustandekommen des Tiefeneffektes. *Psychol. Forsch.* **6**, 298–357.

Lord, M. P., and Wright, W. D. (1948). Eye movements during monocular fixation. *Nature, Lond.* **162**, 25–26.

Lorente do Nó, R. (1933). Vestibulo-ocular reflex arc. *Arch. Neurol. Psychiat., Chicago*, 245–291.

McCouch, G. P., and Adler, F. H. (1932). Extraocular reflexes. *Amer. J. Physiol.* **100**, 78–88.

Mackworth, J. F., and Mackworth, N. H. (1958). Eye fixations recorded on changing visual scenes by the television eye-marker. *J. opt. Soc. Amer.* **48**, 439–445.

Maddox, E. E. (1886). Investigations on the relation between convergence and accommodation of the eyes. *J. Anat.* **20**, 475–508; 565–584.

Maddox, E. E. (1907). "The Clinical Use of Prisms and the Decentring of Lenses", 5th edition, pp. 158–177. John Wright & Company, Bristol.

Magnus, R. (1924). "Koerperstellung; experimentelle physiologische Untersuchungen ueber die einzelnen bei der Koerperstellung in Taetigkeit tretenden Reflexe, ueber ihr Zusammenwirken und ihre Stoerungen". Julius Springer, Berlin.

Marg, E. (1951). Development of electro-oculography: standing potential of the eye in registration of eye movement. *A.M.A. Arch. Ophthal.* **45**, 169–185.

Marg, E., and Morgan, M. W., Jr. (1949). The pupillary near reflex. The relation of pupillary diameter to accommodation and the various components of convergence. *Amer. J. Optom.* **26**, 183–198.

Marg. E., and Morgan, M. W., Jr. (1950a). The pupillary fusion reflex. *Arch. Ophthal. N.Y.* **43**, 871–878.

Marg, E., and Morgan, M. W., Jr. (1950b). Further investigation of the pupillary near reflex; the effect of accommodation, fusional convergence and the proximity factor on pupillary diameter. *Amer. J. Optom.* **27**, 217–225.

Marlow, F. W. (1921). Prolonged monocular occlusion as a test for the muscle balance. *Amer. J. Ophthal.* **4**, 238–250.

Marlow, F. W. (1927). Observations on the prolonged occlusion test. *Amer. J. Ophthal.* **10**, 567–574.

Marlow, F. W. (1930). The prolonged occlusion test. *Brit. J. Ophthal.* **14**, 385–393.

Marlow, F. W. (1933). Recent observations on the prolonged occlusion test. *Amer. J. Ophthal.* **16**, 519–527.

Marshall, W. H., and Talbot, S. A. (1942). Recent evidence for neural mechanisms in vision leading to a general theory of sensory acuity. *Biol. Symp.* **7**, 117–164.

Martens, T. G., and Ogle, K. N. (1959). Observations on accommodative convergence: especially its nonlinear relationship. *Amer. J. Ophthal.* **47** (No. 1, Pt. 2), 455–463.

Maxwell, J. C. (1856). On the unequal sensibility of the foramen centrale to light of different colours. *Rep. Brit. Ass.* **26**, Notices & Abstracts, p. 12.

Morgan, M. W., Jr. (1944a). Accommodation and its relation to convergence. *Amer. J. Optom.* **21**, 183–195.

Morgan, M. W., Jr. (1944b). The clinical aspects of accommodation and convergence. *Amer. J. Optom.* **21**, 301–313.

Morgan, M. W., Jr. (1952). Relationship between accommodation and convergence. *A.M.A. Arch. Ophthal.* **47**, 745–759.

Morgan, M. W., Jr. (1954). The ciliary body in accommodation and accommodative-convergence. *Amer. J. Optom.* **31**, 219–229.

Morgan, M. W., Jr., and Olmstead, J. M. D. (1939). Quantitative measurements of relative accommodation and relative convergence. *Proc. Soc. exp. Biol., N.Y.* **41**, 303–307.

Morgan, M. W., Jr., and Peters, H. B. (1951). Accommodative-convergence in presbyopia. *Amer. J. Optom.* **28**, 3–10.

Mueller, J. (1842). "Elements of Physiology" (translated from the German by W. Baly), Vol. II, p. 1147. Taylor and Walton, London.

Nachmias, J. (1959). Two-dimensional motion of the retinal image during monocular fixation. *J. opt. Soc. Amer.* **49**, 901–908.

Nagel, A. (1861). "Das Sehen mit zwei Augen und die Lehre von den identischen Netzhautstellen", p. 51. C. F. Winter, Leipzig.

Nagel, A. (1868). Ueber das Vorkommen von wahren Rollungen des Auges um die Gesichtslinie. *v. Graefes Arch. Ophthal.* **14** (Abt. 2), 228–246.

Nagel, A. (1880). Die Anomalieen der Refraction und Accommodation des Auges. *In* "Handbuch der gesammten Augenheilkunde" (A. Graefe and T. Saemisch, eds.), Vol. VI, pp. 257–503. W. Engelmann, Leipzig.

Noell, W. K. (1953). Studies on the electrophysiology and the metabolism of the retina. U.S. Air Force School Aviat. Med. Report No. 1, pp. 1–22. Project No. 21–1201–0004.

O'Brien, B. (1951) Vision and resolution in the central retina. *J. opt. Soc. Amer.* **41**, 882–894.

Ogle, K. N. (1950). "Researches in Binocular Vision". W. B. Saunders Company, Philadelphia.

Ogle, K. N. and Ellerbrock, V. J. (1946). Cyclofusional movements. *Arch. Ophthal.*, *N.Y.* **36,** 700–735.

Ogle, K. N., and Martens, T. G. (1957). On the accommodative convergence and the proximal convergence. *A.M.A. Arch. Ophthal.* **57,** 702–715.

Ogle, K. N., and Prangen, A. de H. (1951). Further considerations of fixation disparity and the binocular fusional processes. *Amer. J. Ophthal.* **34** (No. 5, Pt. 2), 57–72.

Ogle, K. N., Mussey, F., and Prangen, A. de H. (1949). Fixation disparity and the fusional processes in binocular single vision. *Amer. J. Ophthal.* **32,** 1069–1087.

Parks, M. M. (1958). Abnormal accommodative convergence in squint. *A.M.A. Arch. Ophthal.* **59,** 364–380.

Pasik, P., Pasik, T. and Krieger, H. P. (1959). Effects of cerebral lesions upon optokinetic nystagmus in monkeys. *J. Neurophysiol,* **22,** 297–304.

Peckham, R. H. (1936). An objective study of binocular vision. *Amer. J. Psychol.* **48,** 474–479.

Percival, A. S. (1892). The relation of convergence to accommodation and its practical bearing. *Ophthal. Rev.* **11,** 313–328.

Pereles, H. (1889). Ueber die relative Accommodationsbreite. *v. Graefes Arch. Ophthal.* **35,** (Abt. 4), 84–115.

Powell, W. H., Jr. (1938). Ocular manifestations of alcohol and a consideration of individual variations in seven cases studied. *J. Aviat. Med.* **9,** 97–103.

Powsner, E. R., and Lion, K. S. (1950). Testing eye muscles. *Electronics* **23** (No. 3), 96–99.

Rashbass, C. (1959). Barbiturate nystagmus and the mechanisms of visual fixation. *Nature, Lond.* **183,** 897–898.

Rashbass, C. (1960). New method for recording eye movements. *J. opt. Soc. Amer.* **50,** 642–644.

Rashbass, C., and Westheimer, G. (1960). Recording rotational eye movements independently of lateral displacements. *J. opt. Soc. Amer.* **50,** 512.

Rashbass, C. and Westheimer, G. (1961). Disjunctive eye movements. *J. Physiol.* **159,** 149–170.

Ratliff, F. (1952). The role of physiological nystagmus in monocular acuity. *J. exp. Psychol.* **43,** 163–172.

Ratliff, F. (1958). Stationary retinal image requiring no attachments to the eye. *J. opt. Soc. Amer.* **48,** 274–275.

Ratliff, F., and Riggs, L. A. (1950). Involuntary motions of the eye during monocular fixation. *J. exp. Psychol.* **40,** 687–701.

Riggs, L. A., and Tulunay, S. Ü. (1959). Visual effects of varying the extent of compensation for eye movements. *J. opt. Soc. Amer.* **49,** 741–745.

Riggs, L. A., Ratliff, F., Cornsweet, J. C., and Cornsweet, T. N. (1953). Disappearance of steadily fixated visual test objects. *J. opt. Soc. Amer.* **43,** 495–501.

Riggs, L. A., Armington, J. C., and Ratliff, F. (1954). Motions of the retinal image during fixation. *J. opt. Soc. Amer.* **44,** 315–321.

Sabin, F. C., and Ogle, K. N. (1958). Accommodation-convergence association: experiments with phenylephrine, pilocarpine, and physostigmine. *A.M.A. Arch. Ophthal.* **59,** 324–332.

Schöne, H. (1954). Statozystenfunktion und statische Lageorientierung bei Dekapoden Krebsen. *Z. vergl. Physiol.* **36,** 241–260.

Schubert, G., and Burian, H. (1936). Die Fusionsreaktion, eine bisher unbekannte Reaktion der Pupille. *Pflüg. Arch. ges. Physiol.* **238**, 184–186.

Schweigger, C. (1894). Die Erfolge der Schieloperation. *Arch. Augenheilk* **29**, 165–220.

Scobee, R. G. (1947). "The Oculorotary Muscles", p. 113. C. V. Mosby Company, St. Louis.

Scobee, R. G., and Green, E. L. (1946). A center for ocular divergence: does it exist? *Amer. J. Ophthal.* **29**, 422–434.

Shackel, B. (1960). Note on mobile eye viewpoint recording. *J. opt. Soc. Amer.* **50**, 763–768.

Sheard, C. (1930). The zones of ocular comfort. *Amer. J. Optom.* **7**, 9–25.

Shepard, C. F. (1941). The most probable expecteds. *Optom. Wkly.* **32**, 538.

Sloan, L. L., Sears, M. L., and Jablonski, M. D. (1960). Convergence-accommodation relationship. Description of a simple clinical test and its application to the evaluation of isoflurophate (DFP) therapy. *A.M.A. Arch. Ophthal.* **63**, 283–306.

Smith, K. U. (1937). The postoperative effects of removal of the striate cortex upon certain unlearned visually controlled reactions in cats. *J. Genet. Psychol.* **50**, 297–304.

Smith, W. M., and Warter, P. J., Jr. (1960). Eye movement and stimulus movement; new photoelectric electromechanical system for recording and measuring tracking motions of the eye. *J. opt. Soc. Amer.* **50**, 245–250.

Stevens, G. T. (1895). Du Strabisme vertical alternant et des déviations symétriques moins prononcées que le strabisme. *Ann. Oculist., Paris* **113**, 225–232; 385–393.

Stewart, C. R. (1950). An investigation of the time characteristics of lateral fusional movements of the eyes. M.Sc. Thesis. The Ohio State University.

Stewart, C. R. (1951). A photographic investigation of lateral fusional movements of the eyes. Ph.D. Thesis. The Ohio State University.

Stroud, J. (1951). Discussion. *In* "Transactions of the Seventh Conference on Cybernetics, March 23–24, 1950" (H. von Foerster, M. Mead, and H. L. Teuber, eds.), pp. 28–32. Josiah Macy, Jr. Foundation, New York.

Swab, C. M. (1930). Latent heterophoria as noted after prolonged monocular occlusion. *Amer. J. Ophthal.* **13**, 1054–1057.

Szentágothai, J. (1950b). The elementary vestibulo-ocular reflex arc. *J. Neurophysiol.* **13**, 395–407.

Tait, E. F. (1933). A reciprocal reflex system in the accommodation-convergence relationships. *Amer. J. Psychol.* **45**, 647–662.

Tait, E. F. (1949). Fusional vergence. *Amer. J. Ophthal.* **32**, 1223–1230.

Tait, E. F. (1951a). Accommodative convergence. *Amer. J. Ophthal.* **34**, 1093–1107.

Tait, E. F. (1951b). "Textbook of Refraction", pp. 22–32. W. B. Saunders Company, Philadelphia.

Tamler, E., Jampolsky, A., and Marg, E. (1958). An electromyographic study of asymmetric convergence. *Amer. J. Ophthal.* **46** (No. 5, Pt. 2), 174–182.

Tani, G. T., Ogle, K. N., Weaver, R. W., and Martens, T. G. (1956). On the precise objective determination of eye movements. *A.M.A. Arch. Ophthal.* **55**, 174–185.

ter Braak, J. W. G. (1936). Untersuchungen ueber optokinetischen Nystagmus. *Arch. néere. physiol.* **21**, 309–376.

Tinker, M. A. (1936a). Eye movement, perception, and legibility in reading. *Psychol. Bull.* **33**, 275–290.

Tinker, M. A. (1936b). Reliability and validity of eye-movement measures of reading. *J. exp. Psychol.* **19**, 732–647.

Tinker, M. A. (1938). Motor efficiency of the eye as a factor in reading. *J. educ. Psychol.* **29**, 167–174.

Tinker, M.A. (1942). Individual and sex differences in speed of saccadic eye movements. *In* "Studies in Personality", pp. 271–280. McGraw-Hill Book Company, Inc., New York.

Tinker, M. A. (1951). Fixation pause duration in reading. *J. Educ. Res.* **44**, 471–479.

Van Hoven, R. C. (1959). Partial cycloplegia and the accommodation-convergence relationship. *Amer. J. Optom.* **36**, 22–39.

Verhoeff, F. H. (1959). Fixation disparity. *Amer. J. Ophthal.* **48**, 339–341.

Warwick, R. (1955). The so-called nucleus of convergence. *Brain* **78**, 92–114.

Wendt, G. R. (1951). Vestibular functions. *In* "Handbook of Experimental Psychology" (S. S. Stevens, ed.), pp. 1193–1223. John Wiley & Sons, Inc., New York.

Westheimer, G. (1954a). Mechanism of saccadic eye movements. *A.M.A. Arch. Ophthal.* **52**, 710–724.

Westheimer, G. (1954b). Eye movement responses to a horizontally moving visual stimulus. *A.M.A. Arch. Ophthal.* **52**, 932–943.

Westheimer, G. (1957). Kinematics of the eye. *J. opt. Soc. Amer.* **47**, 967–974.

Westheimer, G., and Mitchell, A. M. (1956). Eye movement responses to convergence stimuli. *A.M.A. Arch. Ophthal.* **55**, 848–856.

Westheimer, G. and Rashbass, C. (1961). Barbiturates and Eye Vergence. *Nature, Lond.* **191**, 833–834.

Weymouth, F. W., Andersen, E. E., and Averill, H. L. (1923). Retinal mean local sign; a new view of the relation of the retinal mosaic to visual perception. *Amer. J. Physiol.* **63**, 410–411.

Weymouth, F. W., Brust, P. R., and Gobar, F. (1925). Ocular muscle balance at reading distance, and certain related factors. *Amer. J. physiol. Opt.* **6**, 184–205.

Wheatstone, C. (1852). Contributions to the physiology of vision. II. On some remarkable, and hitherto unobserved, phenomena of binocular vision (continued). *Philosoph. Mag. Ser.* 4, **3**, 504–523.

Woellner, R. C., and Graybiel, A. (1959). Counterrolling of the eyes and its dependence on the magnitude of gravitational or inertial force acting laterally on the body. *J. Appl. Physiol.* **14**, 632–634.

Yarbus, A. L. (1957a). Motion of the eye on interchanging fixation points at rest in space. *Biophysics* **2**, 679–683 (translated from *Biofizika* **2**, 698–702.)

Yarbus, A. L. (1957b). The perception of an image fixed with respect to the retina. *Biophysics* **2**, 683–690 (translated from *Biofizika* **2**, 703–712.)

CHAPTER 6

Physiological Characteristics of the Extra-Ocular Muscles

I. Extra-Ocular Myography

While there may be some dispute as to whether the eye muscles are histologically red or white, there can be little doubt, because of the exhaustive experiments of Cooper and Eccles (1930); Brown and Harvey (1941); and Reid (1949), that extra-ocular muscles are extremely fast acting. Cooper and Eccles studied the physiological characteristics of a number of different kinds of mammalian striated muscle, and the eye muscles were the fastest acting of them all. In the medial rectus of the cat they found that, following stimulation of the motor nerve, the interval between the onset of the electrical

TABLE I

CHARACTERISTICS OF VARIOUS MUSCLES OF THE CAT (COOPER AND ECCLES, 1930)

Muscle	Twitch tension (kg.)	Tension double response / Tension Single response	Tetanus tension (kg.)	Tetanus tens. / twitch tens.	Twitch contraction time (msec.)	R = 1/contract time (sec.⁻¹)	Tens. of tetanus at R (kg.)	Tens. at rate R / max. tetanus tens.	Stim. rate needed for complete mechanic fusion (sec.⁻¹)
eus	0.65	1.9	2.44	3.8	100	10	1.85	07.6	—
	0.65	1.9	2.10	3·26	94	10.6	1.73	08.2	33
	0.875	—	2.77	3.26	120	8.3	2.16	07.8	31
stroc- mius	4.64	1.94	14.58	3.30	39	26.6	10.1	0.685	100
tensor	0.63	3.30 †	3.12	4.95 †	23.4	42.7	2.4	0.77	115
itorum gus	0.65	2.2	2.35	3.76	38.2	26.2	1.65	0.74	108
dial tus	0.0093	larger than 3	0.1	10.7	7.5	133	0.07	0.7	350

† Values are high owing to the rather low initial tension used throughout this experiment.

activity and the onset of the contraction (i.e., the contraction-time) could be as short as 7.5 to 10 msec. Brown and Harvey (1941) found that a peak of the twitch-tension could be attained in as little as 7 to 8 msec. Once this peak was achieved the muscle relaxed 50% in only 6.5 to 7 msec. more. The average maximum twitch-tension of the inferior oblique was found to be about 0.96 grammes, which is smaller by a factor of almost 1,000 than that which the soleus can develop. The duration of the twitch of the eye muscle is less than 100 msec., which is about half that of the gastrocnemius and about a fifth

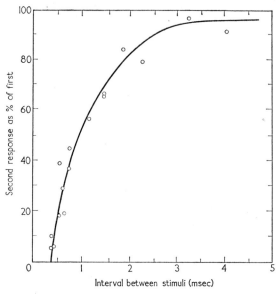

FIG. 1. Percentage of response of the cat inferior oblique to the second of two shocks to its motor nerve according to Brown and Harvey (1941).

that of the soleus. A comparison of some of the characteristics of the medial rectus and other muscles of the cat, obtained by Cooper and Eccles (1930), is summarized in Table I. While the eye muscles develop only a comparatively small tension the ratio of the tetanus- to twitch-tension is almost three times as high as that of the soleus or gastrocnemius in the cat. The eye muscles build up about 70% of their maximum tension when they are stimulated at a rate that is equal to the reciprocal of its contraction-time, and this is what is generally found in other kinds of striped muscle also.

A. REFRACTORY PERIOD

Figure 1 shows the magnitude of the second of two responses to stimulation as a function of the interval between the stimuli, in the extra-ocular muscle of the cat. There is an absolute refractory period smaller than 0.5 msec. and a relative refractory period that has terminated after about 3.5 msec. This is extremely short and, together with the short duration of the twitch, accounts for the fact that the muscle can build up a tetanus-tension about 10 times the twitch-tension.

1. FUSION

It would be expected from examination of these data that the frequency of stimulation required for mechanical fusion of responses would be extremely high and this indeed is the case. In the goat, stimulation at the rate of 250 stimuli per second gave almost complete fusion (Whitteridge, 1959); in the cat, the value is 350 (Cooper and Eccles, 1930). These values are much larger than one finds typically for other kinds of skeletal muscles. In a similar fashion, the frequency of firing of motor units in eye muscles is larger than in other skeletal muscle. Adrian and Bronk (1929) found rates of 20 to 50 per second in the skeletal muscle that they examined. In the case of the eye muscle of the cat, Reid (1949) on the other hand found values of over 170 per second and similar high-frequency discharge rates have been reported for eye muscles of other animals including man.

B HUMAN STUDIES

Recently a considerable amount of effort has been devoted to the study of human extra-ocular muscles by placing small needle-electrodes into them and observing the variations in electrical activity obtained as the eye undergoes various kinds of movement (Adler, 1953; Björk, 1952; Momose, 1957; Sears et al., 1959; Kuboki, 1957; Breinin, 1958; Tamler et al., 1959a, b, c, among others). While the method can undoubtedly be quite informative, it has inherent within it a number of difficulties (Jampolsky et al., 1959).

1. SOURCES OF ERROR

In the human eye activity of adjacent muscles such as the orbicularis may appear in the record even though it is not the subject of study. As in any system in which the electrode attempts to sample a small group of motor units or a single motor unit, one cannot infer anything about the activity of other units in the muscle that are not being sampled. Consequently, one must be extremely cautious about generalizing the results from study of the activity of a few motor units to what other units in the muscle, or the muscle as a whole, or the eye as a whole, may be doing. This seems so obvious that one would hesitate to mention it if the already rather extensive literature in this field were not characterized by numerous examples of such interpretations.

Still another problem in such work is the inherent assumption that the integrated muscle activity, and the tension developed in the muscle, are directly related. This seems to be the case for isometric contraction of skeletal muscle but the eye muscles do not maintain a constant length when they contract *in vivo*. When one studies the activity of a sample of motor units in the eye muscle further complications arise when the muscle contracts.

When the muscle contracts the eye moves, and when the eye moves the muscle moves as well. Under these conditions, the relationship between the position of the electrode (which is adherent to conjunctival and/or lid tissue) with respect to the muscle fibres may very well undergo a change. If this change is rather gross the artifact will probably be obvious and no very great harm result since the data can merely be rejected. On the other hand, the possibility is always at hand that the change between the position of the electrode at the beginning and that at the end of the movement may be so subtle as to go undetected. Despite this fact, the motor units sampled at the beginning of the movement may be quite different from those sampled at the end and one has no clear idea when (or if) the transition occurred.

One final source of error comes from the presence of the electrode within the muscle itself. One cannot be sure how closely the activity so recorded resembles the activity of the muscle in its normal physiological state. To be sure one tries to make the electrode as fine as possible in order to avoid such problems. Working with fine wire electrodes in the inferior oblique muscle of the decerebrate cat, however, Reid (1949) found that the presence of the electrode provoked discharge of single motor units that were being sampled. The discharge patterns he found were similar to those described by Adrian (1930) for isolated injured mammalian nerve. They appeared even when the motor nerve had been cut for as long as 3 hours before, and they could not be inhibited by appropriate head (and therefore eye) movements. While these artifacts appeared readily in the extra-ocular muscles, perhaps because of the fineness of the fibres or the richness of the nerve supply, they were not found in other skeletal muscle.

2. TONIC DISCHARGE

Whatever its reason there seems to be little doubt that electrical activity is readily recorded when electrodes are placed within the muscle, even though the eye itself is virtually motionless. It has been argued that the activity so recorded represents the ordinary tonic activity of the muscles when the eye is in the primary position. If this is true the activity of the eye muscles in tonic contraction is much higher than is found in skeletal muscle in general. When the eye is in the straightforward position, potentials of the order of $20\,\mu V$ to $150\,\mu V$ in amplitude may be recorded but this is still smaller than the values of 400 to $600\,\mu V$ found when the globe is rotated. Single

diphasic spikes can be seen, which last from 1 to 2 msec. These occur at a
rate that may be larger than 100 impulses/second.

3. SACCADIC MOVEMENTS

Saccadic eye movements are characterized by a latent period, which may
be as large as 0.28 second, in the electrical activity of the agonist. This is
somewhat larger, but within experimental (probably sampling) error of the
value of 0.12 to 0.18 second reported by Westheimer (1954) from photographic
record of eye position during such movements. As the eye begins to change
position there is correlated a high-frequency burst of activity in the agonist
and complete inhibition of activity in the antagonist. This phase lasts for

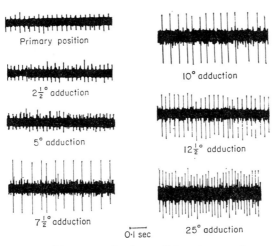

FIG. 2. Electromyographic pattern in the medial rectus muscle one second after a
saccade to various eye positions in the field according to Miller (1958).

around 0.06 second, and this is just a bit less than the duration of the movement (Miller, 1958). Following this, there is a new pattern established: the
agonist firing at a somewhat slower rate than during the burst of activity at
the start but somewhat higher than the activity prior to the movement; the
antagonist firing at a rate somewhat higher than the complete silence during
the movement but somewhat slower than its rate prior to the onset of the
movement. Miller found that when the saccadic movements are very large
(greater than 15°), there may be a second high-frequency burst 0.15 second
after the initial burst and on occasion three or four after-bursts may occur
in serial fashion with an interval of 0.15 to 0.2 second. This has not been
confirmed by Tamler et al. (1959c). During a saccadic eye movement there
increased electrical activity of all muscles except the one reciprocally inhibited (Tamler et al., 1959c).

The examination of the steady-state activity of the eye muscles following saccadic eye movements to various positions can be quite informative. Figure 2 illustrates a record obtained by Miller from the medial rectus when the eye is first in the straightforward position and then at various adducted positions. It is clear that these records are characterized by an increase in firing rate of the motor units as well as an increase in the number of motor units firing as the agonist contracts more and more.

4. BALLISTIC MOVEMENTS

The understanding of movement patterns has developed from a classification described by Stetson and his students (cf. Stetson and McDill, 1923; Hartson, 1939). According to this, movements may be divided into two large classes:

(i) Slow tension movements in which groups of muscles contract in opposition to each other, and

(ii) Ballistic movements in which the agonist muscle-groups contract while the antagonists are completely inhibited.

Stetson and McDill (1923) pointed out that saccadic eye movements were of this latter classification and considerable evidence supports this view. In the first place, as has already been pointed out, saccadic eye movements are extremely fast. Moreover, the saccade is not capable of being changed during its course. The entire movement is determined before the movement begins. The maximum velocity of a saccadic movement increases with the amplitude of the movement. All of these are characteristics of ballistic movements in the sense that Richer (1901) used the word and according to Stetson's classification. In general, electrophysiological data seem to confirm this view. The major finding that the saccade is accompanied by a high-frequency burst of activity in the agonist and complete inhibition of the antagonist is exactly what one would expect if a saccade were a ballistic movement. In most ballistic movements the burst of electrical activity in the muscle does not persist throughout the movement but only during the early part. Eye movements are so rapid and their amplitudes so small (relatively speaking) that the time-characteristics do not permit this particular feature of a ballistic movement to appear in saccades. Thus, in a saccade the high frequency burst of activity of the agonist lasts almost throughout the movement. Westheimer (1954) pointed out that ophthalmographic data show that the eyes begin to decelerate in a saccade earlier than might be expected in a ballistic movement. The extremely rapid time-characteristics of the saccade may explain this feature too. Characteristically, a ballistic movement is stopped by an active contraction of the antagonist muscle group, and electrophysiological evidence for this in the case of the saccade is equivocal. Figure 3 gives one example of positive evidence for such a "checking" action obtained by Björk (1955) from the right medial rectus during a saccade. The first movement is a shift of gaze to the left in which the relevant muscle is the agonist. It shows the typical high-frequency burst and the steady-state increased firing rate. In the second movement the relevant muscle is the antagonist, and it is apparent in this case that there is complete inhibition of firing during most of the movement but that just before the movement is completed a high-frequency burst in the antagonist begins. Miller did not obtain similar data. Tamler *et al.* (1959c) published some records that are quite similar to those in Fig. 3, although some of their data are not, and they conclude on the basis of the latter that saccadic eye movements are not ballistic.

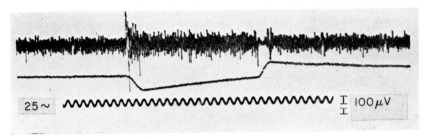

FIG. 3. Electromyographic data from the right medial rectus during a rapid horizontal movement from a point to the right of the mid-line to a point to the left and then back again, according to Björk (1955). The lower record gives an indication of eye position using the method of electro-oculography.

5. CHECKING THE MOVEMENT

If the active contraction of the antagonist does not, in fact, check the movement in a saccade as some (Miller, 1958; Tamler *et al.*, 1959c) maintain, it seems important to determine what does. It is now quite clear that the original description of Westheimer (1954) is much too simple. He proposed the ". . . existence of a one-to-one relation between innervation sets to the extra-ocular muscles and positions of the eye in the orbit. A saccadic movement would then be no more than a practically instantaneous change-over from one innervation pattern to another, and this would occur as a unitary phenomenon . . . the eyeball coming to a stop in the equilibrium position dictated by the new forces applied to it. . . . When the eye is moved from one position to another there is a change-over from one pattern of amplitude and frequency to another, this change-over preceding the actual movement by a brief interval." The electromyographic data emphasize that the actual pattern of amplitude and frequency is much more complicated than this. The way in which the eyes are brought to rest precisely on target at the termination of a saccade, if this is not, in fact, produced by active contraction of the antagonist, remains to be determined.

6. FOLLOWING MOVEMENTS

Whether one classifies saccadic movements as ballistic or merely ballistiform (and a final decision on this matter cannot yet be made) it is at least apparent that the characteristics of saccadic movements are quite different from those of pursuit (following) movements. This latter occurs when an object is moved in the visual field and an observer is instructed to maintain fixation upon it. Electromyographic records during this kind of movement reveal firing patterns quite different from those just described. Figure 4

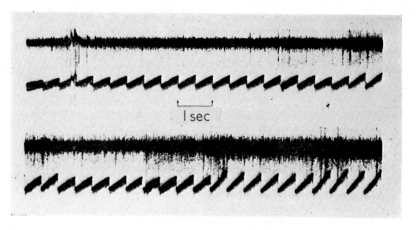

Fig. 4. Electromyographic records from the right medial rectus looking from the right to left in a pursuit movement. The lower channel shows integrated responses, the upper the electrical activity in the muscle. (The data are from Marg, Jampolsky and Tamler, 1959.)

shows a record obtained by Marg *et al.* (1959), for this type of movement, from the right medial rectus when the eye was looking to the extreme right at the beginning of the record. At this point there are only a few motor units responding, and these respond at a relatively slow rate. As the eye follows an object being moved slowly from right to left the muscle starts to contract. The rate of firing of the motor units gradually increases and the number of motor units firing also gradually increases. The pattern blends from a few motor units into a mixed pattern until, when the eye looks to the extreme left, there is an interference pattern above which some units can still be distinguished. The lower channel in the record displays the response of an electronic integrator which automatically resets itself every half-second. The increase of the slope of these segments emphasizes the increase in electrical activity as the eye shift from right to left. Simultaneous records in the antagonist in such a movement indicate just exactly the opposite kind of response, i.e., when the eye is at the extreme right the right lateral rectus is firing at a high rate with a large number of motor units, but as the object the eye is fixating slowly moves to the left the activity gradually subsides. Figure 5 illustrates graphically the results of integrating the activity of, say, the left medial rectus in such a movement. The arrow on each curve in the figure indicates the direction the fixated object was moving when the data were obtained. When the muscle is the agonist the curve is somewhat higher than when the muscle is the antagonist. This difference in height represents the difference in tension in the muscle when it contracts as compared to that obtained when it is relaxing. Momose (1958) proposes that the difference in

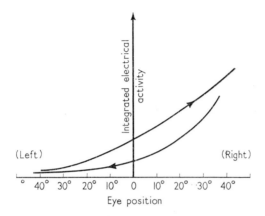

FIG. 5. The integrated electromyographic response of the left medial rectus in various eye positions during a pursuit movement according to Momose (1958). The arrow indicates the direction in which the fixated object was moving.

height of these two curves represents the imbalance in tension that rotates the globe, but this interpretation is not without its difficulties. Data such as this, however, clearly show that following movements of the eye are what Stetson classified as slow tension-movements. These latter are movements associated with a co-contraction of the agonist and antagonist. The movement occurs as a result of only a slight difference in tension in the two muscles. Such movements are typical of many unskilled movements such as might occur when a child learns to write. Slow tension-movements are characterized by the fact that their velocity is not a function of their amplitude, and this is also characteristic of following movements.

7. VARIOUS MOVEMENTS

One can study the activity of muscles when the fixated object is moved in to various parts of the visual field. Figure 6 shows a graph obtained in this way for, say, the left medial rectus (Momose 1958). The curve labelled *H* shows the activity when the eye moves nasalward and is similar to the data in Fig. 5. The curve labelled V shows what happens as the eye moves up and down, and the curve O represents the activity in the medial rectus as the eye fixates an object that moves obliquely into a tertiary position. There are several interesting features in these data. In the first place, they show that the horizontal rectus muscles do not show an increase in electrical activity when the eyes move in a purely vertical direction. Nevertheless the tonic activity of the horizontal rectus muscle, as the eye moves up or down, assists in this vertical movement. Similar records from vertical rectus muscles indicate

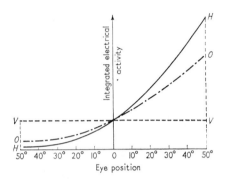

Fig. 6. The integrated electromyographic response of the left medial rectus in various eye positions during the pursuit movement. The curve labelled H indicates results from a horizontal movement, that labelled V from a vertical and that labelled O from an oblique eye movement. (Taken from Momose, 1958.)

that they behave in exactly the same way during a horizontal movement. In this sense, then, the eye muscles do not show an increase in co-activity during following movements (Tamler et al., 1959b). In the oblique movements, however, it is clear that the horizontal rectus muscles do participate and the work of Momose (1959) shows clearly that the limit of activity in the oblique direction is about the same as that in the purely horizontal direction although the electrical activity in the horizontal rectus muscle in the former case is clearly smaller than that in the latter (Fig. 6).

a. Limitation of Movement

What causes the limitation of movement? According to Momose (1959) the horizontal following movement from the primary position is characterized by a contraction of the lateral and medial rectus muscles. The agonist, however, has a slightly greater tension than does the antagonist and the difference between the tensions in the two muscles is what is responsible for the rotation of the globe. As the agonist contracts, its length is shortened and, in order to maintain an isotonic contraction, the motor nerve activity must be increased. Similarly, as the eye turns the antagonist is lengthened, and in order to maintain an isotonic contraction, the motor nerve activity to this muscle must be decreased. This process continues while the eye follows the object of regard. Soon, however, the inhibition of activity of the relaxing agonist has reached its limit (which is about zero). As the eye continues to rotate (since the motor nerve activity cannot be inhibited any further) the antagonist now no longer continues to contract isotonically. On the contrary, the tension in the antagonist starts to build up and the contraction approaches an isometric one. In order for the agonist to continue to rotate the globe it must maintain a differential tension between itself and antagonist, but this becomes more and more difficult. As the agonist continues to contract the activity of its motor nerve must continue to increase in order to maintain an isotonic contraction. Furthermore, the agonist now must also overcome the continuously mounting tension of the isometrically contracting antagonist. Eventually, this combination of effects is too great and the agonist is no longer capable of increasing its activity sufficiently to maintain the tension differential required, and the limit of the movement is reached. Electrical records in the muscle show that, as the limit of movement is reached, the activity recorded from the muscle is always a maximum. What limits the amount of activity to the muscle? Momose suggests two possibilities: (i) all of the motor units are firing at the maximum rate possible; or, (ii) there is an inhibition of the firing of the muscles once the limit is reached. Momose favours the second view because the electrical activity of a given muscle at the limit is smaller when the movement is an oblique one than when the movement is purely horizontal (Fig. 6).

8. OPTO-KINETIC NYSTAGMUS

The distinction between saccadic movements and following movements is most dramatic if one studies the electrical activity in the eye muscle during opto-kinetic nystagmus. Figure 7 shows data from the left medial rectus muscle in such a movement obtained by Björk (1955). In this figure the upper channel is the myogram; the lower channel gives an indication of eye position. At the left-hand part of the record the fast phase of the nystagmus is to the left; at the right-hand part of the figure the drum direction was reversed so that the fast phase is now in the opposite direction. It is apparent that the ballistiform movement of the fast phase of the nystagmus represents a saccade while the tension movement of the slow phase is typical of following movements. (Note that the activity of the muscle during the slow phase of the nystagmus is almost identical irrespective of whether the muscle is serving as the agonist or as the antagonist.)

9. VERGENCE

Electromyographic data showing the activity of all four horizontal rectus muscles during symmetrical convergence and divergence (Jampolsky *et al.*, 1959) is preferable for the interpretation of many features of vergence behaviour. There is a dearth of data of this sort. Some information about

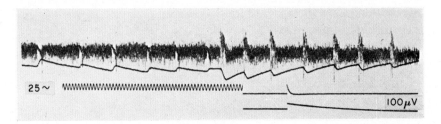

FIG. 7. Electromyographic response of the left medial rectus during opto-kinetic nystagmus according to Björk (1955). Upper record is electromyogram; lower record gives the record of eye position using electro-oculography. The left-hand part of the Figure shows movements with drum rotating to right; the second half the drum rotation was reversed.

vergence movements is available, however. It has been proposed from time to time that the movement of the eyes from a convergent position to a less convergent one was associated with no action of the lateral rectus at all, merely with an inhibition of the activity of the medial rectus. In 1953, however, Adler clearly demonstrated that this was not the case. The shift from a

FIG. 8. Electromyograph data showing activity of the medial rectus muscle during a 15° convergence movement. (According to Miller, 1958.)

large to a somewhat smaller convergent position was associated with a marked increase in the electrical activity of the lateral rectus muscle. Clearly divergence is produced by active contraction of the lateral rectus muscle. Breinin (1957a, b) verified this in a patient with intermittent exotropia. He found an increase in activity in the lateral rectus of the strabismic eye when it assumed the strabismus position. As this patient converged his eyes towards the near point the lateral rectus was completely silent. However, about 20 msec. before the eyes broke from binocular vision a burst of activity appeared in the lateral rectus, implying that the convergence movement was stopped by the active contraction of the antagonistic muscle. It has already been pointed out that this is characteristic of a ballistic movement.

Figure 8 shows a record obtained by Miller (1958) from the medial rectus muscle in a 15° convergence movement. In such movements there is frequently a short pause in firing, which is then followed by a gradual increase in firing. This increase of activity eventually reaches a peak and then subsides to the final steady state firing rate. The decline may last longer than a second for large convergence movements, but these movements are extremely slow (Alpern and Ellen, 1956a, b) and large vergence movements may indeed last this long. Vergence movements never show after-bursts of activity. Data such as this emphasize that vergence movements are associated with electrical activity in the muscle that is different from the changes occurring in the same muscle during a following movement, or for that matter, during a saccade.

a. Reciprocal Innervation

In vergence the agonist contracts, the antagonist through reciprocal innervation being completely inhibited; and the movement is terminated by an active contraction of the antagonist which apparently stops the rotation of the globe and/or (at the limiting value) begins the vergence movement in the opposite direction. The velocity of a vergence movement is a function of its amplitude, and this is another characteristic of a ballistic movement. One hesitates to classify them in this way, however, because the time-characteristics of the movement are so slow. Indeed, it is almost as though the characteristics of a vergence movement were, if anything, even more ballistic-like than a saccade but produced by a neuromuscular apparatus with time-characteristics about one order of magnitude slower (Alpern and Wolter, 1956).

II. Pharmacology of the Extra-Ocular Muscles

A. ACETYLCHOLINE

The eye muscles, like all striated muscles, are cholinergic. It has been shown that these muscles, even while normally innervated, are extremely sensitive to acetylcholine, whereas in ordinary skeletal muscle this is usually true only after complete degeneration of the motor nerve, the acetylcholine being too quickly destroyed by cholinesterase to show its effect. Eye muscles

6

are sensitive in this way whether these drugs reach them slowly through the blood stream or are supplied to the surface of the surviving muscle suspended in Locke's solution (Duke-Elder and Duke-Elder, 1930). Following eserine, when the cholinesterase is inactivated, a single volley applied to the motor nerve of the inferior oblique muscle of the decerebrate cat evokes a regular series of spikes in this muscle. These spikes undergo a logarithmic decrement with time (Brown and Harvey, 1941). Acetylcholine, injected into the carotid artery or into a vein, evokes an enduring contraction of the eye muscle, which is accompanied throughout its course by oscillatory action potentials. After eserine, however, both acetylcholine and repetitive nerve stimulation evoke a contracture, which blocks the propagation of excitation along the muscle fibre.

B. CURARINE

Eye muscles are especially sensitive to curarine. Brown and Harvey (1941) showed, in the cat, that the inferior oblique was affected by smaller doses of curarine than were the skeletal muscles of the lower limb. Similar results have been obtained in man. Smith *et al.* (1947) found that human eye muscles were paralysed very soon after the intravenous injection of *d*-tubocurarine. On the other hand, succinylcholine, which mimics the effect of curarine on most striated muscle fibres, causes a very pronounced contraction of the extra-ocular muscles (Kaller, 1956; Lincoff *et al.*, 1957; Dillon *et al.*, 1957; Macri and Grimes, 1957). The effect found by Lincoff *et al.* (1957) was eliminated by deep anaesthesia but even *in vitro* human eye muscle contracts in response to small doses of succinylcholine and decamethonium. This effect can be blocked by *d*-tubocurarine (Hofman and Lembeck, 1956). Succinylcholine, while similar to curarine in many ways, also causes a cholinergic response (i.e. contraction) of smooth muscle. The similarity in its effect on the eye muscles perhaps means that its curarine-like action blocks the myoneural junction of the fibres innervated by ordinary somatic nerves while at the same time causing contraction of those fibres innervated by the parasympathetic branch of the autonomic nervous system, which Alpern and Wolter (1956) relate to vergence movements. A somewhat similar interpretation of these facts has been suggested independently by Hofman and Lembeck (1956).

III. Proprioception in the Extra-Ocular Muscles

The sensory (afferent) discharge from the extra-ocular muscles and its possible role in the perception of space, motion, stereopsis, and of the position of one's eyes has been a subject of intense interest in the history of eye movement physiology. Classical physiologists such as Helmholtz, Tscherning and

Hering, working at a time when knowledge of proprioception was very limited, believed that one was aware of eye movements in terms of the innervation sent to the muscles in order to displace the globe. Sherrington (1918), on the other hand, believed that sensory discharges from the eye muscles themselves played an important role, not only in the awareness of the positions of one's eyes but in the visual perception of space as well.

A. MUSCLE SPINDLES

Examination of the eye muscles of common laboratory animals, cat, rabbit, small monkeys, reveals no sensory spindles in the extra-ocular muscles analogous to those found in other skeletal muscles. This fact has been over-emphasized while the fact reported earlier (Cilimbaris, 1910) that such spindles were liberally distributed in the eye muscles of sheep and goat, has been more or less ignored. Examination of human material was not pursued to the full advantage afforded by silver staining methods and so until very recently the presence of ordinary muscle spindles (in fact, their rich concentration) in the human extra-ocular muscles was undetected. Moreover, the stretching of the extra-ocular muscles of decerebrate cats (McCouch and Adler, 1932) does not lead to the increase of tonus characteristic of the stretch-reflex of ordinary extensor muscles. Irvine and Ludvigh (1936) showed that the same is true in human extra-ocular muscle and verified further that no vibration sense, to speak of, was present in the human eye muscles.

1. AFFERENT DISCHARGE ON STRETCH

All of these circumstances led to the view that the human extra-ocular muscles supplied no afferent information to the central nervous system. However, in the meantime the muscle spindles in the human extra-ocular muscles were discovered (cf. above) and this raised anew the question of their physiology. While stretching the extra-ocular muscle produces no stretch-reflex there can no longer be any doubt that such stimulation does increase the (afferent) discharge in the oculo-motor nerve. Cooper et al. (1951) first demonstrated this effect in young sheep and goats and it was verified in cats and monkeys by Cooper and Fillenz (1955), Fillenz (1955), even though cat and monkey eye muscles (while they have many sensory endings) have no typical muscle spindles such as are found in the eye muscles of sheep, goats and man. In these experiments the insertion-end of the muscle was detached from the globe and, upon stretching the muscle, action potentials in a single nerve fibre were recorded. The pattern of these discharges was exactly that which Matthews (1933) found from the muscle spindles of the limb. Figure 9 illustrates one such experiment. The stretch of the muscle by 0.6 mm. (Fig. 9a) is associated with a mild increase in activity of the afferent fibre; when the muscle is stretched at a slightly greater amount (0.85 mm.) the muscle spindle fires the afferent fibre at a higher rate.

a. Brain-Stem Responses

Cooper *et al.* (1955) succeeded in tracing these afferent fibres into the brain-stem. As the muscle was stretched, they recorded electrical activity from a branch of the oculomotor nerve as it joined the Vth nerve. In the brain-stem two different varieties of response were recordable. The first of these was the short-latency sustained discharge with low threshold. Stretching the jaw muscle produced activity of this kind in the mesencephalic nucleus of NV; stretching the eye muscle produced similar responses in the rostral and caudal ends of the mesencephalic nucleus of NV. Because of the time-characteristics

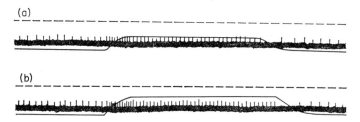

Fig. 9. Afferent impulses from a unit during passive stretch of the inferior oblique muscle of a goat according to Cooper, Daniel and Whitteridge (1951). Stretch of the muscle (indicated by the solid line) was associated with a marked increase in firing of the "motor" nerve which then settled to a steady level. On relaxation a pause is followed by a resumption of firing at the resting rate. (a) weak stretch (0.6 mm.), (b) slightly greater stretch (0.85 mm.).

of these responses Cooper *et al.* (1954) believed that these impulses were travelling in first-order sensory neurones, some cell bodies of which were situated in the mesencephalic nucleus. These investigators also reported responses elsewhere in the brain-stem from stretch of the eye muscles. These had longer (20 to 200 msec.) latencies and somewhat different firing patterns than the low threshold sustained discharges. They suggested that these responses are those of second- (or higher-) order neurones; patterns of this sort were obtained in the medial longitudinal fasciculus, the tegmental tract, the superior cerebellar peduncle, the colliculo-tegmental tract, and in the deeper layers of the superior colliculus.

b. Gamma Efferents

Work of this sort clearly establishes the flow of afferent discharges to the central nervous system from the muscle spindles in the eye muscles. What can be said of the physiology of these muscle spindles? Whitteridge (1959) has studied this matter at some length by stimulating the motor nerve to the eye muscle (goat, superior oblique) while recording electrically from one of the branches of NV. Simultaneous record of the tension in the (isometric) muscle was also obtained. Typical results of one such experiment are illustrated in Fig. 10. In A the whole IVth nerve was stimulated and it is to be noted that, in addition to the increased tension developed in the muscle, the discharge recorded in NV, was increased. In experiments illustrated from B to D in this figure, progressive dissection of the IVth nerve was accomplished and smaller and smaller nerve slips were stimulated. As a consequence,

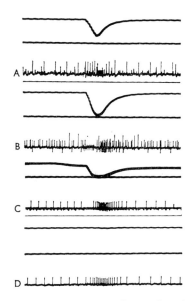

Fig. 10. Isolation of γ-efferent fibre to a single muscle spindle in the goat superior oblique. Upper trace: myogram, increase in tension downward; middle trace: time, 50 cycle ripple; lower trace: action potential in a single afferent branch of NV. In trace A to D successively smaller slips of nerve IV were stimulated until finally a motor fibre was stimulated which caused no change in tension in the muscle but a clear increase in firing of the afferent branch. (Whitteridge, 1959.)

the tension developed in the muscle becomes progressively less, and the activity obtained with the recording electrodes becomes more distinct. In D it is apparent that the small-nerve fibres go exclusively to the intrafusal muscle fibres of the muscle spindle, since no tension is developed by their stimulation. At the same time, stimulation of such motor fibres (which are called gamma-efferent because of their small diameter and slow conduction velocity) does cause an increase in the activity of the afferent fibre recorded in NV. Such gamma-efferent fibres make up approximately 30% of the motor nerve of the eye muscles of the goat, according to Donaldson (1960). The function of the gamma-efferent system is best understood by recording the frequency of discharge in the Vth nerve following various degrees of stretch of the muscle and various rates of firing of the gamma-efferent fibre. Such an experiment is illustrated in Fig. 11. There is a linear relationship between stretch of the muscle and frequency of afferent discharge when the motor nerve was cut. When, however, the gamma-efferent fibres are stimulated, although this linear relation remains, the sensitivity of the spindle to stretch is greatly increased as is shown by the increased slope of the curves in the

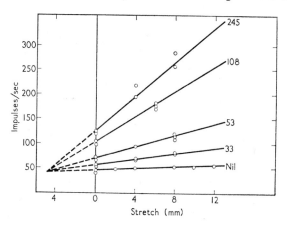

Fig. 11. Frequency response to stretch in an afferent fibre from a muscle spindle during stimulation of the γ-efferent (goat, inferior oblique) at rates of 0, 33, 53, 108 and 245 stimuli/sec. (Whitteridge, 1959.)

figure. The sensitivity changed from 1–5 impulses/sec./mm. without stimulation to 15–20 impulses/sec./mm. during stimulation. If the straight lines in this figure are extrapolated back they all intersect at the same point. This demonstrates the fact that, while gamma-stimulation increased the sensitivity of the primary afferent endings of the muscle spindle to stretch, it had at the same time little or no effect on the threshold of the spindle.

2. VALUE OF AFFERENT DISCHARGE

Thus it is clearly established that the muscle spindles in the eye muscles send information to the central nervous system regarding the extent of stretch of the muscle. How is this information used? It has already been suggested that some physiologists followed Sherrington's lead and felt that such information played an essential role in the visual perception of space, stereopsis and movement. Sherrington (1918) pointed out that the objective vertical was perceived as vertical in the tertiary position of gaze even though according to the principle of Listing's law the vertical meridian of the retina no

longer coincides with objective vertical. Sherrington believed that the proprio‑
ception from the extra-ocular muscles was responsible for the ability of the
organism to correct for false information supplied by retinal stimulation.
This is contrary to the older view that the correction must come about as a
consequence of an "awareness" of the innervation that has been sent to the
eye muscles in order to displace the globe to the tertiary position. Whitteridge
(1960) classifies these two opposite views as the "inflow" and the "outflow"
hypothesis respectively, and emphasizes that the available data support the
latter view.

a. Parametric Feedback

Ludvigh (1952a) showed that, in a dark room, a person could not estimate
better than 75% of the time whether a spot of light was 6 Δ to the left or 6 Δ
to the right. This is an amazingly poor performance in view of the precision
that "inflow" theory would require for the position sense. In clinical patients
the movement of an eye with a paralysed muscle may give rise to apparent

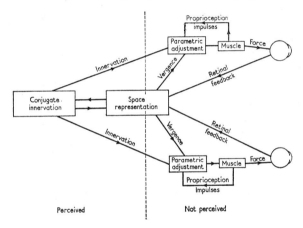

Fig. 12. Ludvigh's (1952b) schema for qualitative explanation of various normal and
abnormal ocular movements in relation to perception of motion.

motion of the visual field. Results of this kind prejudice the "inflow" theory
of visual space perception. Ludvigh (1952a) on the other hand, suggested an
important role for the muscle spindle discharge in what he called *parametric
feedback*. According to this scheme, while the muscle afferents supply no
information regarding the position of the eye, or the accuracy with which an
eye movement has been achieved, it does provide information regarding
gross difference in eye position, difference in tonus and metabolism of the
muscles, and so on. This information is extremely essential for the eye's
ability to shift from one point in space to a second after a latency of only

120–180 msec. with an extremely high-velocity movement, and without any appreciable error. A very small difference in metabolism or tonus of the muscle from one moment to the next would make the execution of such a precise movement impossible without the availability of some variety of parametric feedback. Figure 12 illustrates Ludvigh's scheme. Ludvigh estimates that a 1 % error in the efficiency of the eye muscles could lead to relatively serious errors in eye position. He emphasizes that, since the eye fails to make such errors in normal saccades, the parametric feedback may provide a means by which the proper innervation is sent to the eye muscles in order to complete the required change in fixation. An essential feature of the diagram in Fig. 12 is the retinal feedback. It is the relationship of the information sent to space representation from the retinal feedback to that sent by conjugate innervation that determines whether or not objects are seen to move as the consequence of movements of the eyes. Suppose the eyes make a change of fixation from a point straight ahead to one 15° to the right. To accomplish this, conjugate innervation sends innervation to the space representation that a 15° movement is about to occur. At the same time innervation is sent to parametric adjustment. At this point the innervation is modified according to the feedback from the proprioceptors in the muscles so that exactly the correct innervation is sent to the muscles to effect the 15° movement. If by chance a slight error occurs, the retinal feedback to space representation will cause a further innervation from conjugate innervation and the process must be repeated.

b. *Apparent Movement*

The subject is aware of all events that occur to the left of the dotted line, unaware of those to the right. Thus he knows the amount of innervation sent to space representation but not about the modifications made by the parametric adjustment. As the eye muscles contract to rotate the globe to its new position the environment sweeps across his retina and this information is conveyed to space representation by retinal feedback. When the feedback from the retina coincides with the information sent from conjugate innervation, no movement is perceived. If, however, these two different pieces of information are not in agreement, then the subject will perceive motion. Thus when the eyeball is passively displaced by pressing on the globe the conjugate innervation provides no information regarding a movement and yet the retinal feedback indicates movement has occurred. Under these conditions, clear movement is perceived. If a weak prism is suddenly placed before one eye the retinal feedback from one eye differs from that supplied by the other and this in some way provides a stimulus to vergence movements (cf. above). The eyes move the indicated amount to adjust for this disparity. This is accomplished by vergence innervation to parametric adjustment from space representation; the innervation to the muscles is modified according to the feedback from the muscles and the eyes move the required amount. All of this occurs without the subject being aware of any change occurring at all. If an after-image is placed on the retina and the eye then makes a saccadic movement there is a discrepancy between the retinal feedback and the innervation from conjugate innervation and the after-image is seen to move as the eye moves.

c. Past–Pointing

In fresh paralysis of the eye muscles the innervation to parametric adjustment for an eye movement in the field of action of the paralysed muscle may not be sufficient even after modification from the proprioceptors from the muscles. The movement of the eye will then be smaller than the innervation to space representation so that retinal feedback will disagree with that expected. In this situation the subject, when asked to point to the object (when the hand is not visible) will past-point. The angle of past-pointing will be larger when a gross fixation target is used than when the subject is asked to fixate an object with fine detail in the field of the paralysed muscle (Adler, 1945). This is in keeping with the "out-flow" theory. If visual space were determined by the feedback from the eye muscles, one would expect greater past-pointing with the fine target than with the gross one, since more muscle activity is required to see the former than the latter.

d. Effect of Cutting Tendons

In man, Breinin (1957a, b) reported that the high-frequency firing so characteristic of the eye muscles could be eliminated merely by cutting the muscle tendons. The muscle then behaved, electrically, like ordinary skeletal muscle; firing could be obtained by changes in fixation of the contralateral (i.e., normal) eye. These effects occurred after the muscle was free from the globe; stretching the muscle while it was still attached to the globe was not correlated with an increase in the firing pattern of the muscle, nor was it possible to inhibit the rate of firing of a given muscle by stretching its antagonist.

References

Adler, F. H. (1945). Pathologic physiology of convergent strabismus. *Arch. Ophthal.*, *N.Y.* **33**, 362–377.

Adler, F. H. (1953). Pathologic physiology of strabismus. *A.M.A. Arch. Ophthal., N.Y.* **50**, 19–29.

Adrian, E. D. (1930). The effects of injury on mammalian nerve fibres. *Proc. roy. Soc. B.* **106**, 596–618.

6*

Adrian, E. D., and Bronk, D. W. (1929). The discharge of impulses in motor nerve fibres. II. The frequency of discharge in reflex and voluntary contractions. *J. Physiol.* **67**, 119–151.

Alpern, M., and Ellen, P. (1956). A quantitative analysis of the horizontal movements of the eyes in the experiment of Johannes Mueller. I. Method and results. *Amer. J. Ophthal.* **42** (No. 4, Pt. 2), 289–296.

Alpern, M., and Ellen, P. (1956b). A quantitative analysis of the horizontal movements of the eyes in the experiment of Johannes Mueller. II. Effect of variation in target separation. *Amer. J. Ophthal.* (No. 4, Pt. 2), 296–303.

Alpern, M., and Wolter, J. R. (1956). The relation of horizontal saccadic and vergence movements. *A.M.A. Arch. Ophthal.* **56**, 685–690.

Björk, Å. (1952). Electrical activity of human extrinsic eye muscles. *Experientia* **8**, 226–227.

Björk, Å. (1955). The electromyogram of the extraocular muscles in opticokinetic nystagmus and in reading. *Acta. ophthal., Kbh.* **33**, 437–454.

Breinin, G. M. (1957a). Electromyographic evidence for ocular muscle proprioception in man. *A.M.A. Arch. Ophthal.* **57**, 176–180.

Breinin, G. M. (1957b). The nature of vergence revealed by electromyography. II. Accommodative and fusional vergence. *A.M.A. Arch. Ophthal., N.Y.* **58**, 623–631.

Breinin, G. M. (1958). Analytic studies of the electromyogram of human extraocular muscle. *Amer. J. Ophthal.* **46** (No. 3, Pt. 2), 123–142.

Brown, G. L., and Harvey, A. M. (1941). Neuro-muscular transmission in the extrinsic muscles of the eye. *J. Physiol.* **99**, 379–399.

Cilimbaris, P. A. (1910). Histologische Untersuchungen ueber die Muskelspindeln der Augenmuskeln. *Arch. mikr. Anat.* **75**, 692–747.

Cooper, S., and Daniel, P. M. (1957). Responses from the stretch receptors of the goat's extrinsic eye muscles with an intact motor innervation. *Quart. J. exp. Physiol.* **42**, 222–231.

Cooper, S., and Eccles, J. C. (1930). The isometric responses of mammalian muscles. *J. Physiol.* **69**, 377–385.

Cooper, S., and Fillenz, M. (1955). Afferent discharges in response to stretch from the extraocular muscles of the cat and monkey and the innervation of these muscles. *J. Physiol.* **127**, 400–413.

Cooper, S., Daniel, P. M., and Whitteridge, D. (1951). Afferent impulses in the oculomotor nerve, from the extrinsic eye muscles. *J. Physiol.* **113**, 463–474.

Cooper, S., Daniel, P. M., and Whitteridge, D. (1954). Afferent impulses from the muscle spindles of the extrinsic eye muscles and their course within the brainstem. *Trans. ophthal. Soc. U.K.* **74**, 435–440.

Cooper, S., Daniel, P. M., and Whitteridge, D. (1955). Muscle spindles and other sensory endings in the extrinsic eye muscles; the physiology and anatomy of these receptors and of their connexions with the brain-stem. *Brain* **78**, 564–583.

Dillon, J. B., Sabawala, P., Taylor, D. D., and Gunter, R. (1957). Action of succinylcholine on extraocular muscles and intraocular pressure. *Anesthesiology* **18**, 44–49.

Donaldson, G. W. K. (1960). The diameter of the nerve fibres to the extrinsic eye muscles of the goat. *Quart. J. exp. Physiol.* **45**, 25–34.

Duke-Elder, W. S., and Duke-Elder, P. M. (1930). The contraction of the extrinsic muscles of the eye by choline and nicotine. *Proc. roy. Soc. B.* **107**, 232–243.

Fillenz, M. (1955). Responses in the brainstem of the cat to stretch of extrinsic ocular muscles. *J. Physiol.* **128**, 182–199.

Hartson, L. D. (1939). Contrasting approaches to the analysis of skilled movements. *J. gen. Psychol.* **20**, 276–293.

Hofmann, H., and Lembeck, F. (1956). Pharmakologische Untersuchungen am isolierten, aeusseren Augenmuskel des Menschen. *v. Graefes Arch. Ophthal.* **158**, 277–279.

Irvine, S. R., and Ludvigh, E. J. (1936). Is ocular proprioceptive sense concerned in vision? *Arch. Ophthal. N.Y.* **15**, 1037–1049.

Jampolsky, A., Tamler, E., and Marg, E. (1959). Artifacts and normal variations in human ocular electromyography. *A.M.A. Arch. Ophthal.* **61**, 402–413.

Kaller, H. (1956). Pharmakologische Untersuchungen an der quergestreiften Augenmuskulatur der Ratte. *Arch. exp. Path. Pharmak.* **229**, 297–304.

Kuboki, T. (1957). Studies on discharge intervals of a single motor unit in human extraocular muscles. I. During fixation of the gaze. II. During horizontal movement of the eye. *Tohoku J. exp. Med.* **66**, 91–105.

Lincoff, H. A., Breinin, G. M., and DeVoe, A. G. (1957). The effect of succinylcholine on the extraocular muscles. *Amer. J. Ophthal.* **43**, 440–444.

Ludvigh, E. (1952a). Possible role of proprioception in the extraocular muscles. *A.M.A. Arch. Ophthal.* **48**, 436–441.

Ludvigh, E. (1952b). Control of ocular movements and visual interpretation of environment. *A.M.A. Arch. Ophthal.* **48**, 442–448.

McCouch, G. P., and Adler, F. H. (1932). Extraocular reflexes. *Amer. J. Physiol.* **100**, 78–88.

Macri, F. J., and Grimes, P. A. (1957). The effects of succinyl-choline on the extraocular striate muscles and on the intraocular pressure. *Amer. J. Ophthal.* **44** (No. 4, Pt. 2), 221–230.

Marg, E., Jampolsky, A., and Tamler, E. (1959). Elements of human extraocular electromyography. *A.M.A. Arch. Ophthal.* **61**, 258–269.

Matthews, B. H. C. (1933). Nerve endings in mammalian muscle. *J. Physiol.* **78**, 1–53.

Miller, J. E. (1958). Electromyographic pattern of saccadic eye movements. *Amer. J. Ophthal.* **46** (No. 5, Pt. 2), 183–186.

Momose, H. (1957). Studies on the action of the extraocular muscles by means of the quantitative measurement of integrated EMG. I. Application of an integrator and behaviors of the horizontal and vertical muscles in monocular movements. *Acta Soc. ophthal. japan.* **61**, 1570–1592.

Momose, H. (1958). Studies on the action of the extraocular muscles in monocular movements by means of quantification of integrated EMG. *Jap. J. Ophthal.* **2**, 108–122.

Momose, H. (1959). Electromyographic studies on the mechanism of limitation of uniocular movement. *Jap. J. Ophthal.* **3**, 9–13.

Reid, G. (1949). The rate of discharge of the extraocular motoneurones. *J. Physiol.* **110**, 217–225.

Richer, P. (1901). Locomotion humaine. *In* "Traité de Physique Biologique" (A. d'Arsonval, A. Chauveau, C. Gariel, and E. J. Marey, eds.), Vol. I, p. 158. Masson et Cie, Paris.

Sears, M. L. Teasdall, R. D., and Stone, H. H. (1959). Stretch effects in human extra-ocular muscle; an electromyographic study. *Bull. Johns Hopk. Hosp.* **104**, 174–178.

Sherrington, C. S. (1918). Observations on the sensual rôle of the proprioceptive nerve-supply of the extrinsic ocular muscles. *Brain* **41**, 332–343.

Smith, S. M., Brown, H. O., Toman, J. E. P., and Goodman, L. S. (1947). The lack of cerebral effects of d-tubocurarine. *Anesthesiology* **8**, 1–14.

Stetson, R. H., and McDill, J. A. (1923). Mechanism of the different types of movement with a Preliminary Report of Experimental Data. *Psychol. Monogr.* **32**, No. 3, 18–40.

Tamler, E., Jampolsky, A., and Marg. E. (1959a). Electromyographic study of following movements of the eye between tertiary positions. *A.M.A. Arch. Ophthal.* **62**, 804–809.

Tamler, E., Marg, E., and Jampolsky, A. (1959b). Electromyographic study of co-activity of human extraocular muscles in following movements. *A.M.A. Arch. Ophthal.* **61**, 270–273.

Tamler, E., Marg, E., Jampolsky, A., and Nawratzki, I. (1959c). Electromyography of human saccadic eye movements. *A.M.A. Arch. Ophthal.* **62**, 657–661.

Westheimer, G. (1954). Mechanism of saccadic eye movements. *A.M.A. Arch. Ophthal.* **52**, 710–724.

Whitteridge, D. (1959). The effect of stimulation of intrafusal muscle fibres on sensitivity to stretch of extraocular muscle spindles. *Quart. J. exp. Physiol.* **44**, 385–393.

Whitteridge, D. (1960). Central control of eye movements. *In* "Handbook of Physiology: A Critical, Comprehensive Presentation of Physiological Knowledge and Concepts" Section 1. Neurophysiology (J. Field, H. W. Magoun, and V. E. Hall, eds.), Vol. II, pp. 1089–1109. American Physiological Society, Washington, D.C.

Strabismus

I. Introduction

Strabismus (or squint) is a condition in which the line of sight of one of the two eyes is different when it alone is uncovered from when both eyes are uncovered. Since the line of sight in monocular viewing is invariably very close to the pupillary axis, the characteristic feature of strabismus is a rather obvious failure of the pupillary axis of each eye to intersect in the object of regard when both eyes are uncovered. This deviation may be in either a horizontal or vertical plane or perhaps in both. A horizontal deviation is classified as exotropia or esotropia depending upon whether the eyes are divergent or convergent with respect to the point of fixation. A vertical deviation may be classified as hypertropia or hypotropia depending upon whether the pupillary axis of the squinting eye is above or below that of its fellow. In cyclotropia the orientation of the vertical meridian of one of the two eyes differs when both eyes are uncovered from when it alone is uncovered.

Strabismus is a very old and extensively studied phenomenon and a good deal of relevant information is available about it in standard textbooks. A thorough discussion of such material is obviously beyond the scope of this chapter. For more details, the reader is referred to standard references (Duke-Elder, 1949; Bielschowsky, 1943; Allen, 1950, 1958).

A. DEFINITIONS

Briefly, one can differentiate two basically different kinds of strabismus: *comitant* and *incomitant*. This distinction is of value both theoretically and clinically but the borderline is often not so distinct as one might wish. A comitant strabismus is essentially a defect of the *vergence* mechanism. An incomitant strabismus is a defect of the *version* system. Furthermore, incomitant strabismus results from neurological defects that in general involve the final common pathway to the extra-ocular muscles. It is popular to state that comitant strabismus results from neurological defects that are above the final common pathway to the extra-ocular muscles—i.e., supranuclear disorders. As a matter of fact, virtually nothing at all is definitely known of the basic neurological cause or causes of comitant strabismus.

II. Incomitant Strabismus

Incomitant strabismus is a direct result of a paralysis of one or more of the extra-ocular muscles or of the final common nerve pathway to the muscle. It has a number of characteristic signs, all of which are most obvious when the paralysis is fresh. The paralysis itself may result from a congenital defect, or from an acquired lesion of one or more of the cranial nerves that innervate the ocular muscles. Such lesions include: injury, inflammation, tumour, vascular accidents, and degenerative diseases. Moreover, a paralysis may follow a direct involvement of the muscle as, for example, by injury or muscular dystrophy, or it may follow a gross displacement of the globe within the orbit.

A. PRIMARY AND SECONDARY DEVIATIONS

One outstanding feature of paralytic strabismus is a direct consequence of Hering's law of equal innervation to the yoked extra-ocular muscles. If a given muscle, say the left lateral rectus, is paralysed, the unopposed action of its antagonist, the left medial rectus, will cause the left eye to move nasalward when the right eye is fixating. The angle of strabismus that results is determined only by the unopposed action of the antagonist of the paralysed muscle when the normal eye is fixating. This is called *primary* deviation. On the other hand, when the eye with the paralysed muscle fixates, it is necessary for it to rotate out to the mid-line and to do so requires a further contraction of the paralysed muscle. Because of the paralysis, the innervation required by the paralysed muscle to do this will be much greater than would be otherwise necessary. Because of Hering's law this increased innervation of the paralysed muscle will also be reflected in an increased innervation to its yoked muscle in the other eye (which in this case is the right medial rectus). Thus, when the eye with the paralysed muscle fixates, not only is the deviation of the eyes determined by the relation of actions of the paralysed muscle and its antagonist but by a further increased innervation to the yoke of the paralysed muscle in the contralateral eye as well. Thus, when the eye with the paralysed muscle is fixating, the angle of strabismus (*secondary* deviation) is greater than it is when the normal eye fixates. This difference between primary and secondary deviation is one of the major characteristics of paralytic strabismus.

B. LIMITATIONS OF MOVEMENT

A second feature of incomitant strabismus is a clear limitation of movement. When the eyes move in different extreme tertiary positions of the gaze the rotation of the globe is largely (although not exclusively) obtained by the action of only one or two of the extra-ocular muscles. A fresh paralysis of only a single muscle results in no limitation of movement at all when the eyes are moved in certain directions. However, a rather marked limitation will occur when the eyes are moved into the field of action of the paralysed muscle. The obvious result is that the angle of deviation of the strabismus varies, according to the particular region of the field of fixation into which the observer happens to be directing his gaze. For this reason a paralytic strabismus is called *incomitant* and is sharply distinguished from *comitant* strabismus in which the angle of deviation is the same irrespective of the direction of gaze. This difference, like most of the others, is most pronounced when the paralysis is a fresh one.

1. DIAGNOSTIC POSITIONS OF GAZE

In order to detect this limitation of movement most easily, one asks the patient to fixate upon a light as it is moved through the field, the head remaining fixed. The detection of paralysis of the horizontal muscles is quite easy since the left lateral and right medial rectus rotate the globes to the left, and the right lateral and left medial rotate the globes to the right. To detect limitations of movement of the vertically acting extra-ocular muscles one can first move the fixation light to an extreme (say 51°) horizontal position from the straightforward position. Under these conditions elevation (or depression) of the globe now is largely the function of a single muscle for each eye. For example, if the light is moved horizontally 51° to the left, elevation is a function of the left superior rectus (since any contraction of the other elevator of the left eye—the inferior oblique—will in this extreme position only produce a rolling movement) and of the right inferior oblique. Depression of the eyes from this horizontal position is a function of the left inferior rectus and the right superior oblique. Similarly, rotating the fixation 51° to the right places the eyes in such a position that elevation is the function of the right superior rectus and the left inferior oblique and depression the function of the right inferior rectus and the left superior oblique. Such positions are referred to as the diagnostic positions of gaze.

C. Diplopia

A third symptom of incomitant strabismus, which follows more or less from the limitation of movements, is diplopia or double vision. The sudden onset of a fresh paralysis is always characterized by diplopia but if the paralysis is long standing, suppression of one of the double images may occur, just as seems to be the case in comitant strabismus. In esotropia the diplopia will be homonymous (or uncrossed), since if the patient closes one eye the image on the same side will disappear. If the patient has an exotropia the diplopia will be heteronymous. Vertical strabismus will also show vertical diplopia. Moreover, just as with limitation of movement, the diplopia will increase as the eyes are rotated into the field of action of the paralysed muscle. For example, in a fresh paralysis of the right superior oblique there will be no diplopia at all when the eyes are looking up in any direction since the superior oblique muscle does not contribute to elevation of the globe at all. However, when the patient looks down, a diplopia will appear and the vertical separation of the images will be greatest when the eyes are directed down and to the left (the image seen by the eye with the paralysed muscle being below that seen by the normal eye) since it is in this field that the right superior oblique exerts its greatest depression effect. The angular tilt of the images of the two eyes with respect to one another will be greatest, however, when the eyes look down and to the right because it is in this field that the superior oblique exerts its greatest torsional effect. Just as is the case in the angle of deviation, the diplopia will be greater when the eye with the paralysed muscle fixates than it will be when the normal eye fixates.

D. Past-Pointing

Another sign of incomitant strabismus results when the patient is asked to point to the object of regard when it is being fixated with the eye with the paralysed muscle (particularly in its field of action). The explanation of this as a discrepancy between retinal feedback and muscle innervation has already been discussed. According to Bielschowsky (1943), the angle of past-pointing will exactly coincide with the angle of secondary deviation, the line of sight of the covered (i.e., normal) eye is directed at exactly the same point that the eye with the paralysed muscle locates the object of regard.

E. Postural Changes

Finally, one can recognize an incomitant strabismus by the fact that it is frequently associated with rather definite postural changes of the head and neck. These postural changes come about as a consequence of the rather annoying diplopia that is characteristic of a fresh paralysis. The patient adjusts his head so that the most convenient position for the maintainence of single binocular vision is achieved.

1. PARALYSIS OF HORIZONTAL MUSCLE

For example, if the right lateral rectus is paralysed and the patient is looking straight ahead, he will experience diplopia if he suddenly is required to look at an object in the right part of the field. If, however, he rotates his head to the right so that he does not need to use the paralysed muscle to look at the object, then he sees it without diplopia. Since he has no diplopia when looking to the left the change of posture has minimized the region of his field in which diplopia will appear.

2. PARALYSIS OF VERTICAL MUSCLE

In paralysis of one of the vertical acting muscles, similar considerations apply. If, for example, the right superior rectus muscle is paralysed the face is frequently turned to the right. The reason for this is that the elevation of the right eye in this position is more dependent upon the inferior oblique and less dependent upon the superior rectus than would be the case if the face were directed to the front. Thus diplopia on upward gaze is reduced.

a. Head Tilt

Paralysis of the oblique muscles is frequently associated with a tilting of the head. In trochlear paralysis the head is usually tilted to the shoulder of the sound side and at the same time turned around the vertical axis so that the paretic eye is rotated outward. For example, a paralysis of the right superior oblique causes a tilt of the head to the left shoulder. The patient can now look down and to the right to some extent with less reliance upon the paralysed muscle since the inferior rectus will now also move the right eye into this field. This head tilt also causes a stimulation of the vestibular apparatus and this produces a contraction of the left superior rectus and oblique and contraction of the right inferior rectus and oblique. The co-operation of the paralysed muscle is not required in this compensatory rotation of the eyes and single binocular vision is maintained. If, however, the head is (forcibly) tilted to the side of the paralysed muscle (i.e., the right, in this example) the compensatory rolling induced by the vestibular apparatus would in this case call for an active contraction of the right superior rectus and oblique muscles (and the left inferior rectus and oblique muscles). The greater part of the activity of the right superior rectus is concerned with elevation rather than with torsion and this elevation cannot be opposed by the depression action of the paralysed right superior oblique. Therefore, in addition to the rolling motion, the right eye (i.e., the eye with the paralysed muscle) is elevated. The characteristic elevation of the eye with the paralysed muscle when the head is tilted to the side of the paralysis is one outstanding sign of paralysis of the superior oblique muscle. It was described by Bielschowsky and is referred to as Bielschowsky's sign.

F. Later Phenomena

1. INHIBITIONAL PALSY

All of the characteristics of paralytic strabismus that have just been described are those in which the patient is seen immediately after the onset of paralysis. Very soon, however, the characteristics of the strabismus will begin to show other changes. If paralysis of the superior rectus of the left eye occurs (and the left eye continues to be used for fixation), the inferior rectus of this same eye will be able to move the eye down with less than the usual innervation since this action is no longer opposed by tonus of the paralysed superior rectus. Consequently, this action of the left inferior rectus is associated with smaller innervation to obtain equal amounts of depression. This reduction in the innervation to the left inferior rectus is then associated with reduction of the innervation to its yoked muscle in the contralateral eye according to Hering's law of equal innervation. This muscle, the right superior oblique, will therefore underact. When the eye with normal muscles fixates, both eyes will appear to be able to move in the field of action of the right superior oblique without difficulty and the only limitation of gaze will be in the diagnostic position of gaze of the paralysed muscle, i.e., the left superior rectus. When the eye with the paralysed muscle fixates, the apparent paralysis of the right superior oblique will appear to limit movement of the right eye upon rotation down and to the left. This inhibitional palsy (Chavasse) or underaction (Adler) of the muscle yoked to the antagonist of the paralysed muscle appears when the patient tends to fixate with the paralysed eye but will not if he uses his normal eye routinely to fixate. With this situation the diplopia fields, field of fixation, etc., that have just been described for a fresh case of paralysis will be considerably different after the paralysis has persisted while the patient continues to fixate with the eye with the paralysed muscle. For example, in this situation the patient soon learns to adjust to the changed innervation pattern so far as egocentric localization is concerned and will soon cease to past-point to the object of regard while the eye with the paralysed muscle is fixating. On the other hand, if he now fixates with the normal eye (which he has not been using routinely for fixation) he will past-point to the opposite side.

2. SPREAD OF COMITANCE

The differences between a primary and secondary deviation are greatest when the paralysis is a fresh one and they tend to become smaller and smaller with time. This phenomenon results in the strabismus becoming less and less incomitant and is referred to as the *spread of comitance*. It is the major reason for the statement made above that the borderline between comitant and incomitant strabismus is not always very precise. Two factors seem to be responsible for the spread of comitance: (*a*) The onset of a paralysis (say, of the left lateral rectus) causes the left eye to rotate nasally and this results in a shortening and sometimes also in a strengthening of the antagonist of the paralysed muscle (the left medial rectus). As time goes on this moves the left eye even farther nasally and results in what has been rather loosely referred to as "secondary contracture" of the antagonist of the paralysed muscle and, according to Bielschowsky, may finally result in structural changes so that a strabismus persists even though the patient recovers from the paralysis. (*b*) When fixating with the left eye the patient will have the same kind of underaction of the yoked muscle of the antagonist of the paralysed muscle which was described above. In this case, the underacting muscle will be the right lateral rectus which would also tend toward a convergent strabismus. In this case, however, the strabismus will tend to increase in the field of the right lateral rectus, i.e., with the gaze to the right, while with the original paralysis the strabismus would tend to increase with the gaze to the left. In this way an incomitant strabismus may become more and more comitant.

III. Comitant Strabismus

A. CAUSES

In comitant strabismus the angle of strabismus is essentially the same irrespective of the direction of regard. In brief, the patient is unable to make sufficient fusional movements to overcome any misalignment of the eyes. The reasons for this are not clear. It is felt that the early months of infancy when the macula is developing may be rather crucial as to whether or not adequate single binocular vision will develop. Thus, any anomaly that interferes in this crucial early period may serve as an obstacle to the unification process.

1. OBSTACLES TO UNIFICATION

A number of such obstacles have been proposed. These may be roughly grouped as sensory, motor and refractive. Congenital defects or defects acquired in infancy could interfere with the unification process by, for example, producing a blurred image in one of the two eyes. Such defects as a small corneal scar, hyaloid artery remnants, retrolental fibroplasia and, at a somewhat later age, retinoblastoma and pseudotumours, all can interfere (on the sensory side) with the unification process. The ability of such defects to serve as obstacles to fusion certainly must vary from patient to patient, however, because apparently identical defects will be associated with strabismus in some, and not in other patients. Refractive anomalies, and in particular (in this age group) rather marked amounts of hyperopia, can operate in a similar way. Motor obstacles are essentially consequences of incomitant strabismus which, because of the phenomenon of spread of comitance, become comitant as the crucial age for development of single binocular vision has passed. The eyes remain crossed even though the original cause of the incomitant strabismus may have long since disappeared. In addition to these, there are a large group of patients for whom none of the above factors can be shown to play an obvious role. It has been suggested that in the case of such patients a quite temporary obstacle may result in the diplopia and that this diplopia itself may play a prominent part in the prolongation of the strabismus. Theories of "diplopia phobia" are quite old. Recently it has been suggested that the process of reification of only one of these diplopic images is the necessary step whereby the individual with strabismus is able to exist in his visual world. This very same process, according to this notion, later becomes the major force which then prevents the development of normal single binocular vision (McLaughlin, 1960).

2. VERGENCE

While the basic factors responsible for the development of normal single binocular vision, on the one hand, and comitant strabismus, on the other, are still only poorly understood, it is useful to look at the matter in the light of the categories of vergence developed by Maddox (1886, 1907). This has already been discussed at some length and the relevance of the discussion to problems of strabismus has been pointed out in several different instances. The highly adaptable fusional movements characteristic of the adult observer with good single binocular vision are not to be found in the adult patient with long standing comitant strabismus, although rudimentary fusional movements often can be demonstrated. Thus it is an obvious over simplification to imagine that such a patient continues to be a squinter because two of the types of vergence are not in harmony (i.e., because, for example, his amplitude of negative fusional vergence is not sufficient to overcome the rather large amount of positive tonic convergence). But in the process of learning to live with the strabismus there is little doubt that a number of rather specific sensory adaptations occur. Such adaptations have rather profound effects on the character of the strabismus. For this reason inferences that have been made by studying the characteristics of strabismus in an adult or adolescent observer may have little relevance to the manner in which the strabismus developed when the observer was a child.

a. Tonic Convergence

In the development of comitant strabismus it seems likely that the relationship of the various types of vergence can play a very important role. If, to use the example already cited, the basic tonic vergence is high and insufficient negative fusional vergence is available to bring the eyes within the zone of single binocular vision, then convergent strabismus may result. A considerable amount of recent clinical experience on very young children seems to indicate that this may be an important factor in many cases of comitant strabismus. Moreover, it becomes quite important, following Maddox, to differentiate the two components of a comitant strabismus respectively due to an excess or deficiency of tonic vergence (suggested by what has been called the "basic deviation") and to an excess or deficiency of accommodative vergence. When the strabismus is largely a consequence of the former then surgical intervention is the method of treatment. Other methods are used for treatment of the deviations with an accommodative component. Of course, in any given case either or both of these factors may come into play and tend to bring the position of the eyes outside the zone of single binocular vision. One must decide in each case how much of the deviation at any given distance of fixation may be due to each component.

b. Hyperopia

It has been known since the time of Donders that the hyperopia of early childhood may result in an attempt by the child to accommodate to see even distant objects clearly. As has been emphasized, the innervation to accommodation will be linearly related to a given amount of accommodative vergence but the magnitude of such accommodative vergence associated with a unit change in innervation to accommodation will be different for each child. If the AC/A is high then moderate amounts of hyperopia may suffice to result in the accommodative vergence associated with the accommodation for the uncorrected hyperopia being enough to move the vergence position of the eyes outside the zone of single binocular vision. To put the matter another way, there is insufficient negative fusional vergence to bring the eyes from the position set by the accommodative vergence to the demand point. Strabismus results. Frequently glasses that correct for the hyperopia will suffice to give such patients normal single binocular vision. If the AC/A is somewhat lower the patient may still have sufficient negative fusional amplitude to bring the eyes from the position set by accommodative vergence to the demand point. No strabismus may result, although the use of the eyes may not always be in complete comfort. Two children with the same amount of hyperopia may behave quite differently, the one manifesting a convergent strabismus, the other normal single binocular vision. The difference between the two may only be in the magnitude of their respective AC/A. Even in the absence of hyperopia, or with its correction with suitable convex spectacles, accommodative vergence may play an important role in the strabismus for near distances. Even though single binocular vision is maintained for distance vision when the child accommodates for near there may be insufficient negative fusional convergence to avoid convergent strabismus. Young children, as a consequence of a number of circumstances, are particularly disposed to this state of affairs.

3. OUTGROWING STRABISMUS

From what facts are available, it seems likely that the AC/A is well established at an early age and remains essentially unchanged throughout life. During the early years, however, the size of the separation of the eyes is increasing quite rapidly. Figure 1 emphasizes the fact that a child who has a

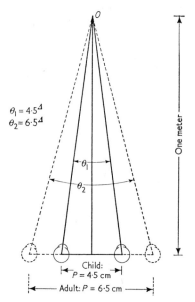

FIG. 1. Difference in magnitude of convergence required for fixating an object at 1 metre distance for a child (interocular separation 4.5 cm.) and an adult (interocular separation 6.5 cm.)

separation of the eyes of only 4.5 cm. needs to converge his eyes 2.0 prismdioptres less in order to see an object at 1 metre than he will have to when he grows to be an adult with an interocular separation of 6.5 cm. Moreover, because of his short arms the child has a visual space-world concentrated much closer to his eyes than does the adult (Gesell *et al.*, 1949). He will usually hold objects closer to his eyes in order to see them in detail than he will when he grows older. When he accommodates to see at this close distance he brings in a great deal of accommodation-convergence, but since his convergence demand for this near distance is not very great (because of the small interpupillary distance) he will over-converge for the near target, especially if his AC/A is very large. Whether or not he will be able to see this near target singly depends only upon whether or not he has sufficient negative fusional convergence to compensate for the excessive amount of accommodative vergence brought into play. If he does, then normal binocular vision will persist; if he does not, then convergent strabismus will appear. One can treat this convergent strabismus with bifocals and/or with DFP, each of which reduces the amount of accommodation-innervation required for seeing the near object sharply (and reduces also thereby the accommodation-vergence), and by attempting to build up the amplitude of fusional divergence with orthoptics. In the meantime, as the child grows older, the separation of the eyes increases, and this increases the amount of convergence required for fixation of the near object and reduces correspondingly the amount he will over-converge as a result of accommodating. At the same time his arms grow longer and he no longer holds near objects as close to his eyes. This further reduces the amount he will accommodate and, as a consequence, the amount of accommodation-vergence he will bring into play while looking at near objects. Thus the child may "outgrow" his strabismus.

References

Allen, J. H., ed. (1950). "Strabismus Ophthalmic Symposium I". C. V. Mosby Co., St. Louis.

Allen, J. H., ed. (1958). "Strabismus Ophthalmic Symposium II". C. V. Mosby Co., St. Louis.

Bielschowsky, A. (1943). "Lectures on Motor Anomalies". Dartmouth College Press, Hanover, N.H.

Duke-Elder, W. S. (1949). "Textbook of Ophthalmology", Vol. IV. C. V. Mosby Company, St. Louis.

Gesell, A., Ilg, F. L., and Bullis, G. E. (1949). "Vision: Its Development in Infant and Child". Paul B. Hoeber, Inc., New York.

McLaughlin, S. C., Jr. (1960). An hypothesis concerning the etiology of nonparalytic strabismus. Amer. J. Ophthal. 49, 1218–1221.

Maddox, E. E. (1886). Investigations on the relation between convergence and accommodation of the eyes. J. Anat., Lond. 20, 475–508; 565–584.

Maddox, E. E. (1907). "The Clinical Use of Prisms and the Decentering of Lenses", 5th edition, pp. 158–177. John Wright & Company, Bristol.

PART II

Accommodation and the Pupil

by

Mathew Alpern

University of Michigan, Ann Arbor, Michigan, U.S.A.

and

Otto Lowenstein and Irene E. Loewenfeld

Columbia University College of Physicians and Surgeons, New York, U.S.A.

Accommodation †

MATHEW ALPERN

I. Introduction

The change in fixation from an object at one distance to that at another is associated with a concomitant change in optical characteristics of the eye. The specific change that occurs is a shift of the location of that point in space which is optically conjugated ‡ to the retina. It is this process that we define as a change in accommodation. If the retinal conjugate focus moves closer

† I would like to acknowledge my indebtedness to Dr. Lloyd M. Barr of the Physiology Department, University of Michigan, Dr. Fergus W. Campbell of the Physiological Laboratory, The University of Cambridge, and to Dr. Gerard van Alphen of the National Institutes of Health for very helpful suggestions in the preparation of this chapter.

‡ Conjugate points in an optical system are two points so located that if an object is placed at one, the image of that object appears at the second.

to the eye, accommodation is said to increase; if it moves farther away, accommodation decreases.

A. TIME-CHARACTERISTICS

Figure 1 illustrates some of the time-characteristics of this process according to Campbell and Westheimer (1960). In this figure the upper trace shows the shift in location of the point conjugated to the retina in dioptres. In the lower trace the change in stimulus conditions is recorded. In this experiment the subject changed fixation from a target at optical infinity to one at an optical

FIG. 1. Record of accommodation responses to a 2D step stimulus and return to zero level of accommodation according to Campbell and Westheimer (1960). Top line, accommodation (horizontal calibration: 1 sec.; vertical calibration: 1D) upward movement represents far-to-near accommodation. The stimulus signal on the bottom line is at the same scale.

distance of 50 cm. from the eye. After a while the second target was turned off, the first turned on and then the whole cycle was repeated. When the stimulus changes from an object at a great distance to one much closer, the eye starts to change accommodation in the correct direction after a reaction-time of 0.36 ± 0.09 second.

1. REACTION-TIME

This is three times as long as the shortest reaction-time for a shift of gaze between two objects at the same distance from the eyes (i.e., for a saccadic eye movement; Westheimer, 1954a). It is almost twice as long as the reaction-time of a fusional vergence movement (Westheimer and Mitchell, 1956). Once the response starts in the correct direction (as it does 19 times out of 20 according to Allen, 1955) it continues in a more or less smooth fashion until levelling off at the new accommodation level. This process can be made considerably less smooth and exact, however, if the near target differs only in focus, but not in size, from the far one (Campbell and Westheimer, 1960). The reaction-time for far-to-near focus is about 20 msec. longer than that from near-to-far on the average, although an occasional subject will respond more quickly to the far target.

2. MOMENTARY STIMULI

The response to a momentary optical defocusing follows each aspect of the stimulus after the usual reaction-time. This suggests that the system is continuously monitoring the state of focus and that accommodation-responses may be halted during its progress and modified according to the new stimulus-conditions (Campbell and Westheimer, 1960). One can contrast this kind of response with the saccadic eye movements, which cannot be modified at all during their execution.

3. SLOW CHANGES

If one gradually moves a fixated object closer to the eyes, the accommodation-change no longer follows the stimulus smoothly, as pursuit eye movements do (Westheimer, 1954b). On the contrary, the response contains discontinuities and fluctuations; it may fail to match the target velocity correctly and may even make rather large changes in the incorrect direction.

This process of changing accommodation represents one of the more remarkable features of vertebrate eyes. The search for an understanding of the way in which it comes about has been long and extensive and if our knowledge is still incomplete, it is because the techniques for accurate investigations are, by and large, relatively recent. The description of the various objective and subjective ways of studying these phenomena is beyond the scope of this chapter. Fortunately, however, a reasonably complete description of the more common methods, as well as references to more detailed discussion of these problems, is available in the recent review by Fry (1959b).

B. THE IMPORTANCE OF THE LENS

Thomas Young (1801) first conclusively elucidated the importance of the lens in the accommodation process. He showed that changes in length of the eyeball did not occur during changes in accommodation by fixing both the anterior and posterior poles of his eye with two small rings, which were clamped together. When the eye changed accommodation he observed no change in the size of the pressure phosphene produced by the posterior clamp as it stimulated the retina mechanically. Young also showed: (i) *The absence of any change in curvature of the cornea during accommodation.* He invented a fluid contact-lens and in this way he eliminated the refracting power of the cornea. Under these conditions he showed that the amplitude of accommodation was still as large as under normal viewing conditions. (ii) *The changes in the shape of the lens must be responsible for changes in accommodation.* He demonstrated the absence of any ability to change accommodation at all in an eye in which the lens was removed for cataract.†

† Miotic pupils in normal eyes enhance the depth of field so that objects located at grossly different distances may continue to be seen clearly even when the retinal conjugate focus remains at a fixed distance (Campbell, 1957). In aphakia this natural miosis of the near response remains when the eye attempts to look at near objects, even though the dioptric power of the eye remains unchanged. The increased miosis and accompanying

This work clearly identified the lens as the structure most intimately involved in the process of changing accommodation. Before going into more detail about the changes that the lens undergoes, the anatomy of the lens and its supporting structures will be briefly summarized.

II. Anatomy

Some of the features of the anatomy of these structures have already been described in Volume I; here we may simply emphasize those characteristics that are important from the present optical point of view.

A. The Lens

1. DIMENSIONS

The lens is a transparent optical structure approximately 10 mm. in equatorial diameter, and 3.8 mm. in saggittal diameter. The shapes of the surfaces of the living lens are not easily described in simple geometrical terms. The anterior surface is more or less convex spherical with a central radius of curvature of 10–12 mm. The posterior surface is not spherical; although, in the centre, it has an approximate spherical shape (with a radius from 4.6 to 7.5 mm.). However, toward the periphery it is much more flattened. All of these figures are for distance-vision and many of them change rather prominently for near-vision.

2. CAPSULE

The substance of the lens is enclosed within an elastic capsule but, despite the absence of a blood supply, continues to grow throughout life by multiplication of the epithelial cells at the equator.

3. GROWTH

Throughout life (Smith, 1883) new lens fibres are laid down at the equator and apply themselves as they develop further to the anterior and posterior

increased depth of field have misled many to the idea that the conjugate focus of the eye could change even though the lens had been removed. A case of this kind, Benjamin Clerk, was reported by Home (1795) to disprove Young's thesis to the Royal Society (1793) which suggested that changes in form of the lens were responsible for the increased refraction of the eye during increased accommodation. In what can only be regarded as a unique example of scientific perseverance, Young first designed an optometer to measure the change in position of the conjugate focus of the retina, and then demonstrated in five aphakic patients that their conjugate retinal focus remained completely fixed. Several years later, in the presence of Home and Henry Cavendish, Young showed that Clerk himself also had no ability at all to change the location of the conjugate focus of the retina in the aphakic eye even though his depth-of-field allowed him to see objects at different distances clearly with it.

surfaces, each fibre bending around the equator. The younger lens fibres are thicker, softer, less coloured. As they grow older they become flatter, closer together and amber coloured. The centrally situated fibres are the oldest. The sclerosis of the lens fibres begins here. Each successive layer of lens fibres is laid down at a different stage in the lens development. Thus, the lens can be envisaged as being made up of layer upon layer of lens fibres much like the layers of an onion, with each layer having a slightly different index of refraction. Gullstrand (1908) called these, iso-indicial surfaces, and computed their optical characteristics. The central zone of the lens (the nucleus, or core) being composed of the oldest fibres also has the highest index of refraction.

a. Optical Zones

Figure 2 illustrates the slit-lamp view of the lens of patients of various ages according to Goldmann (1937). With advancing age the number of elementary zones increases (in a very old person there may be as many as 20), while the individual laminae, showing lenticular sclerosis, become thinner. The distance of the anterior capsule from the posterior boundary of the anterior senile nucleus increases. The senile nucleus may be marked off into zones of discontinuity. Lenses from eyes in the first two decades of life have only one zone, those from the second two decades have two, and those from later ones, three. The isoindicial surfaces have smaller and smaller values for the index of refraction as one approaches the lens surfaces. Gullstrand assigned values of 1.406 for the centre and 1.386 for the vertex. The average weight of the lens was found by Smith (1883) to increase about 1.5 mg./year and the volume to increase by 1.5 mm.^{3}/year.

The lens substance is characteristically regarded as being somewhat elastic. Adler (1959) denies this and regards it as completely plastic. While precise measurements of the elastic properties of the lens substance are unavailable, it is likely from certain characteristics of the lens substance to be described below that it has a certain amount of elasticity.

B. THE LENS CAPSULE

The lens substance is enclosed in a thin, transparent envelope—the lens capsule. The outer layer of the capsule is derived from the zonule and is known as the superficial zonular lamella. Beneath this is the capsule proper. The outstanding physical characteristic of the capsule is its elasticity, although precise measurements of the magnitude of the elasticity have not been reported. If the isolated lens is placed in water the capsule will imbibe some water. This causes the capsule to swell. If the capsule is then punctured it

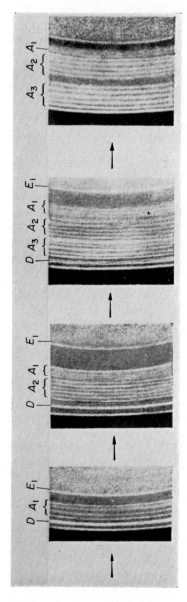

FIG. 2. Changes in the lens fibres with age as seen in the narrowest slit-lamp beam. The pictures show the characteristics of a lens in 13 years, 23 years, 46 years and 60 years old patients, respectively. D = zone of discontinuity. A_1, A_2, A_3 = zone of senile nucleus. E_1 = outer embryonic nucleus. (According to Goldmann, 1937.)

will extrude fluid in a steady stream and then return to its original form around the lens substance.

1. DIMENSIONS

Fincham (1937) found the capsule to vary in thickness in various positions. It was thinnest (2.8 μ) at the posterior pole, increasing to 6.3 μ 2 mm. from the pole on the posterior surface and to 14.83 μ 3 mm. from the pole on the posterior surface. The anterior surface of the capsule, on the other hand, was

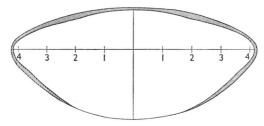

FIG. 3. Diagram showing the relative thickness of various regions of the lens capsule according to Fincham (1937). These thicknesses are magnified for illustration purposes.

much thicker. On average Fincham found: 15.5 μ at the pole on the anterior surface of the capsule, 22.5 μ 2 mm. from the anterior pole but this reduced to 18.5 μ 3 mm. from the pole on the anterior surface. Some of these relations are illustrated in Fig. 3 which shows the relative variation in thickness of the lens capsule according to Fincham (1937). The thicknesses in this figure are exaggerated in order to illustrate the differences between different regions.

C. THE ZONULE OF ZINN

The zonule of Zinn (suspensory ligaments of the lens) consists of a series of delicate homogeneous transparent fibrils which run from the inner surface of the ciliary body to the peripheral parts of the lens capsule in the region of the equator. It is sometimes stated that the zonule is a gel (part of the vitreous) and the fibres are mainly histological artifacts. Wolff (1946) offers clear evidence that the fibres are indeed part of the normal anatomy. These fibres become quite continuous with the internal limiting membrane of the ciliary body. The fibres pass forward and become continuous with the zonular lamella of the lens capsule. The fibres from the posterior ciliary body pass to both posterior and anterior lens capsule near the equator; those from the anterior ciliary body pass also to both the anterior and posterior lens capsule. The zonular fibres pass posteriorly to the edge of the retina at the spikes of the ora serrata (McCulloch, 1954) but fall short of the retina at the bays. It is helpful to think of the zonule as having broad areas of origin, large masses of connecting fibres and large areas of insertion. The fibres do not arise in the ciliary processes, since these have no internal limiting membrane, but in the valleys between the processes.

D. The Ciliary Muscle

The ciliary muscle consists of flat bundles of unstriped muscle. The outermost layers run meridionally from front to back, the innermost layers run circularly around the globe. The ciliary body represents the anterior part of the uvea and is thus continuous with the choroid. The muscle fibres begin to appear in the choroid, even at the equator mainly in the supra-choroidal spaces. These muscle fibres appear first as star-shaped figures, becoming more and more numerous the farther forward one moves. The ciliary muscle proper begins with meshes of the muscle-bundles. A close framework develops out of this. The bundles disposed in various planes unite with one another and the muscle mass becomes thicker and thicker through further branching. This framework is maintained throughout the entire ciliary muscle, although the prevailing directions change gradually so that the ciliary muscle falls into various portions.

1. GROUPING OF FIBRES

Various authors describe different muscle groups in the ciliary muscle. Actually, it is functionally more realistic to regard the meshwork of inter-mingling muscle fibres as different portions of the same muscle. Salzmann (1912) describes three such portions:

a. The *longitudinal fibres* (also called meridional fibres; also called Brueck's muscle) run antero-posteriorly on the outside of the ciliary muscle. These fibres originate in the scleral spur at the corneo-scleral junction and insert into the elastic laminae of the suprachoroid. Con-traction of these fibres does not pull the choroid forward but it does allow the muscle to move forward (Wolff, 1952) as the experiments of Hensen and Voelckers (1873) proved.

b. The *circular fibres* (Mueller's muscle or sphincter muscle) are the innermost fibres and run circularly around the globe.

c. The *radial fibres* (or reticulated portion) appear as an intermingled mesh connecting the circular and meridional bundles.

Contrary to this description of the ciliary muscle as a single system of muscle, Calasans (1953) believes it to be formed by four systems of oblique smooth-muscle bundles. All of these systems take origin in the corneo-scleral meshwork. The bundles run alternately nasalward and temporalward and unite at the end in the shape of a double V. The bundles of the first system, according to Calasans, correspond more or less to the longitudinal fibres of Salzmann. Calasans believes this system is composed of three muscular laminae. The remaining muscular systems are related to the ciliary processes and run in an antero-posterior direction. The bundles of the second system connect to the tails of the ciliary processes, those of the third system to the bodies of the ciliary processes. The bundles of the fourth system connect to the root of the iris and to the head of the ciliary process. Busacca (1955), by gonioscopic examination of an eye with a large peripheral iridectomy, confirmed the idea that certain fibre bundles of the ciliary muscle act as erectors of the ciliary processes and retractors of the base of the iris.

2. INNERVATION

The ciliary muscle is richly supplied with nerves, probably from both the ortho- and parasympathetic divisions of the autonomic nervous system.

III. Physiology

A. CILIARY MUSCLE AND ZONULE

When the eye looks at infinity, that part of the ciliary muscle innervated by the parasympathetic nervous system is relaxed. A discharge in these nerves causes the release of acetylcholine which initiates a contraction of the ciliary muscle. When the ciliary muscle contracts its length is reduced and it moves forward towards the equator of the lens. The demonstration of this was achieved by Hensen and Voelckers (1873) by placing a needle in the equator of the eye and stimulating nerves to the ciliary muscle. The needle promptly moved backwards. It has been suggested that the vascular characteristics of the choroid make it incapable of withstanding the traction imposed by the contraction of the ciliary muscle (Henderson, 1926). However, Wolff (1952) points out that the ciliary muscle does not insert into the vascular layers of the choroid at all but into the elastic lamellae of the suprachoroidal connective tissue.

1. RELAXATION OF SUSPENSORY LIGAMENT

When the ciliary muscle contracts, the fibres of the suspensory ligaments of the lens are relaxed as Helmholtz first suggested in 1855. One can verify this by looking at these fibres directly with a slit lamp during accommodation in a case with aniridia (Fincham, 1937) or with a large peripheral iridectomy (Busacca, 1955). Graves (1925) studied a case in whom penetrating injury to the anterior lens capsule had caused a complete dissolution of all the lens substance while leaving the capsule virtually intact. When this patient's other eye looked at far objects (or homatropine was instilled into the eye

7

without any lens material) the two surfaces of the capsule were rigidly taut. On the other hand, looking at near objects (or putting eserine into the injured eye) caused the capsule to become slack, the anterior capsule showing a definite forward curve, the posterior capsule becoming lax and wrinkled.

2. GRAVITY EFFECT

Hess (1904) demonstrated that the accommodated lens is markedly influenced by the force of gravity while the unaccommodated lens is not. Two plus lenses are optically of greater power when the distance between them is shortened and Hess showed that the maximum amplitude of the accommodating eye was greater when one looks straight down than when one looks straight up. Moreover, the displacement of the lens due to the force of gravity can be verified in eyes with small lenticular opacities when such an observer accommodates. This displacement may be observed by looking at the eye with a slit lamp or it can be demonstrated entoptically.

3. SHAPE OF LENS

Suppose that an eye, which has been made to accommodate for far vision by instillation of atropine, is removed from the orbit and pointed upwards after the cornea and iris have been carefully dissected away. The profile of the front surface of the lens can then be photographed and in this condition it demonstrates the characteristic shape of the lens when the eye is looking at a distant object. When the fibres of the zonule are severed, however, merely by passing the sharp edge of a knife around the lens, the anterior surface of the lens then assumes the shape that it has under maximum accommodation. Figure 4 illustrates an experiment of this kind carried out by Fincham (1937). Clearly tension developed by the fibres of the zonule distorts the lens.

B. THE LENS

1. CURVATURES

The changes in the form of the lens during accommodation are most pronounced on the anterior surface although it should be kept in mind that these changes in form are distributed to each of the isoindicial surfaces of the lens. Figure 4 illustrates these changes quite clearly. In the unaccommodated state the anterior lens surface has more or less spherical shape with (in this case †) a radius of curvature of 12 mm. When the eye accommodates, however, the anterior surface no longer remains spherical but becomes somewhat

---

† Fincham (1937) finds on the average a value of 11 mm. with the classical writers assigning a value closer to 10 mm.

hyperboloid. The central (3 mm.) region of the anterior surface is indeed more or less spherical. Moreover, the radius of this region is greatly shortened during accommodation. In the case illustrated in Fig. 4, it is only 5 mm. The peripheral part of the anterior surface of the lens, however, does not show any

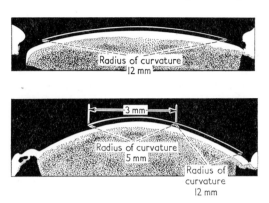

FIG. 4. The form of the anterior surface of the lens of a child under normal suspension by the zonule, and with zonule severed. (According to Fincham, 1937)

increase in curvature at all and indeed in many cases its curvature may actually be flatter in the eye accommodated for near-vision than when it is accommodated for far-vision.

a. Ophthalmophakometry

While the data illustrated in Fig. 4 are from an enucleated eye with zonule fibres severed it is quite evident that identical changes can be demonstrated in the intact eye accommodating for near distances. In order to do this Tscherning (1900) measured the radius of curvature in the living lens using a device which he called the *ophthalmophakometer*. In principle this consists of treating the cornea and anterior surfaces of the lens as a pair of convex mirrors. He arranged objects in the field so that the image of one object formed by reflexion at the cornea was the same size as the image of the second object formed by reflexion at the anterior lens surface.† Provided these two objects are sufficiently far away (as is always the case) optical considerations show that the ratio of the sizes of the two objects under these conditions is

† These reflected images are referred to as the Purkinje-Sanson images. The first three are respectively formed by reflexion at the anterior and posterior corneal surfaces and the anterior lens surface, all of which are convex toward the observer. Hence all of these images are upright. The fourth Purkinje-Sanson image is formed by reflexion at the posterior surface of the lens (a concave mirror) and is thus inverted. The second image is of low luminance and so close to the bright first image that it cannot normally be seen.

inversely proportional to the radii of the respective reflecting surfaces.† In this way it is easy enough to measure the radius of curvature of the anterior surface of the lens. Using this method Tscherning first showed that during accommodation the central region of the anterior surface of the lens increased markedly in curvature but that the peripheral part of this surface was considerably flattened during accommodation.

b. Spherical Aberrations

This same conclusion can be obtained by examination of the spherical aberration characteristics of the eye under various accommodation states. Tscherning (1900) demonstrated with an " aberrascope" that the spherical aberration of the eye changes during accommodation. Gullstrand (1924) criticized Tscherning's method but his essential conclusions have been verified

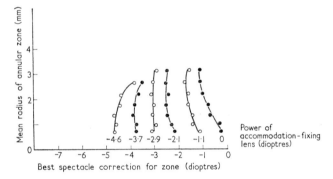

Fig. 5. Spherical aberration of the eye for accommodation at different levels according to Koomen *et al.* (1949). The ordinate represents the radius of annular zone held centred in front of the eye-pupil while the abscissa shows the optimal spherical lens necessary to correct the focus of that zone, when the accommodation was fixed at various stimulus values.

by more precise quantitative experiments (Koomen *et al.*, 1949; Ivanoff, 1956). Figure 5 illustrates the data obtained by Koomen *et al.* on one subject. It is apparent in this subject that the spherical aberration for viewing at a distance is positive (or under-corrected). This means that light passing through the edge of the pupil is brought to a focus in front of light passing through the centre of the pupil. As the eye accommodates more and more,

† The radius of the anterior surface of the lens obtained in this way, however, is only the *apparent* radius. To calculate the actual lens radius one must correct for the refraction of the cornea using the image-object equation of first order optical theory. For this calculation one also needs to know the radius of curvature of the corneal surface and the distance of the anterior surface of the lens from the anterior surface of the cornea, each of which must be obtained empirically. The former is measured using the ophthalmometer, the latter using the ophthalmophakometer.

the extent of the aberration gets less and less and when the eye accommodates 2.9 D (in this case) there is essentially no spherical aberration at all. When the eye accommodates more than this the aberration becomes negative (or over-corrected) which means that rays entering through the edge of the pupil are brought to a focus behind those passing through the centre. While individual differences in experiments of this kind are prominent, the general trends are invariably similar.

Tscherning (1900) correctly attributed this change in the spherical aberration characteristics of the eye during accommodation to the hyperbolic form that the anterior surface of the lens assumes when the ciliary muscle contracts. However, he incorrectly assumed that this shape was due to an increase in tension of the fibres of the suspensory ligament which are, in fact, relaxed when the ciliary muscle contracts.

c. Posterior Surface

In contrast to the changes that occur on the anterior surface of the lens during accommodation the posterior surface of the lens changes its curvature very little, if at all. This has been apparent to investigators at least since the experiments of Helmholtz (1855) and no very sharp disagreement exists on it. One can verify it easily enough by using the ophthalmophakometer or by photographing the fourth Purkinje-Sanson images with the eye respectively accommodated for infinity and for nearness. By such techniques Fincham (1937) showed a decrease in radius from 5.18 to 5.05 mm. in one case, and from 5.74 to 4.87 mm. in a second, for an accommodation change from 1D to 9D.

2. EQUATORIAL DIAMETER

A considerable disagreement existed, however, regarding the change in the equatorial diameter of the lens during accommodation. If contraction of the ciliary muscle increased the zonular tension, then an increase in equatorial diameter should occur during increasing accommodation. The Helmholtz view that accommodation was associated with relaxed tension of the zonular fibres predicts that the equatorial diameter would become smaller as the accommodation increases. This argument was finally resolved in favour of the latter interpretation by studying the diameter of the lens in an eye with congenital absence of the iris. In this eye the equatorial diameter of the lens could be observed and photographed first while looking at far, and then while looking at near objects. It was found to be 0.4 to 0.45 mm. smaller in the latter case (Fincham, 1937).

3. FORWARD BULGING

The pole of the anterior surface of the lens bulges forward during accommodation, as Fig. 4 clearly demonstrates. In changing from 1D of accommodation to 9D, Fincham found a forward movement of 0.34 mm. in one case and of 0.27 mm. in the second. This was primarily due to an increase in the central thickness of the lens which changed from 3.66 to 4.24 mm. in the first case and from 3.84 to 4.20 mm. in the second.

C. The Capsule

1. variable thickness

How are the changes in the form of the lens induced by the relaxation of the zonule when the ciliary muscle contracts? Fincham (1937) believes that the variable thickness of the lens capsule plays an essential role. When the eye is looking at a far object, the tension of the zonule releases the lens substance from the elastic force of the capsule. The elasticity of the lens substance itself causes it to assume the shape of the unaccommodated lens which is that of a highly convex posterior curve (of radius of about 5.5 mm.) and much less convex curve on the anterior surface (radius about 11 mm.). When the ciliary muscle contracts the tension of the zonule fibres is relaxed and the elastic capsule then contracts and exerts its tension onto the lens substance and in this way moulds it. The capsule on its anterior surface will give way where it is thinnest (in the centre) and in this way the centre of the anterior surface of the lens becomes more highly curved and its pole bulges forward. The peripheral part of the anterior surface of the lens, which has a much thicker capsule, will not increase in curve at all so that the anterior surface of the lens changes from the spherical shape (far-vision) to the hyperboloid shape (near-vision). At the same time, the equatorial diameter of the lens gets smaller and the lens substance is moulded to the central bulge. The saggittal diameter increases while the curvature of the posterior lens surface at the centre (where the capsule is thinnest) does not increase at all.

a. Posterior Surface

It may not be apparent how the curve at the centre of the posterior surface remains relatively unchanged when accommodation changes even though the capsule is thinnest at this point. Stuhlman (1943) attributes this to the fact that the tension of the fibres running from the anterior border of the ciliary body to the posterior surface of the lens capsule is uninfluenced by the change in length of the ciliary muscle. Another explanation can be found, however, in the geometry of the unaccommodated lens. Assume that all lens changes are restricted to the central regions because of the thick capsule in the periphery. Under these conditions it can be shown that the rate of change of the angle of slope of the tangents to the surface at the centre with change in the equatorial diameter varies inversely with the cube of the cosine of the angle of slope. Since the anterior curve is flattest its angle of slope is largest and it therefore must undergo the greatest curvature change when the accommodation changes.

Figure 6 shows the appearance of the lens of the eye while looking at far (left) and at near (right) objects. These are photographs of the lens and the cornea obtained with oblique illumination in a case of congenital aniridia (Fincham, 1937).

Unaccommodated   Accommodated

FIG. 6. The cornea and lens, in the unaccommodated and accommodated states, in a case of congenital absence of the iris as observed by slit-lamp illumination. The photographs have been corrected for the oblique angle of the axis of the camera so that the view is what is obtained by observing the process in a perpendicular direction. (Fincham, 1937)

2. KINETICS OF CHANGE

The kinetics of the changes in the lens substance during accommodation as a result of the moulding influence of the elastic capsule, according to this theory, have never been described in quantitative terms (Fry, 1959b). Until such time as this has been done it will be difficult to understand just how an elastic ellipsoidal membrane like the lens capsule with varying thickness in different zones produces the necessary changes in lens shape. None the less, a certain degree of plausibility has been given to this theory by the demonstration that the primate lens, free from zonular tension, has the shape of the lens in an eye accommodated for near-vision while the same lens from which the capsule has been removed has the shape of the lens in an eye looking at far objects (Fincham, 1928). If the experiment is repeated on lenses from animals (such as sheep) in which little variation in capsule thickness can be found (and which also presumably have very little accommodation) the shape of the lens with and without the capsule remains essentially the same.

D. INTRACAPSULAR MECHANISMS

The changes in the lens that have just been described occur on its anterior surface. However, Gullstrand (1908) emphasized that each of the various iso-indicial surfaces of the lens would be considerably changed in shape and position during the process of accommodation. Gullstrand pointed out that a slight increase in the index of refraction at any given point in the lens might result from the interpenetration of individual lens fibres, even though the physical indexes of the individual fibres did not change. Moreover, the shifting of individual parts in the direction of the axis during increased sagittal thickness of the lens was, according to Gullstrand, greatest in the equatorial plane. In this plane the parts lying near the axis should move more than those near the equator. In this way the modified forms and positions of the iso-indicial surfaces produce an increase of the "total index" of refraction of the lens and this tends to increase its refracting power also.

1. ELECTRIC CURRENTS

Resurgence of interest in these problems may be anticipated as a result of the recent experiments of Kleifeld (1956) who applied currents to the lens *in vitro*. With small amounts of d.c. stimulation (2.0 mA.) reversible changes were produced both in whole lenses and in lens fibres. The fibres become thicker and thinner, displace some of their contents and move towards one another. Kleifeld suggests the possibility that the lens fibres possess a primitive contractile system.† In order to support this speculation, Kleifeld showed that animal lenses during accommodation show a decrease in the sugar and lactic acid content while oxygen consumption is increased. Moreover, extract of young lens nuclei is capable of building up ATP in important quantities.

While the interpretation of results of this kind must await much more crucial quantitative experiments, this work is valuable because it tends to emphasize that aspect of the mechanism of accommodation which has been most ignored by theoretical approaches after Gullstrand. It seems quite clear that before we can hope to have any better understanding of the accommodation process we will need to know a good deal more about: (i) the elasticity (and compressibility) of the lens fibres and of the cement substance; (ii) the form of the various layers of the lens fibres at various ages; and, (iii) the nature of the adhesions between: (*a*) each lamina of lens fibres and the other laminae, and (*b*) the lens fibres and the capsule.

IV. Presbyopia

The ability of one's eye to vary its optical characteristics in order to focus objects at different distances shows very large decrements as one grows older. Measurements of this phenomenon were reported almost a century ago by Donders (1864). His values were revised by Duane (1912). Figure 7 illustrates the results of these latter studies, which were obtained as the nearest point

† This idea can be traced directly to Thomas Young (1793). It is commonly described as the one hypothesis in his Bakerian lecture of November 27, 1800 that has not been substantiated by subsequent research.

that a 3.0 × 0.2 mm. vertical blank line on a white background could be seen without blur. It is evident that the amplitude of accommodation progressively decreases with age. In the older age group this results in an inability to read or do close work with the lenses which correct only for optical defects of far distance sight. In this case, it is essential to prescribe additional positive lenses for near work, in the form of reading glasses or bifocals. This condition is known as *presbyopia*.

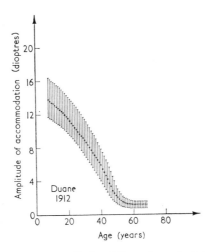

FIG. 7. Mean and upper and lower limits of the reciprocal of the near point of accommodation at various ages, according to the measurements of Duane (1912).

A. VARIATION OF AMPLITUDE WITH AGE

The onset of disability due to presbyopia usually occurs around the age of 45 years † although, according to Fig. 7, the mean amplitude at this age is almost 4D and this should be sufficient to allow clear vision about 25 cm. from the spectacle plane. It is necessary to point out, however, that the data illustrated in Fig. 7 were obtained by a subjective blur criterion. This means that they may not in fact represent the extent to which the eye can vary its dioptric power at various ages, since one utilizes one extreme of the depth of field for determining the far point of the eye and the other for the determination of the near point. If we define the amplitude of accommodation

† It will be earlier in hyperopia, later in myopia, because spectacle lenses correct for the ametropia some 11 or 12 mm. in front of the principal planes of the eye. Thus to fixate an object at a given distance from the eyes the myope will have to accommodate less, the hyperope more, while looking through correcting spectacle lenses (Neumuller, 1937; Alpern, 1949).

7*

as the maximum extent to which the eye can vary the position of the retinal conjugate focus point, then clearly the ordinate in Fig. 7 does not represent accommodation amplitude. Using the method of stigmatoscopy, Hamasaki *et al.* (1956) determined the extent to which the amplitude of accommodation (as just defined) varied with age in the presbyopic group. Their results are illustrated as the filled circles in Fig. 8. For comparison on the same graph are

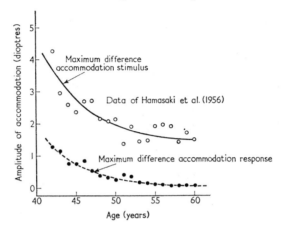

FIG. 8. Mean values for the maximum amount the dioptric power of the eye can increase (filled circles) for various ages according to the data of Hamasaki *et al.* (1956). The open circles represent near-point determinations by the push-up method in the same population sample.

measurements of the "amplitude" using the subjective push-up to "blur" method on the same population sample. It is quite apparent that, while both sets of data show a continued decrement with age, the amplitude of accommodation at any age is at least 1.5D smaller than would be suggested by the "near-point" measurements. For example, at 42 years of age the amplitude is only 1.25D on the average, while Duane's data show 5D and Donders's about 4.4D for this age.†

B. LENTICULAR SCLEROSIS

With increasing age the lens increases in weight, volume, specific gravity and in thickness. The latter is due to an increase in thickness of the cortex while the nucleus apparently decreases in thickness. The number of elementary zones greatly increases while individual laminae become thinner. These

† It is of some clinical interest that the sum of amplitude of accommodation (as defined above) at any age and the power of the additional positive (reading) lens usually prescribed for presbyopes of this same age (Hofstetter, 1949) is about the same value (a little bit more than 2D) for every age up to 60 years.

changes constitute what has become known as lenticular "sclerosis." It is assumed that under these conditions the lens fibres are much more rigid, much less plastic, than in younger ages. It is generally agreed that this is the physiological basis for presbyopia. Gullstrand (1908), taking careful notice of the way in which the lens fibres are laid down, believed the sclerosis was largely confined to the fibres that had been laid down earlier (thus, those closest to the nucleus) while those new fibres in the cortex were believed to have little or no sclerosis. For this reason Gullstrand, following Helmholtz, believed that to produce a dioptre change of accommodation at any age would require the same amount of change in length of the ciliary muscle (if the lens were capable of accommodating that much at all).

C. DONDERS'S HYPOTHESIS

Gullstrand's view has not been universally accepted and has even come into disrepute in recent years. Donders (1864), Duane (1925) and recently Fincham (1932, 1955), in order to account for the decline of amplitude with age, have all supported the idea that the amount of shortening of the ciliary muscle, required to produce a unit change in refraction of the eye, increases with age. The assumption is that the ciliary muscle itself remains relatively constant throughout life. Fincham (1932) believes this must be true if the capsule does in fact mould the shape of lens of the accommodated eye. He states:

"As the lens-substance becomes more rigid with age it will suffer less change in form for a given pressure of the capsule. Thus, to produce a given amount of accommodation a greater pressure from the capsule and therefore a greater ciliary contraction will be necessary in age than in youth."

The evidence that Fincham offers to support this view will be discussed presently. However, we do not know enough about the kinetics of the elastic forces in the capsule and their relation to the rigidity of the lens fibres in different positions within the lens to be able to make any quantitative test of the accuracy of the statement quoted above. This point must be emphasized because it does not necessarily follow that if this theory of presbyopia is wrong the capsular theory of accommodation must also be incorrect.

The evidence for this theory of presbyopia may briefly be summarized in four categories:

1. CLINICAL EVIDENCE

It has been maintained that the full amplitude of accommodation cannot be maintained for long periods with comfort. Moreover, the presbyopic observer is said to need positive lenses for near seeing even though the near point may not lie beyond the normal reading distance. However, it has been pointed out already that this is based upon subjective estimates of the near point which include a rather large amount of depth of field changes. Analysis of the problem in terms of objective measurements of accommodation frequently leads to the opposite conclusion.

2. CHARACTERISTICS OF AN ACCOMMODATION MODEL

Fincham (1932) used as a model of his accommodation theory a mechanism consisting of a lens made of rubber suspended from spiral springs. He found that more change in tension of the springs was required when the lens was made of hard rubber than when it was made of soft rubber in order to produce a given change in thickness.†

3. CONVERGENT ACCOMMODATION

The variation in the stimulus to convergence was found by Fincham (1955) to produce an accommodation response provided the vergence of the light at the retina was not permitted to influence the refractive state of the eye. Moreover, he found that the amount of change in refractive state induced by a unit change in convergence-stimulus showed a progressive decrement as age progressed. Fincham (1955) assumes that the innervation to the ciliary muscle evoked by a given convergence-stimulus remains constant at all ages. If this is true then a given amount of shortening of the ciliary muscle produces a smaller amount of change in dioptric power of the eye with increased age. When homatropine is applied, the amount of accommodation induced by convergence becomes smaller and this happens as soon as there is any measurable reduction in the amplitude of accommodation. Finally, when eserine is applied the amount of accommodation induced by a unit change in convergence-stimulus increases and so does the maximum amount of accommodation induced by convergence.

This last is the most crucial piece of evidence. It implies that an additional shortening of the ciliary muscle mustered by the anticholinesterase activity of eserine was helpful in relaxing the tension on the zonule a little more than is usually obtained with maximum amplitude. If this were true then the lens itself could hardly be the limiting factor on the maximum accommodation. The evidence is, however, still inconclusive. Maximum amplitude obtained using convergence as the only accommodation-stimulus has been found by Balsam and Fry (1959) among others, to be considerably smaller (as much as 1.6D) than the maximum amplitude obtainable under optimal stimulus conditions. Furthermore, the site of action of eserine topically applied to the eye, as it influences changes in accommodation, is unknown. It is possible, for example, that such a substance (or acetylcholine) directly influences the intracapsular accommodation mechanisms. Data supporting this idea are not extensive, but Gillessen (1938) showed that the injection of very small amounts of acetylcholine and histamine directly into the lens caused a large transient increase in dioptric power in monkeys, dogs and rabbits without any influence at all on the pupil. Control injections of equal amounts of aqueous produced no change in refraction.

4. MONOCULAR AND BINOCULAR AMPLITUDE

Duane (1925) points out cases in which the binocular amplitude of accommodation is larger than the monocular. He maintains that this could not be the case if the sclerosis of the fibres of the lens limited the accommodation amplitude. Since in these data reported the technique of "push-up to subjective blur" was used as a criterion, the argument is not definitive. It has already been emphasized that depth of focus (hence pupil size) may alter the "near-point" of accommodation when examined in this way. Evidence of this kind would be more convincing if it could be demonstrated that the maximum amount the eye can change its focus when both eyes fixate is considerably greater than when only one fixates.‡

† How closely this model resembles the condition of the accommodating lens has yet to be determined.

‡ Preliminary experiments (Schapero and Nadell, 1957) suggest this possibility. These results are not definitive, however, since they do not include enough measurements to permit one to compare the near and far points in monocular and binocular conditions.

D. The Gullstrand Theory

It has already been pointed out how Gullstrand (1908), reasoning from the characteristic changes that the lens fibres undergo during life, had developed the idea that the amount of shortening of the ciliary muscle required to produce a unit change in dioptric power of the eye remained constant throughout life. This theory has one prediction: If the amplitude of accommodation declines with age due to sclerosis of lens fibres, but a given change in length of the muscle causes unit change in refraction at all ages, then as one grows older, one's ciliary muscle has an ever increasing ability to change its length which remains "latent" because of its inability to produce any effect on the lens (Hess, 1901). According to the terminology of Flieringa and van der Hoeve (1924), the term *myodioptre* represents the amount of change in length of the ciliary muscle necessary to produce one dioptre change in the refracting power of the eye. Thus as presbyopia proceeds, fewer and fewer myodioptres are used to change the refracting power of the lens and more and more myodioptres remain unrelated to any refractive change at all. The *physical* amplitude of accommodation represents the maximum number of dioptres the eye can change its refractive power. The *physiological* amplitude represents the maximum number of myodioptres the ciliary muscle can change its length. Except at a very young age, the latter should be always greater than the former and presumably remains constant throughout life.

The evidence for this theory of presbyopia may be summarized as follows:

1. PROLONGED FIXATION AT THE NEAR POINT

If only a part of the total available myodioptres are used for obtaining the near point, then it should be quite difficult to show a decrement in accommodation-amplitude by continued practice. As a matter of fact, this is exactly what has been found. If one continues to look at an object at the near point of accommodation, bringing the object in until blurred and moving it back until cleared, the amplitude shows no decrement with continued performance. On the contrary, under such conditions the near point approaches the eye! (Lancaster and Williams, 1914; Hofstetter, 1943.)

When one carries out such attempts to "fatigue" accommodation, even over prolonged periods of time, they are done almost invariably without any asthenopic symptoms such as one might anticipate if maximum shortening of the ciliary muscle were required for maximum amplitude. It should be noted that this is precisely opposite to the statements made by Fincham (1932) about this matter. No quantitative evaluation of discomfort has ever been made under these conditions but those empirical studies that have been done (Hofstetter, 1949; Lancaster and Williams, 1914) do not support Fincham's view.†

2. RELATION OF ACCOMMODATION TO CONVERGENCE

When one eye changes its refractive power during the process of accommodation and the other is occluded, the latter undergoes a vergence movement. The characteristics of

† Fuchs (1922) believed that the apparent asthenopia that occasionally occurs in early uncorrected presbyopia was due not to the excess shortening of the ciliary muscle which such cases may employ in a vain effort to increase the refracting power of the lens. On the contrary, he suggested that the increased vergence associated with this increased innervation to the ciliary muscle displaced the near-point phoria outside the zone of ocular comfort. Since to maintain single binocular vision an excess of fusional convergence would be necessary, *this* results in the symptoms one occasionally finds in cases of this kind.

the relationship between the inward rotation of the eyes and the increased accommodation are summarized in the chapter on eye movements. Suffice it to say that the available evidence is best explained with the assumption that the innervations to both functions are evoked at a common point within the central nervous system. The characteristics of the relation between accommodation and vergence can be quantified by the magnitude of innervation (i.e., effector discharge) to vergence associated with a unit change in the magnitude of the innervation (i.e., effector discharge) to accommodation. Under suitable measurement conditions this can be shown to be identical to the magnitude of change in vergence obtained by changing the accommodation-response one dioptre. (Alpern *et al.*, 1959). This is the AC/A. It varies widely in the population but for an given individual it seems to remain quite fixed.

The way in which vergence changes as accommodation changes throughout the range of accommodation-values is important for the theory of presbyopia. The results of an experiment of this kind are illustrated in Fig. 9. In the figure the abscissa shows the vergence obtained for each accommodation-value. The experiment is monocular in the sense

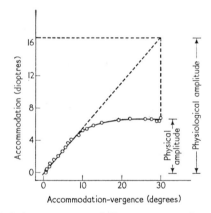

Accommodation-vergence (degrees)

FIG. 9. Relationship between accommodation-vergence and accommodation throughout the range of possible accommodation-stimulation. The dotted line is extrapolated to the physiological amplitude of accommodation according to the theory of the relation of these two functions of Alpern *et al.* (1959).

that no stimulus for fusional movements is present. Throughout almost the entire range of accommodation-values it is clear that increasing accommodation is linearly related to the accommodation-vergence. The reciprocal of the slope of this line is the (response) AC/A. However, as the limit of the amplitude of accommodation is approached there is a marked departure from this straight line. It is to be noted that rather marked increases in accommodative vergence continue to occur as the accommodation stimulus is increased to higher and higher values, even though these latter increases in stimulus no longer evoke any increase in refraction of the eye at all. A variety of evidence seems to emphasize that this increase in vergence is associated with a simultaneous increase in innervation to accommodation, which is no longer manifest by an increase in refraction because of the limitation placed on the lens by its sclerosed fibres (Alpern, 1950). Theoretically the amount of the innervation to vergence per unit change in amount of innervation to the ciliary muscle remains exactly the same as that obtained at lower accommodation levels. If this is the case, one can predict from the graph the maximum amplitude of accommodation the observer had at a very young age (16.75 dioptres)—i.e., the physiological amplitude of accommodation.

3. EFFECT OF AGE ON AC/A

The model that has just been described seems the most reasonable to explain all of the changes in vergence associated with accommodation (Alpern *et al.*, 1959). If this model is correct, a test of the relative merits of the Donders and Gullstrand theories of presbyopia is offered by studying the effect of age on the AC/A. If more and more innervation to the ciliary muscle is necessary to produce a unit change in refraction of the eye as age progresses, as the Donders's hypothesis assumes, then one can predict that the AC/A will increase with age. As a point of fact, according to this theory, age and partial cycloplegia would have identical effects upon AC/A. It is easy enough to demonstrate a very rapid increase in AC/A with partial cycloplegia (by topical homatropine, for example) and to show that this increase in AC/A is associated with the increased innervation to the ciliary muscle required under partial cycloplegia to produce a unit accommodation change (Alpern and Larson, 1960). However, there seems to be no very obvious change in AC/A with age, and this is precisely what one would anticipate if Gullstrand's theory of presbyopia were correct.†

4. CHANGE IN PUPIL-SIZE

In the chapter on eye movements it was pointed out that ciliary muscle innervation aroused by a change in accommodation-stimulus is also related to an increased innervation to iris sphincter as well as increased innervation to vergence. If the Gullstrand theory is correct then one might expect that the pupil-diameter would continue to decrease when accommodation-stimulus increased even beyond the near point of accommodation. Donders's theory, on the other hand, would lead to the prediction that pupil-size would be smallest of all when the *ciliary muscle innervation* and, therefore, accommodation-response were maximal. The data on this matter are less definitive than those described so far. However, Fig. 10 shows preliminary data of this kind which strongly support the Gullstrand theory. Measurements in ordinary room light were made as the accommodation stimulus was varied between zero and 9.5 dioptres (Alpern *et al.*, 1958). This subject had a maximum accommodation-response evoked by a stimulus of about 6D and yet the pupil-size continued to decrease even when the accommodation-stimulus was 9.5D. It is evident that further increase in the stimulus would eventually no longer produce any change in the magnitude of pupil-size and a limit would be achieved. That this limit is not the anatomical limit imposed by iris muscle is demonstrated by the fact that the pupil can be made considerably smaller than this limit merely by increasing light intensity to the contralateral eye. Probably this limit on the change in pupil-size with increase in the stimulus to accommodation is imposed by the maximum possible innervation to the ciliary muscle. This matter can by no means be regarded as conclusively established but experiments currently underway in our laboratory seem to substantiate this view and, therefore, Gullstrand's theory of presbyopia.

5. LATENT CILIARY MUSCLE CONTRACTION RANGE

It is necessary now to turn to the one aspect of the Gullstrand theory that has shown the least empirical confirmation. This is the notion that as age progresses a greater and

† The evidence for the statement of the effects of age on the AC/A are discussed in detail in Chapter 5.

greater amount of change in length of the ciliary muscle remains "latent" because the lens is incapable of altering its form beyond a very limited extent (Hess, 1901). Many attempts to verify this have been made. Fuchs (1922) reported that Treutler found that a single drop of 2% euphthalmine, which reduced the amplitude of accommodation by 4D in an 11-year-old, had no effect at all on the accommodation of a 38-year-old man. Apparently in the latter case the drug affected only changes in length of the ciliary muscle

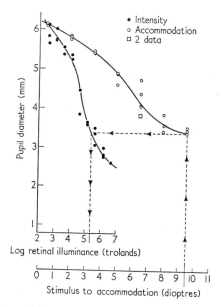

Fig. 10. Relation of pupil-diameter to change in accommodation-stimulus in a subject in whom the maximum accommodation-response was obtained for 6.0 accommodation-stimulus. Normal room illumination was used. The data with filled circles were obtained by exposing the contralateral eye to 16·4° Maxwellian view of various intensities (Alpern et al., 1958).

which were not related to changes in lens form. Duane (1922) was first convinced by this argument. In 1925, however, he reported that the onset of paralysis following cyclo-plegic drugs was, if anything, sooner in older age groups than in the younger. Morgan (1954) verified this. Although the experiment is far from crucial one might expect the opposite result if all the "latent ciliary muscle contraction" must be paralysed before any of the "manifest" were to be paralysed, all other factors being equal.

a. Partial Paralysis of Ciliary Muscle

The most convincing demonstration of a shortening of the ciliary muscle unrelated to changes in refraction was the experiment of Flieringa and van der Hoeve (1924). They found (after several months of extensive training) that a partial paralysis of ciliary muscle by 1% homatropine could result in the reduction of the *relative* near point of accommodation while the absolute near point of accommodation remained uninfluenced by the drug. Moreover, the degree of paralysis, as indicated by the reduction of the relative near point at different angles of convergence, was always the same at a given time interval in the onset of or, in the actual case, the recovery from, paralysis. This suggested that the value of a myodioptre is the same regardless of whether it is required to change the accommodation from 0 to 1 dioptre or from 11 to 12 dioptres.

Using the degree of paralysis as indicated by the reduction of the relative near-point measurements, Flieringa and van der Hoeve computed the physiological amplitude by multiplying its reciprocal by the physical amplitude of accommodation determined at that same moment. For example, 8/27 paralysis produced an accommodation amplitude of 7.4D, the physiological amplitude was then computed as $7.4 \times 27/8 = 24.975$ myodioptres. The average of five measurements on the former 31-year-old subject gave a value of 24.3 myodipotres; on the latter subject (24 years old) the average was only 20 myodioptres.

Morgan (1954) (a highly practised observer) repeated these experiments on his own eyes using the accommodative convergence measurements of phoria like those illustrated in Fig. 9. Computing physiological amplitude from a graph like this he obtained 10.8 myodioptres. When the ciliary muscle was partially paralysed, he found values of 10.25, 10.33, 9.99, 9.20 and 10.08 myodioptres. This confirms the basic findings of Flieringa and van der Hoeve.

Other attempts to repeat these experimental results, however, have not been as successful. Van Hoven (1959) made measurements on four young adults and found on two of them that, after homatropine paralysis, the amplitude of accommodation returned to maximum value at the same time as the AC/A. Moreover, in the other two the amplitude of accommodation returned *after* the AC/A had returned to a normal value. Fincham (1955) found that homatropine caused a decrease in the accommodation stimulated by any given submaximal convergence at the same moment that any decrease in the maximum amplitude could be detected. Goldmann and Aschmann (1946) calculated the extent of paralysis of the ciliary muscle by the ratio of the accommodations that the two eyes used to fixate a submaximal accommodation target when only one eye was partially paralysed by homatropine. The extent of reduction in the physical amplitude of accommodation in the eye was then used to compute the physiological amplitude of accommodation. These measurements showed that the physiological amplitude of accommodation was always larger than the physical, but the difference between the two seemed to get *smaller* as age increased (see also Goldmann, 1947). According to the Gullstrand theory, one would expect the difference between physiological and physical amplitude to get *larger* as age increased.

Similarly, Morgan and Harrigan (1951) observed a patient with a unilateral paresis of accommodation associated with Adie's syndrome. In this case the AC/A varied, depending upon the eye that fixated, and (using the ratios of these and the physical amplitude) one could then calculate the physiological amplitude of accommodation. It was found to be only very slightly larger than the physical amplitude of accommodation in the normal eye.

b. Changes in Ciliary Muscle

Thus the conclusion seems inescapable that the amount of the shortening of the ciliary muscle unrelated to changes in form of the lens is, with rare exceptions, considerably smaller than what would be anticipated on theoretical grounds. What explanation for this dilemma can be made? From the very beginning the idea that only the lens fibres sclerosed, and no concurrent morphological changes in the ciliary muscle occurred, has been explicitly or implicitly assumed. It now seems quite evident that this assumption is completely unwarranted. As a matter of fact, it is clear that changes in the histology of the ciliary muscle continue throughout life (Stieve, 1949) and that both the morphological and physiological characteristics of the ciliary body are undergoing as precipitous age changes as are those of the lens fibres themselves. Kornzweig (1951) has established the rather continuous atrophy of ciliary muscle fibres that takes place as age progresses. Increase in age is also associated with a decline in the facility of aqueous outflow, as well as the rate of aqueous secretion by the ciliary body (Becker, 1958). While the extent to which these changes become manifest at each age-level in the life-span has not yet been completely described, it seems quite likely that, just as the sclerosis of the lens fibres increases and the amplitude of accommodation decreases throughout life in a continuous way, so does the atrophy of the ciliary muscle increase. It is quite clear that other muscles of the body become atrophic because of lack of use and there is no good reason for imagining that the ciliary muscle behaves any differently. In a normal individual, as he grows older, a certain amount of ciliary muscle contraction becomes ineffective because of the sclerosis of the lens fibres. Lack of use of this part of the ciliary muscle renders it atrophic. Thus at all ages almost maximum shortening of the ciliary muscle is required to produce maximum accommodation *and* the same change in length of the ciliary muscle is required to produce one dioptre of accommodation at all ages. Parallel to (and because of) the sclerosis of the fibres of the lens, there is a more or less continuous decrement in the maximum ability of the ciliary muscle to change its length. In one or two rare cases (such as the well-trained eyes of Morgan or the younger (31 years) Flieringa and his other (24 years) observer, in whom continuous practice with accommodation-convergence experiments over several months preceded the measurements) the development of the atrophic process can be suitably delayed.† This accounts for the variable results obtained by different experimenters who made measurements on observers with varying amounts of training in experiments of this kind. According to this view, the physiological amplitude of accommodation no longer represents the extent to which the ciliary muscle can change its length without changing accommodation as Hess (1901) conceived it. The curved part of Fig. 9 at the upper levels of accommodation represents innervation to convergence associated with the innervation to accommodation which neither produces any change in the lens nor (in the usual unpractised observer) any further change in length of the muscle (since the muscle has no longer the ability to change its length much more than that associated with maximum amplitude). In this way one can account for the variety of results that fail to demonstrate the "latent ciliary muscle contraction range" (Fry, 1959a; Van Hoven, 1959) and still maintain the fundamental basis of Gullstrand's theory that the same change in length of the ciliary muscle is required to produce unit change in the refraction of the eye at every age.

E. Evaluation of Theories of Presbyopia

It is still too early to make a decisive choice between these two antagonistic views of presbyopia. Either the same change in length of the ciliary muscle is required for one dioptre change in lens form at all ages (Gullstrand) or more and more change in length of the muscle is necessary to produce one dioptre change in refraction with increased age (Donders).‡ Hess (1901) was the first to emphasize that if one accepts the Donders's

† Even this is a relative matter, however. Morgan, who at the time of the experiments was 41 years old, had only 10.8 myodioptres which is one half the range obtained by the younger subjects, Flieringa and van der Hoeve.

‡ A compromise suggested by Morgan (1954) that at lower accommodation levels the Gullstrand system persists but as the maximum amplitude is approached at high levels

view, then the invariability of the relationship between the acommodative response (in dioptres) and the accommodative vergence (in degrees of eye rotation) with age means that the relation between the *innervation* to the ciliary muscle and the *innervation* to vergence as a result of an accommodation-stimulus must be continuously changing through life. This would imply a highly flexible relation between these two characteristics and one might anticipate that training procedures, prolonged use of the eyes after topical eserine or homatropine, etc., would then result in drastic variation in the AC/A. It was emphasized in the chapter on eye movements, however, that such changes in AC/A are extremely difficult to establish. This implies a quite inflexible interrelation of the variables as the model proposed by Alpern *et al.* (1959) requires.

In the last analysis a decision on the theory of presbyopia awaits a decision on the theory of the synkinesis of vergence and accommodation. Fincham and Walton (1957) have adopted the view that convergence stimulates accommodation and that this forms the basis for the near-reaction. They do not deny that the act of accommodation may automatically evoke some convergence but believe that the amount of such an effect is small and unimportant for the basic process of near-seeing. If this theory can be proved correct then the Donders's theory of presbyopia also seems reasonable since convergence-accommodation declines regularly with age and the failure of the AC/A to increase assumes no great importance. On the other hand, if one adopts the modification of the theory of Maddox (1886) and Fry (1937, 1939) incorporated in the model of Alpern *et al.* (1959), the constancy of the AC/A with age forms strong circumstantial evidence in support of the Gullstrand theory of presbyopia. According to that model, the accommodative convergence evoked by the vergence of the light at the retina (or other possible stimuli to accommodation, see below) forms the basis for the near response. It is not denied that in usual circumstances fusional convergence may also evoke accommodation but it is felt that this effect is small and relatively unimportant for the basic process of near-seeing. Which of these views of the near response is more tenable? Fry (1939) argued convincingly that the evidence then available supported the latter view. Jampel (1959) has recently established excellent neurophysiological evidence to support this model. More recent psychophysical data also tend to support it. For example, very large changes in accommodation, with the stimulus for binocular convergence held fixed, result in no detectable movements of the eyes at all (Alpern, 1957) even though fixation-disparity experiments (Ogle and Martens, 1957) clearly emphasize that the normal accommodative convergence system must be operating. Even so, the matter can by no means be considered settled. A final decision must await a much more informative appraisal of the relative importance of convergent accommodation and accommodative convergence in the process of binocular near-vision. The fact that a decision on presbyopia theory also depends upon this appraisal makes definitive analysis all the more important.

V. Neurology of Accommodation

A. OCULOMOTOR NUCLEUS

The ciliary muscle is innervated by the IIIrd cranial nerve. The majority of neurones to the muscle originate in the ciliary ganglion, and the neurones

greater and greater ciliary contraction would be required, also is possible, of course. However, in a very real sense this begs the question. For as age proceeds the amplitude gets less and less. Does that final one dioptre in presbyopia act like the lower level (Gullstrand) or the upper level (Donders) of the younger age?

that activate them arise in the mid-line nuclei of the oculomotor complex (Warwick, 1954). In the ciliary ganglion only 3% of the nuclei are related to the sphincter of the iris while 97% of the cells in the ciliary ganglion innervate the intrinsic ocular muscles. Some authors have proposed (e.g., Morgan and Harrigan, 1951), on the basis of observation on clinical material, that the small episcleral ganglion described by Axenfeld (1907) contains nuclei for some of the parasympathetic nerve fibres that supply the ciliary muscle. Stotler (1937), however, showed that the ciliary muscle was completely denervated by ciliary ganglionectomy in the cat.

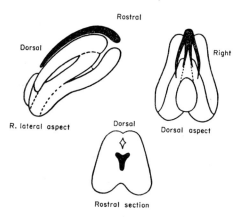

FIG. 11. The oculomotor complex in the rhesus monkey according to Warwick (1954). The parasympathetic nuclei (in black) are the Edinger-Westphal columns (dorsal to the somatic nuclei), and the mid-line antero-median nucleus (formed by the coalescence of these columns at the cephalic or rostral end).

Ciliary ganglionectomy and division of the IIIrd cranial nerve (in monkeys) caused a retrograde reaction of striking degree in most of the cells of the ipsilateral Edinger-Westphal nucleus and in the ipsilateral half of the antero-median nucleus. These two nuclei, in fact, form a continuous small-celled mass in the Macaque. Figure 11 illustrates the topographical structure of the oculomotor complex and the relation of the parasympathetic nuclei (in black), according to these experiments of Warwick (1954).

B. SUPRANUCLEAR CONNEXIONS

Virtually nothing is known of the supranuclear connexions of these brain-stem nuclei. However, recently Jampel (1959) obtained increased refraction of both eyes by unilateral faradic stimulation of area 19 of the occipital cortex. These responses were invariably also associated with a convergence movement and usually with a pupil constriction as well. The relation of the findings to the model of the vergence-accommodation relationship proposed by Alpern *et al.* (1959) has been discussed in detail in the chapter on eye movements. The projection of area 19 on to the mid-brain oculomotor complex is by way of the internal corticotectal tract. The exact fibre connexions between specific regions producing these responses upon electrical stimulation and the small-celled parasympathetic nuclei of the oculo-motor complex have not yet been traced, but there seems to be little doubt that they do occur.

C. Possible Sympathetic Innervations

Until relatively recently it was commonly believed that the ciliary muscle was the only example of smooth muscle innervated by only one (the parasympathetic) division of the autonomic nervous system. It now seems likely, however, that the ciliary muscle is also innervated by two types of nerve (Génis-Gálvez, 1957). The primary innervation is, of course, from the parasympathetic nervous system. However, a second type of nerve, which coincides with the fundamental vegetative plexus, also can be seen to innervate ciliary muscle fibres.† This occurs throughout the ciliary muscle. These orthosympathetic fibres do not, therefore, set up an antagonism with the parasympathetic fibres based on separate innervation to different muscle groups.

1. EFFECT OF SYMPATHETIC STIMULATION

Jessop (1886) reported that a relaxation of the ciliary muscle occurs after the instillation of cocaine into the eye. Morat and Doyon (1891) observed a flattening of the lens following stimulation of the cervical sympathetic nerve. Cogan (1937) observed five cases in whom a portion of the sympathetic chain was surgically removed, and noted the increased accommodation-amplitude on the ipsilateral side. Cogan (1937); Siebeck (1953b) and Biggs *et al.* (1959) have noted a decrement in the amplitude of accommodation in man following sympathetic stimulation by the local instillation of sympathomimetic drugs. The latter two groups of investigators also confirmed an increase in hyperopia as a result of these drugs. Morgan *et al.* (1940) made extensive observations of the effect of stimulation of the cervical sympathetic

† A certain amount of confusion still surrounds this matter, however. In the cat, superior cervical sympathetic ganglionectomy failed to result in any obvious degeneration of the nerve supply to the ciliary muscle, and ciliary ganglionectomy left this muscle without any obvious nerve supply (Stotler, 1937). Since the cat ciliary ganglion is not thought to be supplied with any sympathetic roots these results are not in harmony with Génis-Gálvez's (1957) findings, if one can be certain that the surgical procedures left connexions to the short ciliary nerves from the long ciliary nerves, as well as the long ciliary nerves themselves, intact. Of course, these orthosympathetic endings had not yet been described at the time of Stotler's experiments.

ganglion in rabbits, cats and dogs and in each case observed an increased hyperopia irrespective of whether or not the eye were atropinized, the IIIrd nerve cut, or the extra-ocular muscles severed from the globe. The effect amounts only to about 1.5D while stimulation of the IIIrd nerve causes increased myopia of as much as 10D in these same animals. They also obtained these responses by stimulation of the neural roots of C8 and T1–3. These fibres pass to and synapse at the superior cervical sympathetic ganglion and then move along the trunk of the internal carotid to the cavernous plexus. They pass to the eye as two long ciliary nerves (Morgan, 1944) and probably, as short ciliary nerves, by way of the sympathetic root to the ciliary ganglion as well (Wolff, 1933). These experiments also proved that the effect was indeed due to a flattening of the lens.

2. MECHANISM OF SYMPATHETIC ACTION

a. Vascular Effect

How does the flattening come about? Morgan (1946) believes that it is merely the result of vasoconstriction in the blood vessels of the ciliary body. The reduced vascular bed also reduces the mass of the ciliary body and increases the tension on the fibres of the zonule and this flattens the lens. Fleming (1957) showed that the changes in refraction were quite parallel to changes in the ear-temperature following stimulation or extirpation of the superior cervical ganglion. Fleming (1959) also found that the flattened lens and increased hyperopia were associated with decreased blood volume of the ciliary body following prolonged stimulation of the sympathetic nerve. All of these results are in good agreement with Morgan's theory.

b. Effect on Ciliary Muscle

However, there is evidence that the matter is more complex than this. Movements of the ciliary body and ciliary muscle have been recorded in the enucleated eye (which is thus completely divorced from the circulatory system) following stimulation of the sympathetic effectors by drugs (Meesmann, 1952) and by electrical stimulation of the long ciliary nerves (Melton et al., 1955). Such experiments suggest that the contraction of the ciliary muscle itself (or at least part of it) may be influenced by stimulation of the sympathetic nerves, and in turn influences the flattening of the lens observed. If the sympathetic nerve endings described by Génis-Gálvez (1957) are responsible for this effect, then it must be assumed that all parts of the ciliary muscle are equally concerned with the process. This could mean that the parasympathetic endings excite the ciliary muscle, while the sympathetic endings inhibit it, just as Morat and Doyon (1891) proposed almost seventy years ago. If this were true, the smooth muscle of the ciliary body would behave pharmacologically in much the same way that the smooth muscle of the intestine does † (Vaughan Williams, 1954).

VI. The Stimulus to Accommodation

A. THE STATE OF ACCOMMODATION IN THE ABSENCE OF ANY STIMULUS

When an observer sits in a totally dark room the far point of his eye is not localized in the same point in space as that obtained when his visual field is highly structured. Apparently Rayleigh (1883) was the first to point out that ". . . in a nearly dark room I am distinctly shortsighted." This so-called night myopia has since been the subject of a number of experiments. An extensive summary of such work is clearly beyond the scope of this chapter. Fortunately, a rather extensive review of the available data as of a few years ago has been given by Knoll (1952). If one measures the far point as the luminance of a test field is gradually reduced, one finds that the eye starts to become myopic. The greater the reduction in luminance, the larger the degree of myopia. At very low light levels (about 0.1 troland of retinal illuminance) the mean of four observers showed about 2D more myopia over the optimum measurements in the well-structured visual field (Alpern and David, 1958). Wide differences among individuals exist and so the results obtained by different experimenters do not always agree. The myopia persists even when the target is viewed through a small (2 mm.) artificial pupil so that spherical aberration associated with a wide pupil, which otherwise plays a quite prominent role (Koomen et al., 1951), cannot be the entire explanation. Part of the effect is related to the chromatic aberration of the eye and the Purkinje phenomenon associated with the transition from cone to rod vision. In addition, it seems quite evident that the centre of the front surface of the lens at low levels of illuminance has a more convex shape than it does when the eye looks in a well-structured and well-illuminated field.

Campbell (1954b) photographed the size of the Purkinje images reflected from the front surface of the lens in total darkness and found this surface to have the same shape on the average that it does when the eye is accommodated 0.65D in normal room illuminance.

1. RECESSION OF NEAR POINT

The reduction in the level of illumination is associated not only with an approach of the far point but a recession of the near point as well. The characteristics of this "night presbyopia" are still only poorly defined but it

---

† Van Alphen (personal communication) has recently succeeded in suspending isolated strips of ciliary muscle-choroid combination in a muscle bath and in recording the tension which they develop during isometric contraction with a strain gauge. Adrenergic substances when added to the bath cause a reduction, cholinergic substances an increase, in the tension recorded.

resembles the recession of the near point with increase in age in that the AC/A remains essentially unchanged as the amplitude of accommodation gets smaller and smaller (Alpern and Larson, 1960).

2. REDUCTION OF CONTRAST

The changes in the accommodation ability of the eye at low levels of illumination are not due to the low light level *per se*. It is easy enough to demonstrate, rather, that it is the reduction in the contrast of objects of regard associated with the reduced light intensity which is responsible for the effect. The effects can be made to disappear in a totally dark room provided only a very small, infinitesimally wide, luminous cross is presented in the field of view (Alpern and David, 1958). Moreover, Whiteside (1952) found an increase in refractive power (of about 1.1D on the average) under very bright photopic conditions when the eye was presented with a visual field containing no detail. Thus it appears that "night myopia" and "empty-space myopia" are very closely-related phenomena.

B. THE STIMULUS

1. OSCILLATIONS IN ACCOMMODATION

When the eye steadily fixates an object inside optical infinity, the refractive power does not remain constant but varies over a small range. These microfluctuations of accommodation were described by Arnulf *et al.* (1955). They estimated the amplitude to be 0.04 to 0.14D. Whiteside (1957) photographed the reflexions of light from the first surface of the crystalline lens and found similar fluctuations which varied from peak to peak as much as 0.25D. The most extensive measurements are those of Campbell *et al.* (1959) with the high speed infra-red optometer (Campbell and Robson, 1959). They show wide individual differences. Occasionally values almost as large as 0.4D can be detected. These fluctuations were found by Campbell *et al.* (1959) to be eliminated by homatropine or by fixation at infinity. The dominant frequency components appear to be in a region 0–0.5 cycles/sec. and another in the region 2 cycles/sec. This latter frequency is greatly reduced or absent, while the former is greatly increased, when the effective-entrance pupil-size is reduced to 1 mm. Under these conditions the depth of focus is greatly increased. Moreover, if the fixated target oscillates in the visual field the responses follow these oscillations with a time lag of 0.4 sec. and the amplitude of the accommodation oscillations is a function of the frequency of the target oscillations.

a. Effect of Luminance

It is of some interest that the amplitude of the oscillations increases remarkably when the observer looks into a completely empty visual field

(Campbell *et al.*, 1959). If the observer views a target whose luminance is progressively reduced, the variability of measurements of the accommodative state progressively increases. This effect is illustrated in Fig. 12 which shows the mean standard deviation of ten stigmatoscope settings by four observers (Alpern, 1958) at various levels of retinal illumination. The points are empirical, the curves are theoretical, based on the assumption that the limitation on the variation in focus is a direct function of intensity discrimination (Δ I/I) of the retina.

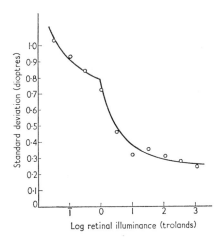

Log retinal illuminance (trolands)

FIG. 12. The variability of successive stigmatoscope settings as the retinal illuminance of a target is systematically varied. The data are the mean of the results from four observers, each of whom made ten successive settings at each light level. The points are empirical, the curve theoretical. (From Alpern, 1958)

b. Significance

On the basis of evidence of this kind it has been proposed (Campbell, 1954a; Alpern, 1958, among others) that oscillations of accommodation play an important role in the determination of the posture of the lens necessary for accurate focus. The evidence for such a hypothesis is not very extensive. This suggestion has been criticized, moreover, on the grounds that the reaction-time characteristic of the accommodation-response is in agreement with the high frequency oscillations and these disappear in an empty field (Campbell *et al.*, 1958).†

† This criticism has two implicit assumptions: (*a*) that reaction-time characteristics of accommodation are invariant regardless of the characteristics (contrast, form, luminance, etc.) of the visual field and (*b*) that the frequency of accommodation oscillations does not shift gradually from one value to an adjacent value as target characteristics are gradually changed. More exact examination of the validity of these assumptions would seem to be worthwhile.

2. MONOCHROMATIC LIGHT

If the accommodation oscillations do not play an important role in influencing the magnitude of accommodation employed while the eye is fixating an object at a given distance, what sensory factors are important? Quite obviously in ordinary everyday seeing a variety of complex stimuli provided by stereoscopic factors, kinesthesis, apparent size and distance are readily available for this purpose (Campbell and Westheimer, 1959). Under laboratory conditions, however, arrangements can be made so that none of these factors operate and the accommodation mechanism still responds immediately (and correctly) to a defocused target while it does not so respond to a target suddenly blurred but not defocused (Fincham, 1951).

Fincham (1951) found that about sixty per cent. of the subjects lost this ability, however, if the target was viewed in monochromatic light. This suggested to him that the chromatic aberration of the eye helped to provide an adequate stimulus for the change in accommodation. Campbell and Westheimer (1959) used an eye-hand analogue of the accommodation process and found that one of their four subjects behaved in a similar way. It proved to be a comparatively easy process to teach this subject to learn to respond correctly, however. Fincham's other subjects were capable of responding to a monochromatic light entering through a peripheral annular pupillary zone which limited the distribution of spherical aberration in the retinal image of the target. Campbell and Westheimer's subjects were not able to do this. In analysing the difference between the experiments of Fincham, in which accommodative responses were directly observed and those of Campbell and Westheimer in which the subjects moved the target by hand (with accommodation paralysed) to bring it in sharpest focus, there is one obvious difference in sensory input. This is proprioception from the motor responses, well established for arm and hand movements, never demonstrated for ciliary muscle contraction.†

3. SCANNING MOVEMENTS

Still another factor found by Fincham (1951) to play an important role in the ability of the eye to respond correctly to a change in accommodation-stimulus was scanning movements of the eye. Using monochromatic light (or white light in the case of those who couldn't respond in monochromatic light) a correct response to the change in stimulus was observed when scanning movements were permitted. It did not occur when the eye remained fixed. Fincham believes that this permitted correct detection of difference in

† It is not obvious, however, how this difference in experimental procedure can account for the discrepancy in the results of the two experiments carried out with monochromatic light and an annular pupil.

direction of retinal defocus by using the signal afforded by the directional sensitivity of the cones. Campbell (1954b) showed that the light minimum required to elicit the accommodation response, indeed, was only 0.25 log units greater than the foveal (and, therefore, cone) visibility threshold. In summary, when normally viewing near objects, apparent size, stereopsis, and apparent distance probably play important roles in the determination of the direction and amount of accommodation change that is evoked. When these factors are obviated, other factors including chromatic aberration, spherical aberration, astigmatism, perhaps also oscillations of accommodation and scanning movements of the eye, may become important. If all of these are removed, or if the signals from one of these is in the opposite direction to the signal from the others, then accommodative readjustment may be in error.

References

Adler, F. H. (1959). "Physiology of the Eye", 3rd edition, Chap. 8, pp. 244–271. C. V. Mosby Co., St. Louis.

Allen, M. J. (1955). The stimulus to accommodation. *Amer. J. Optom.* **32**, 422–431.

Alpern, M. (1949). Accommodation and convergence with contact lenses. *Amer. J. Optom.* **26**, 379–387.

Alpern, M. (1950). The zone of clear single vision at the upper levels of accommodation and convergence. *Amer. J. Optom.* **27**, 491–513.

Alpern, M. (1957). Does relative accommodation exist? *Amer. J. Ophth.* **43**, 464.

Alpern, M. (1958). Variability of accommodation during steady fixation at various levels of illuminance. *J. opt. Soc. Amer.* **48**, 193–197.

Alpern, M., and David, H. (1958). Effects of illuminance quantity on accommodation of the eyes. *Industr. Med.* **27**, 551–555.

Alpern, M., and Larson, B. F. (1960). Vergence and accommodation: IV. Effect of luminance quantity on the AC/A. *Amer. J. Ophthal.* **49**, 1140–1149.

Alpern, M., Ellen, P., and Goldsmith, R. I. (1958). The electrical response of the human eye in far-to-near accommodation. *A.M.A. Arch. Ophthal.* **60**, 592–602.

Alpern, M., Kincaid, W. M., and Lubeck, M. J. (1959). Vergence and accommodation: III. Proposed definitions of the AC/A ratios. *Amer. J. Ophthal.* **48** (No. 1, Pt. 2), 141–148.

Arnulf, A., Dupuy, O., and Flamant, F. (1955). Les microfluctuations d'accommodation de l'oeil. *Ann. Opt. Ocul.* **3**, 109–118.

Axenfeld, T. (1907). Demonstrationen: 1. Accessorische episklerale Ciliarganglien. *Ber. ophth. Ges. Heidelberg* **34**, 300–301.

Balsam, M. H., and Fry, G. A. (1959). Convergence accommodation. *Amer. J. Optom.* **36**, 567–575.

Becker, B. (1958). The decline in aqueous secretion and outflow facility with age. *Amer. J. Ophthal.* **46**, 731–736.

Biggs, R. D., Alpern, M., and Bennett, D. R. (1959). The effect of sympathomimetic drugs upon the amplitude of accommodation. *Amer. J. Ophthal.* **48** (No. 1, Pt. 2), 169–172.

Busacca, A. (1955). La physiologie du muscle ciliaire étudiée par la gonioscopie. *Ann. Oculist., Paris* **188**, 1–19.

Calasans, O. M. (1953). Arquitetura do músculo ciliar no homen. *Ann. Fac. Med. S. Paulo* **27**, 3–98.

Campbell, F. W. (1954a). Accommodation reflex. *Brit. orthop. J.* **11**, 13–17.

Campbell, F. W. (1954b). The minimum quantity of light required to elicit the accommodation reflex in man. *J. Physiol.* **123**, 357–366.

Campbell, F. W. (1957). The depth of field of the human eye. *Optica Acta* **4**, 157–164.

Campbell, F. W., and Robson, J. G. (1959). High-speed infrared optometer. *J. opt. Soc. Amer.* **49**, 268–272.

Campbell, F. W., and Westheimer, G. (1959). Factors influencing accommodation responses of the human eye. *J. opt. Soc. Amer.* **49**, 568–571.

Campbell, F. W., and Westheimer, G. (1960). Dynamics of accommodation responses of the human eye. *J. Physiol.* **151**, 285–295.

Campbell, F. W., Westheimer, G., and Robson, J. G. (1958). Significance of fluctuations in accommodation. *J. opt. Soc. Amer.* **48**, 669.

Campbell, F. W., Robson, J. G., and Westheimer, G. (1959). Fluctuations of accommodation under steady viewing conditions. *J. Physiol.* **145**, 579–594.

Cogan, D. G. (1937). Accommodation and the autonomic nervous system. *Arch. Ophthal. N.Y.* **18**, 739–766.

Donders, F. C. (1864). "On the Anomalies of Accommodation and Refraction of the Eye. With a Preliminary Essay on Physiological Dioptrics" (translated by W. D. Moore). The New Sydenham Society, London.

Duane, A. (1912). Normal values of the accommodation at all ages. *Trans. Ophth. Amer. med. Ass.* 383–391.

Duane, A. (1922). Discussion of paper on "Presbyopia" by E. Fuchs, *Arch. Ophthal. N.Y.* **51**, 63–66.

Duane, A. (1925). Are the current theories of accommodation correct? *Amer. J. Ophthal.* **8**, 196–202.

Fincham, E. F. (1928). The function of the lens capsule in the accommodation of the eye. *Trans. opt. Soc., Lond.* **30**, 101–117.

Fincham, E. F. (1932). The mechanism of accommodation and the recession of the near point. Report of Phys. & Optical Societies Disc. on Vision. pp. 294–308.

Fincham, E. F. (1937). The mechanism of accommodation. *Brit. J. Ophthal. Suppl.* **8**, 5–80.

Fincham, E. F. (1951). The accommodation reflex and its stimulus. *Brit. J. Ophthal.* **35**, 381–393.

Fincham, E. F. (1955). The proportion of ciliary muscular force required for accommodation. *J. Physiol.* **128**, 99–112.

Fincham, E. F., and Walton, J. (1957). The reciprocal actions of accommodation and convergence. *J. Physiol.* **137**, 488–508.

Fleming, D. G. (1957). The role of the sympathetics in visual accommodation. *Amer. J. Ophthal.* **43**, 789.

Fleming, D. G. (1959). A mechanism for the sympathetic control of visual accommodation. *Amer. J. Ophthal.* **47**, 585–586.

Flieringa, H. J., and van der Hoeve, J. (1924). Arbeiten aus dem Gebiete der Akkommodation. *v. Graefes Arch. Ophthal.* **114**, 1–46.

Fry, G. A. (1937). An experimental analysis of the accommodation-convergence relation. (*Trans. Amer. Acad. Optom.* **11**, 64–76) also *Amer. J. Optom.* **14**, 402–414.

Fry, G. A. (1939). Further experiments on the accommodation convergence relationship. (*Trans. Amer. Acad. Optom.* **12**, 65–73; also *Amer. J. Optom.* **16**, 325–336.)

Fry, G. A. (1959a). The effect of homatropine upon accommodation-convergence relations. *Amer. J. Optom.* **36**, 525–531.

Fry, G. A. (1959b). The image-forming mechanism of the eye. *In* "Handbook of Physiology, A Critical, Comprehensive Presentation of Physiological Knowledge and Concepts. Sec. I. Neurophysiology" (J. Field, H. W. Maguon, and V. E. Hall, eds.), Vol. I, pp. 647–670. The American Physiological Society, Washington, D.C.

Fuchs, E. (1922). Presbyopia. *Arch. Ophthal. N.Y.* **51**, 21–28.

Génis-Gálvez, J. M. (1957). Innervation of the ciliary muscle. *Anat. Rec.* **127**, 219–229.

Gillessen, P. (1938). Experimentelle Untersuchungen zur Frage der Kontraktilitaet der Linsenfasern. *v. Graefes Arch. Ophthal.* **138**, 598–619.

Goldmann, H. (1937). Studien ueber den Alterskernstreifen der Linse. *Arch. Augenheilk.* **110**, 405–414.

Goldmann, H. (1947). Some subjective aspects of accommodation. *In* "Modern Trends in Ophthalmology" (A. Sorsby, ed.), Vol. II, Chap. 8, pp. 79–86. Paul B. Hoeber, Inc., New York.

Goldmann, H., and Aschmann, A. (1946). Studien ueber Akkommodation (ueber Korrektur von Akkommodationsparese sowie ueber "physikalische und physiologische Akkommodationsbreite"). *Ophthalmologica, Basel* **111**, 182–186.

Graves, B. (1925). The response of the lens capsules in the act of accommodation. *Trans. Amer. ophthal. Soc.* **23**, 184–198.

Gullstrand, A. (1908). Die optische Abbildung in heterogenen Medien die Dioptrik der Kristallinse des Menschen. *K. svensk. Vetensk. Akad. Handl.* **43**, (No. 2), 1–58.

Gullstrand, A. (1924). Appendices to Part I. *In* "Helmholtz's Treatise on Physiological Optics" by H. L. F. von Helmholtz (translated from the 3rd German edition by J. P. C. Southall, ed.), Vol. I, pp. 261–482. The Optical Society of America, Rochester.

Hamasaki, D., Ong, J., and Marg, E. (1956). The amplitude of accommodation in presbyopia. *Amer. J. Optom.* **33**, 3–14.

Helmholtz, H. (1855). Uber die Accommodation des Auges. *v. Graefes Arch. Ophthal.* **1** (Abt. 2), 1–74.

Henderson, T. (1926). The anatomy and physiology of accommodation in mammalia. *Trans. ophthal. Soc. U.K.* **46**, 280–308.

Hensen and Voelckers. (1873). Ueber die Accommodationsbewegung der Chorioides im Auge des Menschen des Affen und der Katze. *v. Graefes Arch. Ophth.* **19** (Abt. 1), 156–162.

Hess, C. (1901). Arbeiten aus dem Gebiete der Accommodationslehre. VI. Die relative Accommodation. *v. Graefes Arch. Ophthal.* **52**, 143–174.

Hess, C. (1904). Beobachtungen ueber den Akkommodationsvorgang. *Klin. Mbl. Augenheilk.* **42**, 309–315.

Hofstetter, H. W. (1943). An ergographic analysis of fatigue of accommodation. *Amer. J. Optom.* **20**, 115–135.

Hofstetter, H. W. (1949). A survey of practices in prescribing presbyopic adds. *Amer. J. Optom.* **26**, 144–160.

Home, E. (1795). On muscular motion. Pt. 1. *Phil. Trans.* **85**, 1–23.

Invanoff, A. (1956). Au sujet de l'aberration sphérique de l'oeil. *Optica Acta* **3**, 47–48.

Jampel, R. S. (1959). Representation of the near-response on the cerebral cortex of the Macaque. *Amer. J. Ophthal.* **48** (No. 5, Pt. 2), 573–582.

Jessop, W. H. (1886). On the anatomy, histology and physiology of the intraocular muscles of mammals. (Abst.) *Proc. roy. Soc.* **40**, 478–484.

Kleifeld, O. (1956). Beitraege zum intrakapsulaeren Akkomodations-mechanismus. *Docum. ophth.* **10**, 132–173.

Knoll, H. A. (1952). A brief history of "nocturnal myopia" and related phenomena. *Amer. J. Optom.* **29**, 69–81.

Koomen, M., Tousey, R., and Scolnik, R. (1949). The spherical aberration of the eye. *J. opt. Soc. Amer.* **39**, 370–376.

Koomen, M., Scolnik, R., and Tousey, R. (1951). A study of night myopia. *J. opt. Soc. Amer.* **41**, 80–90.

Kornzweig, A. L. (1951). Pathology of the eye in old age. III. Changes attributed to the aging process. *Trans. Amer. Acad. Ophthal. Oto-laryng.* **55**, 261–276.

Lancaster, W. B., and Williams, E. R. (1914). New light on the theory of accommodation, with practical applications. *Trans. Amer. Acad. Ophthal. Oto-laryng.* **19**, 170–195.

McCulloch, C. (1954). The zonule of Zinn: its origin, course, and insertion, and its relation to neighbouring structures. *Trans. Amer. ophthal. Soc.* **52**, 525–585.

Maddox, E. E. (1886). Investigations on the relation between convergence and accommodation of the eyes. *J. Anat., Lond.* **20**, 475–508; 565–584.

Meesmann, A. (1952). Experimentelle Untersuchungen ueber die antagonistische Innervation der Ciliarmuskulatur. *v. Graefes Arch. Ophthal.* **152**, 335–356.

Melton, C. E., Purnell, E. W., and Brecher, G. A. (1955). The effect of sympathetic nerve impulses on the ciliary muscle. *Amer. J. Ophthal* **40** (No. 5, Pt. 2), 155–162.

Morat, J. P., and Doyon, M. (1891). Le grand sympathique, nerf de l'accommodation pour la vision des objets éloignés. *Ann. Oculist., Paris* **106**, 28–30.

Morgan, M. W., Jr. (1944). The nervous control of accommodation. *Amer. J. Optom.* **21**, 87–93.

Morgan, M. W., Jr. (1946). A new theory for the control of accommodation. *Amer. J. Optom.* **23**, 99–110.

Morgan, M. W., Jr. (1954). The ciliary body in accommodation and accommodative-convergence. *Amer. J. Optom.* **31**, 219–229.

Morgan, M. W., Jr., and Harrigan, R. F. (1951). Accommodation and convergence in a patient with Adie's pupil. *Amer. J. Optom.* **28**, 242–253.

Morgan, M. W., Jr., Olmsted, J. M. D., and Watrous, W. G. (1940). Sympathetic action in accommodation for far vision. *Amer. J. Physiol.* **128**, 588–591.

Neumuller, J. (1937). The effect of the ametropic distance correction upon the accommodation and reading addition. *Trans. Amer. Acad. Optom.* **11**, 20–28.

Ogle, K. N., and Martens, T. G. (1957). On the accommodative convergence and the proximal convergence. *A.M.A. Arch. Opthal.* **57**, 702–715.

Rayleigh, (1883). On the invisibility of small objects in a bad light. *Proc. Camb. phil. Soc.* **4**, 324.

Salzmann, M. (1912). "The Anatomy and Histology of the Human Eyeball in the Normal State; Its Development and Senescence", (translated by E. V. L. Brown), pp. 111–115. The University of Chicago Press, Chicago.

Schapero, M., and Nadell, M. (1957). Accommodation and convergence responses in beginning and absolute presbyopes. *Amer. J. Optom.* **34**, 606–622.

Siebeck, R. (1953a). Die antagonistische Innervation der Akkommodation und die Akkommodationsruhelage. *v. Graefes Arch. Ophthal.* **153**, 425–437.

Siebeck, R. (1953b). Akkommodationsimpuls und Akkommodationserfolg unter medikamentoesem Einfluss. *v. Graefes Arch. Ophthal.* **153**, 438–450.

Smith, P. (1883). On the growth of the crystalline lens. *Trans. ophthal. Soc. U.K.* **3**, 79–99.

Stieve, R. (1949). Ueber den Bau des menschlichen Ciliarmuskels, seine Veraenderungen waehrend des Lebens und seine Bedeutung fuer die Akkommodation. *Anat. Anz.* **97**, 69–79.

Stotler, W. A. (1937). The innervation of the intrinsic muscles of the eye; an experimental study. *Proc. Soc. exp. Biol. N.Y.* **36**, 576–577.

Stuhlman, O. (1943). "An Introduction to Biophysics", Chap. 3, p. 107. John Wiley and Sons, Inc., New York.

Tscherning, M. H. E. (1900). "Physiologic Optics, Dioptrics of the Eye. Functions of the Retina, Ocular Movements, and Binocular Vision", (translated by C. Weiland), Chap. 12, pp. 160–189. The Keystone Publishing Company, Philadelphia.

Van Hoven, R. C. (1959). Partial cycloplegia and the accommodation-convergence relationship. *Amer. J. Optom.* **36**, 22–39.

Vaughan Williams, E. M. (1954). The mode of action of drugs upon intestinal motility. *Pharmacol. Rev.* **6**, 159–190.

Warwick, R. (1954). The ocular parasympathetic nerve supply and its mesencephalic sources. *J. Anat., Lond.* **88**, 71–93.

Westheimer, G. (1954a). Mechanism of saccadic eye movements. *A.M.A. Arch. Ophthal.* **52**, 710–724.

Westheimer, G. (1954b). Eye movement responses to horizontally moving visual stimulus. *A.M.A. Arch. Ophthal.* **52**, 932–941.

Westheimer, G., and Mitchell, A. M. (1956). Eye movement responses to convergence stimuli. *A.M.A. Arch. Ophthal.* **55**, 848–856.

Whiteside, T. C. D. (1952). Accommodation of the human eye in a bright and empty visual field. *J. Physiol.* **118**, 65P.

Whiteside, T. C. D. (1957). "The Problems of Vision in Flight at High Altitude", p. 153. Butterworth, London.

Wolff, E. (1933). "The Anatomy of the Eye and Orbit; Including the Central Connections, Development, and Comparative Anatomy of the Visual Apparatus", p. 173. P. Blakiston's Sons and Company, Philadelphia.

Wolff, E. (1946). Some aspects of the normal histology of the suspensory ligament of the lens. *Proc. R. Soc. Med.* **39**, 252–254.

Wolff, E. (1952). Discussion of a paper by T. Henderson. *Trans. ophthal. Soc. U.K.* **72**, 538–539.

Young, T. (1793). Observations on vision. *Phil. Trans. B.* pp. 169–181.

Young, T. (1801). On the mechanism of the eye. *Phil. Trans. B.* pp. 23–88.

CHAPTER 9

The Pupil †

OTTO LOWENSTEIN AND IRENE E. LOEWENFELD

I. Introduction

The iris diaphragm controls the aperture of the refracting system of the eye. With its central portion pushed forward by the lens, the iris resembles the envelope of a flat, cut-off cone. The outer, ciliary edge, or iris root, has a diameter of about 12 mm. in man. The inner border of the iris is formed by the pupil, situated slightly nasal to the centre of the iris. In thickness, the iris measures about 0.6 mm., depending upon the state of pupillary contraction.

Within the optical system of the eye, a mobile pupil serves three main functions:

(1) It regulates the amount of light entering the eye.

(2) It increases the depth of focus of the eye by decreasing the aperture of the optical system.

(3) It reduces chromatic and spherical aberrations, especially in bright light, when the pupil is small.

The iris is an extraordinarily mobile structure. In man, the pupillary diameter may vary from about 1.3 to almost 10 mm., and in some other species

† This work was supported by the Harriman Fund and by a grant from the U.S. Public Health Service (Sens. Dis. B–253).

(e.g., cats) the range of movement is even larger.† The delicate responsiveness of the iris, and the extensiveness of the nervous network controlling it, make it an ideal indicator for studies on the physiology of the autonomic nervous system and, clinically, for the detection of lesions within the centres and pathways of pupillary control. Consequently, a vast literature on the physiology and pathology of pupillary movements has been accumulated during the last two centuries. Because of the great mass and complexity of these discussions, we will omit all but a small number of bibliographical references.‡ Similarly, we will mention only some of the chief controversies in the literature, since limitations of space do not permit a more detailed consideration.

II. The Iris Muscles

A. The Sphincter Pupillae

The pupillary sphincter consists of an annular band of smooth-muscle fibres, about 0.7 to 1 mm. wide, which encircles the pupil. The contractile capacity of this muscle is remarkable. The normal pupil can constrict from 8 mm. (in darkness) to 2 mm. (in bright light) within seconds. During this process, the sphincter pupillae must shrink to one quarter of its original length. Under the influence of drugs, even greater variations of pupillary size are possible.

B. The Dilator Pupillae

Unlike the pupillary sphincter whose existence was firmly established around 1840, the dilator pupillæ has long remained a controversial structure. Its anatomical identity and functional role have been proved repeatedly, only to again be doubted in an endless row of repetitive debates.

On the negative side of these discussions (especially Grünhagen, 1863–93, and later authors), the existence of radial muscle fibres in the iris was denied, and pupillary dilatation was thought to be caused by:
  (i) active (adrenergic) or passive relaxation of the sphincter pupillae, with recoil of elastic tissue in the iris;
  (ii) relaxation of the sphincter pupillae, aided by steady, unchanging pull of radial elements of unspecified structure;

† All measurements in this chapter refer to the *apparent* pupillary diameter, as measured in the living eye. The actual diameters are somewhat smaller. All measurements pertain to the human eye unless otherwise specified.
‡ A few larger, comprehensive publications, some of them with extended rendition of the literature, are listed at the end of this chapter. They were chosen from approximately 7,000 publications in our files as the references most likely to acquaint the reader with the problems of pupillary innervation.

(iii) contraction of iris vessels, or reduction of blood content of these vessels, with or without additional sphincter relaxation.

A careful analysis of these various theories, however, leaves no doubt that they are anatomically and physiologically ill-founded (Loewenfeld, 1958).

An understanding of the structure and function of the pupillary dilator has been obtained by studies which revealed its embryological origin, its great variability among species and among individuals, and its functional changes in appearance.

1. MYO-EPITHELIAL CELLS

Both the pupillary sphincter and dilator are derived from neural ecto-derm, i.e., from the anterior epithelial layer of the primitive optic cup. During development, some of the epithelial cells move into the iris stroma and develop into the true smooth-muscle cells of the sphincter pupillae. In contrast, the majority of the dilator cells remain in their original position and retain a primitive myo-epithelial structure. They become the cells of Bruch's membrane (Fig. 1). They line the entire posterior surface of the iris, covered only by the single layer of pigmented posterior epithelium. In the region of the sphincter, dilatator bundles dip forward into the iris stroma, turn towards a circular course and, interlacing in loops and "arcades," merge with the sphincter strands. Near the ciliary iris margin, similar anas-tomosing muscle arcades form a thin ring plexus from which final insertion bundles emerge radially to pass into the ciliary muscle and pectinate liga-ment.

The myo-epithelial elements of Bruch's membrane are so unusual in structure that their muscular nature was often denied even though they showed the same staining reactions as the other intra-ocular smooth muscles (Henle, 1866 and later authors) and in spite of the fact that their ability to contract was proved: When the pupil dilates, all parts of the iris, the stroma as well as the pigmented posterior epithelium, are thrown into folds. The only structure which never folds is Bruch's membrane; it merely becomes thicker when the pupil dilates and thinner when it contracts (Fuchs, 1885 and later authors).

2. REINFORCEMENT BUNDLES

In addition to the myo-epithelial cell layer of Bruch's membrane, radial strands of smooth-muscle tissue converge upon the pupil similar to wheel spokes. Situated in front of Bruch's membrane toward the iris stroma, these "reinforcement bundles" vary considerably from species to species and even among individuals. When they are strongly developed the iris, in cross-section, appears to possess a smooth-muscle dilator several cell layers thick while in another iris, or in other portions of the same iris, the fascicles may be entirely missing.

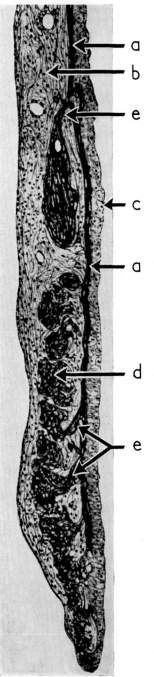

FIG. 1. Iris Muscles. Depigmented Radial Section Through the Pupillary Portion of a Dog's Iris [Fig. 20 of Klinge (1908)]. The letters added by us indicate: a = continuous layer of dilator pupillae (Bruch's membrane); b = iris stroma; c = posterior layer of pigmented epithelium; d = sphincter bundles, cut at right angles to their course; e = connecting muscle strands between sphincter and dilatator.

III. Innervation of Iris Muscles

The pupillary sphincter muscle is activated by parasympathetic (cholinergic) nerve fibres from the ciliary ganglion, the dilator muscle by sympathetic (adrenergic) nerves from the superior cervical ganglion. The iris is, thus, a representative of all smooth-muscle structures reciprocally innervated by the autonomic nervous system.

A. PUPILLARY PLAY

When observed in ordinary room illumination, the pupil is found to be in almost constant motion. These movements of the iris are the result of spontaneous or reactive shifts in the dynamic equilibrium of its sympathetic-parasympathetic innervation. The following are the main causes of such shifts:

(1) The amount of illumination present at the moment of observation. In complete darkness, the pupils of normal, alert subjects are usually large and relatively quiet. With increasing light, they become smaller and more active. We will return to this phenomenon of "pupillary unrest" in a later part of this chapter (cf. pages 261–262).

(2) Spontaneous or reactive changes in the level of consciousness or, neurologically speaking, changes in the degree of cortico-thalamo-hypothalamic activity. Such activity is increased by sensory or emotional stimulation, or by spontaneous thoughts or emotions (cf. also pp. 251–257). It decreases during fatigue and is absent during normal sleep or induced narcosis. Cortico-thalamo-hypothalamic impulses dilate the pupil (a) by giving rise to sympathetic impulses which reach the dilator pupillae via the cervical cord and the peripheral sympathetic chain (cf. pp. 254–256), and (b) by inhibiting the activity of the oculomotor nucleus, with consequent relaxation of the sphincter pupillae (cf. p. 276 and Fig. 8). Even in complete darkness, therefore, the pupil may oscillate over a wide range, especially when the subject is tired.

The iris is, thus, at all times under the influence of a labile, dynamic equilibrium of its autonomic innervation, whereby sympathetic, parasympathetic and supranuclear mechanisms are simultaneously active in varying degrees. Specific reflexes are superimposed on this constantly shifting basic equilibrium that influences the extent and shape of the reactions. The same stimulus may therefore elicit an extensive reflex at one moment and remain without response at the next moment. These facts, which were not always understood, as well as the difficulties in observing accurately an organ as small and as mobile as the iris, have been mainly responsible for the lengthy controversies in the literature concerning the pupil.

IV. Pupillary Reactions

The following main pupillary reactions will be considered:

A. *The Light-Reflex*: The response of the pupil to stimulation of the retina by an increase of light.

B. *The Reaction to Near Vision*: The contraction of the pupil which coincides with convergence of the eyes and accommodation of the lens upon viewing a near object.

C. *Pupillary Reflex Dilatation*: Pupillary dilatation elicited by sensory or emotional stimuli, or by spontaneous thoughts or emotions.

D. *The Darkness-Reflex*: The pupillary response brought about by short interruption of a steady level of light-adaptation.

E. *The Lid-Closure Reflex*: Pupillary movements which accompany (*a*) spontaneous, (*b*) intentional, or (*c*) reactive short closing of the eyelids.

F. *"Pupillary Unrest" and "Hippus"*: Apparently spontaneous oscillations of the pupil under steady conditions of illumination.

Additional pupillary reactions, often mentioned in the literature but owing their popularity mainly to faulty observations or misconceptions, will be mentioned only briefly.

A. THE LIGHT-REFLEX

When the eye of a normal subject is exposed to light, the homolateral pupil (direct reaction) as well as the contralateral pupil (consensual reaction) constricts.

1. EFFECT OF VARIOUS LIGHT STIMULI

a. Stimulus Intensity

When the stimulating light is of very low intensity, the latent period is very long (more than 0.5 second) and the contraction is slow, inextensive and of short duration (Fig. 2A). With increasing stimulus-intensity the latent period becomes shorter (0.2–0.3 second) and the contraction faster, more extensive and longer lasting (Fig. 2B, C). When the two eyes are stimulated simultaneously, there is a summation of the responses, so that the reflex is more extensive than when either eye is stimulated alone.

b. Stimulus Duration and Frequency

When the light-stimulus is short (less than 1 second), the pupillary reaction is usually shortlasting and less extensive than with longer stimulation by light of equal intensity. When such short light-flashes are presented in rapid succession, the individual pupillary oscillations summate so that, with increasing stimulus-frequency, the mean pupillary diameter decreases. Since the smooth

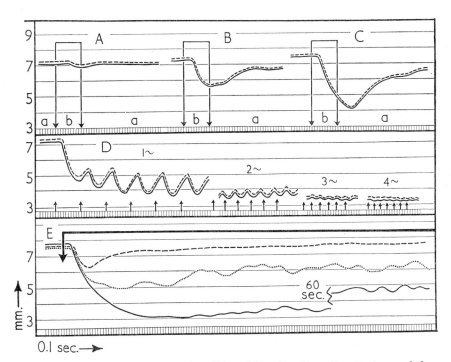

Fig. 2. Pupillary Reactions to Light in Normal Man. Pupillary diameter is recorded as the ordinate (in mm.) against time as the abscissa (in 0.1 second units), whereby the solid lines represent the right pupil's reactions, the broken lines the left pupil's simultaneous responses (except in E). The records were obtained with the "Electronic Pupillograph," an infrared-sensitive recording device (Lowenstein and Loewenfeld, 1958).

First Row (A, B, and C): At a, the subject's eyes were in darkness. During the 1-second periods b (outlined by double arrows) white light flashes were presented (furnished by a Sylvania Glow Modulator tube, controlled electronically as described elsewhere (Lowenstein and Loewenfeld, 1959)). Light intensity was varied by neutral grey filters. In A, the light was one, in B four and in C eight logarithmic units brighter than the intensity needed to reach the subject's absolute visual threshold. With increasing stimulus intensity, the pupillary reflexes increased in extent and speed and the latent period shortened. The reactions were equal on the two sides although only the right eye was stimulated while the left eye remained in darkness.

Second Row (D): At the moments marked by the small arrows, short, bright light flashes (5 msec. duration, same brightness as in C) were presented to the subject's right eye at the rates of 1 to 4 times per second. With increasing rate of stimulation, the pupillary oscillations became smaller and the mean pupillary diameter decreased.

Third Row (E): Pupillary movements elicited by prolonged light stimulation (duration framed by arrow). Only the right pupil's movements are shown. The intensities were eight (solid line), five (dotted line) and two (broken line) logarithmic units above the subject's visual threshold. After the initial contraction, the pupil dilated partially, more so when the light was dim than when it was bright. Pupillary oscillations appeared which were faster in bright than in dim light (cf. text, p. 262).

muscles of the iris move relatively slowly, individual oscillations due to individual light-flashes tend to fuse at a rate of about 3 to 4 per second (Fig. 2D). The pupillary movements elicited by prolonged light-stimulation will be considered later (cf. "pupillary unrest," pp. 261–262).

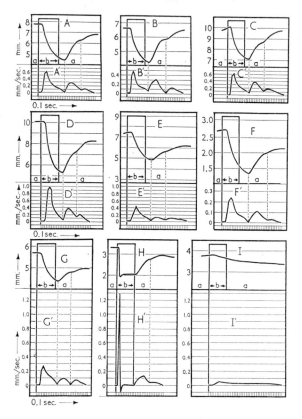

FIG. 3. Pupillary Light-Reflex in Normal Man and Some Animals. A-I: Pupillary diameter is recorded as the ordinate (in mm.) against time as the abscissa (in 0.1 second units). The species represented are: A = man; B = monkey (macaca mulatta); C = dog; D = cat; E = rabbit; F = rat; G = guinea pig; H = pigeon; I = frog. Only one pupil is shown in each pupillogram. For animals with small eyes, the ordinate of the graph was enlarged, using the ratio of the diameter of the animal's iris to that of man as multiplying factor. Note the similarity of the reactions in mammals, as compared with the fast contraction and short latent period (0.06 second) in birds and the slow, prolonged contraction in frogs.

A'-I': The differential curves of the pupillograms A to I show the speed at which the pupillary movements occurred. This speed is recorded as the ordinate (in mm. per second) against time as the abscissa (in 0.1 second units). Note the presence of a single wave of acceleration and deceleration for pupillary contraction (termed C-wave), two waves for redilatation (termed D- and E-waves) (cf. Lowenstein and Loewenfeld, 1950).

2. SENSITIVITY OF IRIS

In lower vertebrate species such as frogs and some fishes, the pupil can be constricted by illuminating the iris itself after the optic nerve has been cut or the iris removed from the eye. But these slow, primitive movements have nothing in common with the light-reflex observed in mammals (Fig. 3). In mammals, the iris itself is insensitive to light and the reaction is elicited via the reflex pathways only. The pupil of a blind eye will remain large and immobile upon intense illumination if experimental errors such as stray of light to the normal eye or changes in accommodation are avoided.

3. THE RETINAL RECEPTORS AND THE AFFERENT PATH TO THE MID-BRAIN

Since the pupillary light-reflex and visual perception share a large portion of their afferent path, from the retina via the optic nerve and chiasm to the posterior third of the optic tract, the study of pupillary reflexes in response to light-stimuli of various intensities, areas, colours, durations and retinal location should be useful for a clearer understanding of some aspects of the visual sensory mechanism. Much work has therefore been done with the aim of relating pupillary movements and visual perception (cf. an excellent summary by Schweitzer, 1955).

a. The Rods and Cones

Many authors believed the retinal cones to be the only receptors for the pupillary light-reflex (cf. especially v. Hess, 1907, 1908; Harms, 1949). When the pupil was observed in dim light, stimulation of the retinal periphery was found relatively ineffective in producing a pupillary response. A brighter light-stimulus was needed to elicit an energetic reaction from the peripheral retina than from the fovea. More recent investigations on pupillary threshold reactions, elicited by low intensity test-stimuli of various colours and retinal locations, leave, however, no doubt that both rods and cones are receptors for the pupillary reflex (Engelking, 1919; Schweitzer, 1955; Lowenstein and Loewenfeld, 1959). There is a close parallel between pupillary reactions and visual sensation:

(i) Just as for vision, the cone function and rod function have separate thresholds, whereby in the dark-adapted eye, the rod-threshold (peripheral stimulation by white, green or blue light) is much lower than the cone-threshold (central stimulation by red light).

(ii) The pupillary threshold reactions are suppressed by light-adaptation and reappear during dark-adaptation in exactly the same manner as vision. Reactions to white, green or blue (peripheral) test-stimuli are suppressed more profoundly, and they require a much longer time to be restored, than reactions to red (central) stimuli.

(iii) Just as for vision, pupillary reactions have been found to show the Purkinje shift of spectral sensitivity after light-adaptation (Abelsdorff, 1900).

(iv) The stimulus-intensity needed to obtain pupillary threshold responses is always somewhat greater than that required for vision. This difference between visual and pupillary thresholds is slightly greater for peripheral than for central test-stimuli of equal area. Furthermore, when the intensity of the light-stimuli is raised above the value needed for pupillary threshold responses, the increase of pupillary activity with equal increments of stimulus-intensity is greater for central than for peripheral stimulation. A similar difference between the effects of foveal and of peripheral light-stimulation is shown by the visual flicker-fusion phenomenon. Equal increments of stimulus-intensity lead to greater increases in flicker-fusion frequency when foveal rather than peripheral light-flashes are used (Fig. 4).

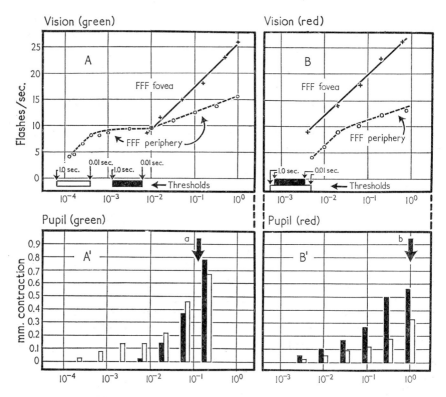

Fig. 4. Normal Pupillary Reactions, Visual Thresholds and Visual Flicker Fusion Frequencies for Red and Green Test-Stimuli in the Fovea and the Retinal Periphery. In all experiments, the subject's eyes were fully dark-adapted. The abscissa represents stimulus intensity, expressed in log unit steps from 10^0 to 10^{-4}, with the full intensity of available light termed as 10^0. Light intensity was varied with neutral grey filters. The stimulus area was a small (1° visual angle) round, white cardboard disk with black velvet background, illuminated by the Sylvania Glow Modulator tube. The colour of the stimulus light was varied by Wratten filters (No. 29 red and No. 99 green). The flash duration was 0.01 second for visual flicker fusion tests and 1.0 second for elicitation of pupillary reactions. The visual thresholds were determined for red and for green flashes

Just as for vision, the cones, though less sensitive, are thus more effective for the production of fast and extensive pupillary reactions. When such experiments are carried out in dim light rather than after dark-adaptation, the sensitive rod responses may be reduced or abolished by retinal adaptation. These facts probably account for the widespread erroneous belief that the retinal periphery does not elicit pupillomotor activity.

b. Retinal Ganglion Cells to Pretectal Area

Afferent impulses for the pupillary light-reflex travel from each retina via the optic nerve, chiasm and tracts to the mid-brain. Some authors maintain that pupillary and visual impulses arise from the same retinal ganglion cells. According to this theory the afferent fibres bifurcate in the optic tract. The visual fibres continue to the lateral geniculate body while the pupillary collaterals descend to the mid-brain. A second group of authors believe that separate visual and pupillary ganglion cells in the retina generate separate visual and pupillary afferent impulses. Up to the present, no conclusive anatomical proof has been brought forth in support of either theory (cf. Magoun and Ranson, 1935).

It was sometimes stated that the pupillary fibres do not cross in the optic chiasm (cf. for example Magitot, 1946). But experiments on monkeys, cats and rabbits, as well as pupillary reactions recorded in patients with optic

---

(*Legend to Fig. 4 continued*)

of 0.01 and of 1.0 second duration (horizontal bars), both in the fovea (solid bars) and the retinal periphery (15°, nasal field, open bars).

A and *B*: The foveal visual thresholds, both for green light (A) and for red light (B) were high. The lowest flicker fusion rate (*FFF*) for both colours was 8–9 per second, obtained at the threshold intensity for single 0.01 second flashes. With increasing light intensity, the *FFF* rose sharply and linearly for both colours (crosses and solid lines). In contrast, the peripheral visual threshold was much lower for green light (A) than for red light (B). For green light, the lowest obtainable *FFF* was 4. The fusion rate rose gradually to a plateau of 9 (rod function) with further increase when the light intensity exceeded the cone-threshold (open circles and broken line in A). For red light, the low threshold and plateau at *FFF* 9 were missing (open circles and broken line in B). For both colours, the peripheral *FFF* showed a shallower rise than the foveal *FFF*.

A' and *B'*: Pupillary reactions were tested in the intensity range from 0.5 log unit above visual threshold for 1-second flashes to 0.1 log unit above the intensity at which the flashes became visible when directed on the subject's blind spot (marked by arrows *a* and *b*). In parallel to the visual functions, the foveal pupillary thresholds were high for both red and green light, and the extent of the reactions increased sharply with increasing stimulus intensity (solid black vertical columns in A' and B'). In contrast, peripheral stimulation by green light (open columns in A') had a much lower threshold than peripheral stimulation by red light (open columns in B'). Peripheral stimulation elicited much less increase in pupillary reactivity with increasing stimulus intensity than foveal stimulation.

8*

tract lesions, indicate that the degree of crossing of pupillary fibres in the optic chiasm parallels the distribution of crossed and uncrossed visual fibres (cf. Magoun and Ranson, 1935; and Fig. 5).

The pupillary light-reflex fibres leave the optic tract in its posterior (central) third and travel by way of the brachia of the anterior colliculi to the pretectal area where they synapse with the rather diffuse group of cells of the "pretectal nucleus." In the older literature, the superior colliculi were thought to be the site of this first central synapse, but more recent work has shown that the light-reflex is not impaired by destruction of the colliculi while it is absent when lesions are limited to the pretectal area (cf. especially Magoun and Ranson, 1935).

Based on anatomical work, some authors (for example Szentágothai, 1942) have stated that the synapse is located in the pregeniculate nucleus, with the post-ganglionic fibres travelling via the pretectal area to the third nerve nuclei. To date, this view has not been generally accepted.

4. THE INTERCALATED NEURONE: DIRECT AND CONSENSUAL LIGHT-REFLEX

The pretectal fibres of each side carry the light-reflex impulses to the anterior small-celled portion of the oculomotor nuclei (Edinger-Westphal nuclei) of the homolateral and the heterolateral side. In cats, the majority of the pretectal fibres cross in the posterior commissure and reach the opposite Edinger-Westphal nucleus while the minority of fibres arch around the central grey matter to the oculomotor nucleus of the same side. In man and monkeys, this central hemidecussation is symmetrical. Consequently, the direct and the consensual light-reflex are equal in normal man and monkeys while in normal cats, the direct reaction of the illuminated eye exceeds the consensual reflex of the eye in darkness.

It was frequently stated that pupillary inequality could be produced by uneven illumination of the two eyes in normal man. It is believed that in man as well as in lower mammals the majority of pupillary fibres cross in the optic chiasm and re-cross in the posterior commissure and that consequently, the direct light-reflex is more extensive than the consensual one. But pupillographic records show that in *normal* man and monkeys the pupils remain equal when one eye is illuminated while its fellow-eye remains in darkness. The erroneous opinion of unequal fibre distribution takes its origin mainly from the following facts:

(i) Apparent pupillary inequality may be an optical illusion on the part of the observer, whereby the pupil of the dimly lighted eye appears larger than the brightly illuminated one.

(ii) Many clinical cases exist with damage to the region of the pretectal area and posterior commissure (Lowenstein, 1954, 1956). In these patients, indeed, the direct light-reflex is more extensive than the consensual one. It is, however, difficult to accept these findings as normal because (a) the syndrome is far more often unilateral than bilateral, i.e., the pupils become unequal when one but not when the other eye is illuminated, and (b) among the bilateral cases, only very few are symmetrical. In contrast, in cats with normally unequal fibre distribution, the phenomenon is always bilateral and symmetrical.

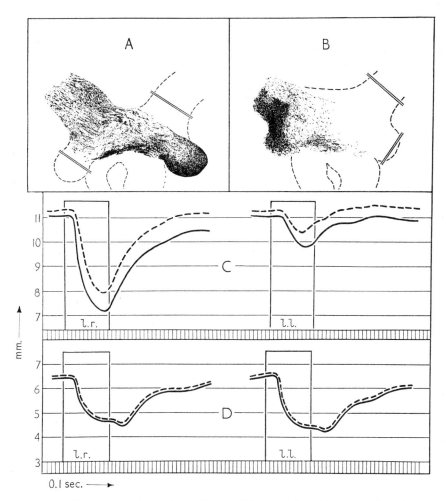

Fig. 5. Fibre Distribution in Optic Chiasm of Cats (A, B), and Pupillary Reactions in Cat (C) and in Man (D) with Lesions in the Optic Tract.

A and B: Crossed (A) and uncrossed (B) fibres in the optic chiasm of two cats. Pen-and-ink camera obscura drawings were made from the original anatomical slides (Davenport silver stain). In A, the animal's right optic nerve and left optic tract had been cut some time previously and all but the crossed optic fibres had degenerated (lesions indicated by double lines). In B, the animal's right optic nerve and right optic tract had been divided, leaving only uncrossed fibres intact. It is evident than in cats, the number of crossed optic fibres is much greater than that of uncrossed fibres.

C: Pupillary reactions of a third cat whose right optic tract had been cut some time before. When the right eye was exposed to light (l.r., with only crossed optic fibres remaining), the pupillary reaction was much more extensive than when the left eye was stimulated (l.l., with only uncrossed optic fibres). It should be noted that in either case the right pupil reacted more extensively, i.e. the pupil opposite to the pretectal nucleus

The distribution of crossed and uncrossed afferent impulses from the pre-tectal area to the Edinger-Westphal nuclei is independent of the distribution of crossed and uncrossed retinal fibres:

(i) In man and monkeys, lesions in the retina, optic nerve or optic tract—unless complicated by additional damage in other pupillary neurones—never lead to pupillary inequality (Fig. 5D).

(ii) In cats, it is always the pupil opposite to the more intensely stimulated pretectal nucleus which becomes the smaller one, regardless of whether the pretectal area receives impulses from the homolateral or the heterolateral retina (Fig. 5C).

5. THE OCULOMOTOR NUCLEUS AND THE EFFERENT PATH OF THE LIGHT-REFLEX

The efferent fibres for the pupillary reaction to light pass, without further crossing, with the third nerve to the ciliary ganglion. The short ciliary fibres, arising from the cells of the ciliary ganglion, provide the final path to the pupillary sphincter. Lesions in the efferent path of the light-reflex lead to mydriatic pupils with slow and inextensive or absent light-reflexes (Fig. 6, 6 and 7). In contrast to the effect of lesions involving the pretectal neurone, it is always the same pupil which reacts poorly, no matter which eye is illum-inated.

6. SYMPATHETIC AND SUPRANUCLEAR MECHANISMS AFFECTING THE PUPILLARY LIGHT-REFLEX

When normal man or animals are subjected to sensory or emotional stimu-lation, the pupillary light-reflex is inhibited; it can be completely suppressed if the interfering stimulus is sufficiently strong. This interference is accom-plished by the simultaneous elicitation of two mechanisms.

a. Sympathetic Activation

Since the pupillary dilator is the antagonist of the pupillary sphincter, it is to be expected that interruption of sympathetic impulses will increase the pupillary contraction to light. This is, indeed, the case. When the sympa-thetic innervation of the eye is interrupted, the pupil on the side of the lesion always contracts to light more rapidly, and under certain conditions more ex-tensively, than the normal pupil (Fig. 7A). Correspondingly, when stimulation

---

(continued from previous page)

which received afferent stimulation from the homolateral (*l.r.*) or from the heterolateral eye (*l.l.*).

D: Pupillary reactions in a patient with right-sided optic tract lesion. The reactions elicited from the right eye (crossed optic fibres) and from the left eye (uncrossed optic fibres) were quite similar, and the pupils remained equal at all times (cf. text, pp. 242–244).

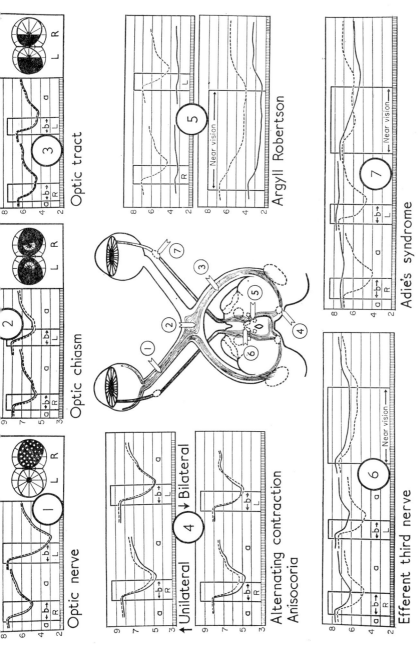

FIG. 6 Diagram of Pupillary Light-Reflex Pathways and Pupillary Reactions (in Man) Resulting from Various Lesions. (Fig. 10 of Lowenstein and Loewenfeld, 1958). The sites of the lesions and the corresponding changes in the pupillary reflex pattern are indicated by the numbers 1–7.

of the eye by light and electrical stimulation of the sympathetic chain coincide, the light-reflex becomes somewhat reduced (Fig. 7B).

It can, however, be seen from Fig. 7B that the inhibiting effect of even maximal sympathetic stimulation upon the light-reflex is not very marked. On the other hand, psycho-sensory stimulation in normal man and animals, and electrical brain stimulation in animals, inhibit the light-reflex almost as effectively in a sympathectomized as in a normal pupil (Fig. 7C).

b. Supranuclear Inhibition

To understand the mechanism of psycho-sensory suppression of the light-reflex, it must be remembered that the pupillary light-reflex pathway is not an isolated reflex arc, independent of the rest of the nervous system. Like all other motor nuclei, the oculomotor nucleus is subject to inhibitory influences from supranuclear structures (Fig. 8, dotted lines). Cortico-thalamo-hypo-thalamic impulses, elicited by sensory and emotional stimuli, and by psychological processes such as spontaneous thoughts and emotions, converge upon the oculomotor nucleus and prevent it from sending constrictor impulses to the pupillary sphincter.

Some authors believe that inhibition of the sphincter pupillae is brought about by active (adrenergic) inhibitory impulses which are thought to reach the sphincter pupillae by way of the peripheral sympathetic path (Grünhagen, 1886 and later authors). But the action of the peripheral sympathetic system plays only a minor role in the suppression of the light-reflex, as shown in the preceding paragraph. In addition, the following experiment demonstrates that the pupillary sphincter and its peripheral cholinergic nerve fibres are *not* inhibited by the interfering stimulus.

In Fig. 7D the same brain stimulus was used as in the experiment of Fig. 7C, but intermittent stimulation of the sphincter pupillae was brought about by intermittent electrical stimulation of the third nerve rather than by stimulation of the retina by light (as in Fig. 7C). While the brain stimulus was able to block completely the light-reflexes in the experiment of Fig. 7C, the pupillary contractions due to third nerve stimulation were not at all inhibited (Fig. 7D).

Inhibition of the Edinger-Westphal nucleus by interfering psycho-sensory or brain stimuli is, therefore, a central nervous event. The interfering impulses reach the third nerve nucleus both via direct afferent connexions in the diffuse reticular formation (Harris et al., 1944) and from higher brain centres. These facts are in agreement with the concept of Sherrington's reciprocal reflex inhibition, which takes place in the central nervous system and is not caused by active impulses via peripheral paths to the effector cells.

c. Psycho-sensory Restitution

It should be noted that suppression of the light-reflex is not the only function of the sympathetic and supranuclear inhibitory mechanisms. On the contrary, a certain degree of sympathetic and supranuclear activity is necessary to establish the delicate dynamic equilibrium that is necessary for the

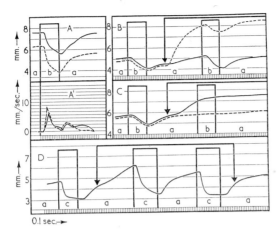

0.1 sec.—➤

FIG. 7. Influence of Peripheral Sympathetic Discharges and of Supranuclear Inhibition upon Pupillary Contractions (Monkey). In A, B, C and D, pupillary diameter is recorded as the ordinate (in mm.) against time as the abscissa (in 0.1 second units), whereby the solid lines represent the reactions of the right, the broken lines those of the left pupil. At *a*, the animals' eyes were in darkness. During the intervals *b* (experiments A, B, C) they were exposed to light of 15 foot-candle intensity. In the experiment D, the animal remained in darkness; the light-stimuli were replaced by intermittent electrical stimulation of the third nerve (*c* = thyratron stimuli, 8 V at 50/sec.). In A', the differential curve shows the increasing and decreasing speed of the pupillary movements shown in A (in mm. per second).

A and A': Light-reflex in awake monkey (macaca mulatta), some weeks after removal of the left superior cervical ganglion. The contraction of the (smaller) sympathectomized pupil was slightly more extensive and faster than the one of the normal pupil. The second wave of pupillary redilatation was missing on the side of the lesion (especially visible in the differential curve, broken line in A').

B: Light-reflexes in anaesthetized, normal monkey. During the time framed by the arrow, the left cervical sympathetic nerve was strongly stimulated (thyratron, 100 V at 50/sec.). Even though the left pupil dilated maximally, the light-reflex was only slightly less extensive than on the right side.

C: Light-reflexes in the same monkey used in B after the left sympathetic chain had been cut (some minutes after B). During the time framed by the arrow, a hypothalamic stimulus was given (square wave, 4 V at 120/sec.). The normal right pupil dilated strongly, the sympathectomized pupil only slightly. The light-reflex was blocked on both sides.

D: Same monkey, some minutes after experiment C. The pupillogram for the right eye is shown (normal sympathetic innervation). The brain stimulus was identical to the one used in C (time framed by double arrow). The pupillary contractions elicited by electrical stimulation of the third nerve were not inhibited (cf. discussion in the text, p. 246).

development of optimal light-reflexes. When the sympathetic and supranuclear impulses are missing, as during sleep and narcosis, the pupil becomes
miotic and the reactions to light inextensive and sluggish. Psycho-sensory

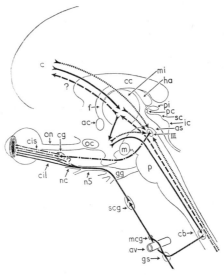

Fig. 8. Schematic Representation of Mammalian Brain (Sagittal View). (Fig. 60 of
Loewenfeld, 1958.)

Solid lines: Efferent sympathetic path from cortex, thalamus and hypothalamus via
the cervical cord and peripheral sympathetic chain to the dilator pupillae.

Broken lines: Afferent sensory path to the thalamus and cortex.

Dash-dot lines: Efferent parasympathetic path from the oculomotor nucleus via the
third nerve and ciliary ganglion to the iris sphincter.

Dotted lines: Inhibitory paths to the oculomotor nucleus; (1) direct afferent connexions
in the brain-stem reticular formation and (2) descending connexions from cortex, thalamus and hypothalamus.

ac = anterior commissure; as = aqueduct of Sylvius; av = ansa of Vieussens; c =
cortex; cb = ciliospinal "centre" of Budge (mostly T1 and T2); cc = corpus callosum;
cg = ciliary ganglion; cis = short ciliary nerves; cil = long ciliary nerves; f = fornix;
gg = Gasserian ganglion; gs = ganglion stellatum; ha = habenular nucleus; ic = inferior
colliculus; m = mammillary body; mcg = middle cervical ganglion; mi = massa inter-
media; nc = nasociliary branch of the ophthalmic 5th nerve; $n5$ = ophthalmic division
of the 5th nerve; oc = optic chiasm; on = optic nerve; p = pons; pc = posterior commissure; pi = pineal body; sc = superior colliculus; scg = superior cervical ganglion;
III = oculomotor nucleus.

stimuli that awaken the sleeping subject, or experimental brain stimuli that
inhibit the oculomotor nucleus and activate sympathetic discharges in narcotized animals, restore the sympathetic-parasympathetic balance and re-
integrate the reduced light-reflex to its optimum (Lowenstein, 1937; Lowenstein and Loewenfeld, 1950, 1951; Fig. 9).

The phenomenon of psycho-sensory restitution is not limited to the pupil. It is a general integrative mechanism affecting all organs reciprocally innervated (Lowenstein, 1937). It re-establishes the labile equilibrium of innervation which is necessary for the development of optimal functional responsiveness of the individual. During recent years, the phenomenon has received much attention under the new name of "arousal phenomenon."

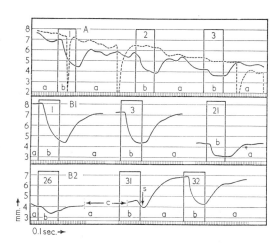

FIG. 9. Pupillary Light-Reflexes in Monkey (A) and in Tired Man (B1, 2). Pupillary diameter (solid lines) and width of palpebral fissure (broken line) are recorded as the ordinate (in mm.) against time as the abscissa (in 0.1 second units). At *a* the eyes were in darkness; at *b* they were exposed to 1-second light flashes of 15 foot-candle intensity.

A: Monkey (Macaca mulatta), gradually falling asleep. The traces for the right palpebral fissure and the directly reacting right pupil are shown. Pupil and palpebral fissure became small, the light-reflexes inextensive.

*B*1, 2: Light-reflexes elicited in a normal 35-year-old man, gradually falling asleep. The direct reactions of the right pupil are shown. The pupil became gradually smaller while the light-reflexes deteriorated. Between the 26th and the 31st stimuli, the subject slept (*c*), with eyes rolled upward and eyelids closed. When he was awakened by a sudden sensory stimulus (sound, *s*), the pupil dilated and the normal reflex was restored.

B. THE PUPILLARY CONTRACTION TO NEAR VISION

The three components of the near vision reaction, namely accommodation, convergence and pupillary contraction, have separate centres within the third nerve nucleus, and separate efferent paths. While the third nerve fibres for convergence reach the internal rectus muscle without interruption, the fibres to the intra-ocular smooth-muscles pass through the ciliary ganglion. The nerve impulses for both pupillary contraction and accommodation undergo synapses in the ciliary ganglion, as is proved by the fact that—in monkeys and cats—both functions can no longer be elicited by electrical stimulation of the third nerve after retrobulbar injection of nicotine (Langley and Anderson, 1902; Lowenstein, 1956).

1. ACCOMMODATION, CONVERGENCE AND PUPILLARY CONSTRICTION

There are many discussions in the literature in regard to the dependence of the pupillary contraction upon either convergence or accommodation. Both clinically and experimentally, however, any one of the three functions can be abolished without interference with the others. For example, convergence or accommodation may be eliminated by the use of prisms or lenses, the pupillary constriction alone by small doses of atropine-like substances or of retrobulbar nicotine, both accommodation and pupillary constriction by larger doses. In cats, dogs and monkeys, isolated pupillary constriction, accommodation of the lens, or contraction of the internal rectus, were obtained by electrical stimulation of the efferent third nerve (Lowenstein, 1956) or of various sites within the third nerve nuclear complex (Hensen and Völckers, 1878; Bender and Weinstein, 1943).

These experiments by no means prove the existence, within the third nerve, of separate fibres for pupillary contraction to light on the one hand and for pupillary constriction to near vision on the other hand. But they lead necessarily to the conclusion that the nervous impulses that cause accommodation, convergence, and pupillary constriction must arise from different cell groups in the third nerve nucleus. Accommodation, convergence and pupillary constriction are associated, synchronized and controlled by supranuclear connexions; they are not caused by one another.

2. ARGYLL ROBERTSON PUPIL

In the Argyll Robertson pupillary syndrome, the pupil is miotic and the pupillary reflex to light is poor or absent. In contrast, the pupillary contraction to near vision is relatively well-preserved. This dissociation makes it necessary to assume the existence of separate centres or pathways for the two kinds of pupillary contraction. The question of the location of the lesion that causes the Argyll Robertson syndrome has been debated ever since it was first described (1869).

(i) The iris muscles and the autonomic nerve-nets and -endings in the iris must be excluded as possible sites because of the selective loss of the light- and darkness-reflexes with preservation of the near-vision reaction, reflex dilatation, and pupillary responses to miotic and mydriatic drugs.

(ii) The ciliary ganglion and short ciliary fibres, likewise, cannot be considered because damage to these structures would lead to mydriasis and tonicity of the near-vision reaction, if this reaction were preserved. In addition, lesions in the final parasympathetic neurone render the sphincter hypersensitive to parasympatheticomimetic drugs (Anderson, 1903 and later authors). The pupillary syndrome in such cases is therefore that of

Adie's pupillotonic pseudotabes and not that of Argyll Robertson (Fig. 6, 7; cf. especially Scheie, 1940).

(iii) Destruction or damage in the third nerve nucleus or the efferent third nerve would also lead to mydriatic pupils, and the miosis found in the typical Argyll Robertson syndrome would remain unexplained (Fig. 6, 6).

(iv) Lesions in the afferent path of the light-reflex, i.e., the retinal fibres within the optic nerve or tract, are excluded because of the absence of visual defects. Damage to these fibres after they emerge from the optic tract would have to involve both pupils equally, and would not lead to miosis.

The Argyll Robertson syndrome would be explained by the assumption of a pre-nuclear lesion, close to the oculomotor nucleus, that interfered with both the crossed and uncrossed pretectal fibres (cf. above, pp. 242–244 and Fig. 6, 5). Such a lesion would interrupt the light-reflex arc, leaving the supra-nuclear paths for the near-vision reaction, as well as the Edinger-Westphal nucleus and the efferent parasympathetic pathways, intact.

This location of the lesion responsible for the Argyll Robertson syndrome was denied by some authors who felt that the miosis found in typical cases must be explained by interruption of the sympathetic pathways to the iris. This belief is, however, erroneous, as proved by the following facts:

(i) The miosis of Argyll Robertson pupils usually is far more pronounced than that caused by interruption of the cervical sympathetic chain.

(ii) Pupillary reflex dilatation, a predominantly sympathetic reaction (cf. below), often is not abolished and may even be exaggerated; in addition, in many cases the affected pupil dilates well when cocaine is instilled into the conjunctival sac which it would fail to do if the sympathetic pathways to the iris were interrupted. (Fig. 10 C, E.)

(iii) Although the Argyll Robertson pupil fails to dilate in darkness, it dilates readily after conjunctival administration of atropine or other parasympatheticolytic drugs (Fig. 10 D) as long as such dilatation is not prevented by damage to the iris.

These facts make the conclusion imperative that miosis in the Argyll Robertson pupillary syndrome is caused by abnormal cholinergic activity. Such activity is most easily explained by the assumption that the Edinger-Westphal nucleus, deprived of the major portion of its afferent innervation by interruption of the pretectal fibres, close to the nucleus (cf. above) had become hypersensitive to cholinergic substances. Such substances, released from other neural complexes in close proximity to the constrictor nucleus, would stimulate the nucleus which, consequently, would send a constant barrage of impulses via the unimpaired efferent pathways to the iris.

C. PUPILLARY REFLEX DILATATION

Pupillary reflex dilatation has been the subject of more voluminous and bitter controversies than all other pupillary movements. Some of these quar-rels, begun more than a century ago, had their origin in the anatomical disagreement regarding the existence in the iris of a radially contractile dilator pupillæ (cf. pp. 232–233). But even after a settlement of the anatomical question had been achieved, discussions about the functional role of the

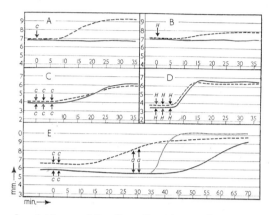

FIG. 10. Normal and Abnormal Pupillary Reactions to Some Drugs (Man). The ordinate represents pupillary diameter (in mm.), the abscissa time (in minutes; note the contraction of the time axis, as compared to the usual pupillograms). The solid lines represent the right, the broken lines the left pupils.

A and B: Normal subject. At the moments marked by the arrows, one drop of cocaine hydrochloride (2%, *c* in A) or of homatropine hydrobromide (2%, *H* in B) was instilled into the left conjunctival sac. The right pupil served as control. Instillation of cocaine caused maximal mydriasis. In contrast, the pupil was only slightly enlarged by homatropine. Since, in darkness, the normal pupillary sphincter had relaxed, the parasympatheticolytic drug could add but little pupillary dilatation.

C and D: Cocaine- and homatropine-tests in a patient with bilateral Argyll Robertson syndrome. Both pupils were dilated by cocaine (3 drops 2%, arrows *c* in C), indicating that their sympathetic innervation was not impaired (cf. below). In contrast to the normal pupil, the Argyll Robertson pupils dilated extensively after instillation of homatropine (3 drops 2%, arrows *H* in D), proving that the miosis, which had persisted in darkness, was cholinergic in nature.

E: Cocaine-adrenaline test in a patient with unilateral damage to the peripheral sympathetic innervation (preganglionic). The normal pupil (broken line) dilated after instillation of cocaine (2 drops 2%, arrows *c*) and failed to respond to the additional application of adrenaline hydrochloride (2 drops 1: 1000, arrows *a*). The pupil on the side of the sympathetic lesion failed to dilate to cocaine (solid line) but did dilate after adrenaline instillation. In cases with complete postganglionic sympathetic lesions the adrenaline reaction is even more pronounced and leads to "paradoxical pupillary dilatation" (dotted line; cf. text, pp. 256–257).

dilator in pupillary reflex dilatation were continued. Most of the more recent polemics were, unfortunately, based upon lack of knowledge, or disregard, of the literature and of established experimental facts. It is to be hoped that the endless repetition of arguments long since exhausted will be discontinued in the future.†

In waking animals and man, sensory or emotional stimuli, and experimental stimulation of various centres in the brain, bring about pupillary reflex dilatation. After a latent period, which varies from 0.2 sec. (cat, monkey) to 0.3–0.5 second (rat, man), the pupils dilate. Among the species examined by us, by far the most dramatic reactions were found in cats, followed, in the order of relative extensiveness, by monkeys, rats, dogs, man, rabbits and guinea-pigs. In birds and frogs, the reactions are much poorer than in mammals and do not follow the same pattern (Fig. 11).

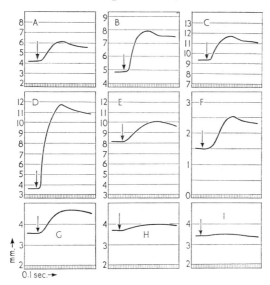

FIG. 11. Pupillary Reflex Dilatation in Normal Man and Some Animals (Fig. 34 of Loewenfeld, 1958). Only one pupil is shown in each pupillogram. Pupillary diameter is recorded as the ordinate (in mm.) against time as the abscissa (in 0.1 second steps). For animals with small eyes, the ordinate of the graph was enlarged, using the ratio of the diameter of the animal's iris to that of man as multiplying factor. The following species are represented: A = man; B = monkey (macaca mulatta); C = dog; D = cat; E = rabbit; F = rat; G = guinea-pig; H = pigeon; I = frog. (Cf. text, pp. 251–253).

In response to a powerful stimulus, the mammalian pupil dilates rapidly and becomes maximally enlarged; it may remain very large for minutes (solid line of Fig. 12). When the dilatation movement is analysed by the method of selective denervation and other experimental procedures, it is found to consist of four factors, two of them due to neural and two to humoral mechanisms.

† The lengthy discussions about this subject are omitted for lack of space. A detailed historical-experimental analysis was published recently (Loewenfeld, 1958).

1. NEURAL MECHANISMS OF PUPILLARY REFLEX DILATATION

The two neural factors that take part in pupillary reflex dilatation are (i) active sympathetic discharges, which reach the dilator pupillæ and cause it to contract (Fig. 12, line of crosses), and (ii) inhibitory impulses, which suppress the activity of the Edinger-Westphal nucleus and thereby cause the sphincter pupillæ to relax (Fig. 12, dotted line).

During general anaesthesia, the active sympathetic component of pupillary reflex dilatation is abolished, and the pupils are dilated by parasympathetic inhibition alone. The mechanism of parasympathetic inhibition has been discussed above (pp. 246–248).

a. Sympathetic Pathway

The peripheral sympathetic path that innervates the dilator pupillæ takes its origin from the cervico-thoracic spinal cord (cf. Fig. 8). Most of the *preganglionic fibres* leave the cord by the ventral roots of the first and second thoracic segments, pass to the first thoracic sympathetic ganglion and continue their uninterrupted course *via* the inferior cervical ganglion, the subclavian ansa of Vieussens, middle cervical ganglion and cervical sympathetic nerve in order to synapse with the cells of the superior cervical ganglion. The *postganglionic fibres* leave the anterior pole of the superior cervical ganglion and accompany the internal carotid artery to its bony canal. They traverse the tympanic cavity, enter the cranial vault and join the Vth nerve near the peripheral end of the Gasserian ganglion. They accompany the ophthalmic branch of the Vth nerve to the orbit where they continue in its nasociliary division. In cats and dogs, all sympathetic fibres bypass the ciliary ganglion and reach the eye by way of the long ciliary nerves. In monkeys, at least some of the fibres take the same course. While it is undecided whether in man and monkeys part of the pupillary dilator fibres traverse the ciliary ganglion, it is certain that they do not enter into synaptic connexions peripheral to the superior cervical ganglion.

b. Reflex Centre

In the early literature (Budge and Waller, 1851) the opinion prevailed that pupillary dilator impulses evoked by sensory stimuli reached the eye directly from the afferent paths in the spinal cord *via* the peripheral sympathetic chain. Later work showed that "Budge's centre" in the cervico-thoracic spinal cord is not the reflex "centre" but only a cell station in the efferent path of the dilatation-reflex.

The *reflex centre* for the active sympathetic component of pupillary reflex dilatation must be situated cephalad to the mid-brain. Transection of the mid-brain at its anterior border causes marked miosis. After such lesions, pupillary dilatation to stimulation of sensory nerves is not abolished entirely, but the remnant responses are incomplete and slow. They are due to inhibition of the oculomotor nucleus since they are not further diminished by peripheral sympathectomy and are abolished when the oculomoter nerve is cut or when the sphincter pupillæ is paralysed by atropine.

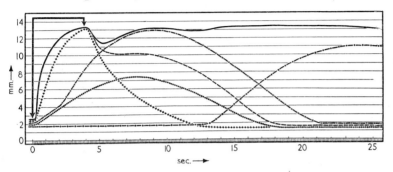

Fig. 12. Mechanisms of Pupillary Dilatation Elicited by Sensory, Psychological or Central Nervous Stimulation (Fig. 61 of Loewenfeld, 1958). Extent and duration of the reactions summarized in this diagram are based on experiments with cats. Pupillary diameter is plotted as the ordinate (in mm.) against time (in seconds). The double-arrow marks the time of stimulation. The solid line represents the response of a normal pupil to a powerful stimulus (cortical, diencephalic or sensory stimuli in waking cats, hypothalamic stimuli in narcotized animals (cf. text, p. 254)). The analysis of this movement reveals the following component mechanisms:

1. Active innervation of the dilatator pupillæ by sympathetic impulses, characterized by relatively fast dilatation and recontraction (line of crosses, cf. pp. 254–256).

2. Inhibition of the oculomotor nucleus, a slower, somewhat longer-lasting movement (dotted line, cf. p. 246).

3. A fast-acting humoral mechanism independent of the adrenal glands (dash-cross line, cf. p. 257).

4. Adrenal epinephrine, arriving at the eye about 9–15 seconds after the start of stimulation (dash-dot line, cf. pp. 256–257).

In response to *strong* stimuli, the humoral factors intensify and prolong the pupillary dilatation movement initiated by the synergistic combination of the two neural mechanisms. In contrast, stimulation by *moderate* stimuli does not appear to evoke the production of humoral substances in sufficient quantity to affect the normal iris (i.e., an iris not rendered hypersensitive by sympathetic denervation), and the normal pupil is dilated by the neural mechanisms alone (broken line). It should be remembered, however, that *normal* blood vessels are at least as sensitive to adrenergic substances as the hypersensitive iris.

Destruction of the thalamus or hypothalamus, likewise, leads to miosis, ptosis and reduction of pupillary reflex dilatation. In contrast, maximal pupillary dilatation can readily be provoked in animals after removal of the entire cerebral cortex or interruption of the cortico-diencephalic connexions.

The reaction threshold to sensory stimulation is reported to become even lower than in the normal animal. All autonomic and somatic functions normally associated with emotional excitement show this hypersensitivity after decortication (Goltz, 1892; Braunstein, 1894; Rothmann, 1923; Cannon and Britton, 1925; Bard, 1929 and later authors). Because of the continued presence of maximal pupillary reflex dilatation after destruction of the cortex it is today widely believed that the sympathetic component of this reaction is transmitted subcortically, i.e., from the thalamus to the efferent centres in the hypothalamus. However, such facts as (i) the early loss of the sympathetic reflex component in anaesthesia, or (ii) the strong sympathetic discharges obtained in normal, awake animals by weak cortical stimulation throw doubt upon this theory. Because of the evident hypersensitivity of the diencephalic centres after decortication, the existence of subcortical transmission in decorticate animals does not furnish conclusive proof that the response is similarly mediated in the intact, awake animal. Under normal conditions, the impulses may run partly or entirely *via* the cortex to the diencephalic efferent centres.

c. Efferent Pathway

The efferent path of sympathetic pupillary dilatation takes its beginning in the ventral diencephalon (Karplus and Kreidl, 1909 and later authors). Since unilateral hypothalamic stimulation with weak currents usually results in bilateral pupillary dilatation, a hemidecussation of the descending pathways must take place somewhere between the hypothalamus and Budge's cilio-spinal centre. The location of this decussation, as well as the precise course of the descending neurone(s) in the lower brain-stem have not yet been demonstrated anatomically in sufficient detail. Within the cervical cord the descending path runs in the lateral and antero-lateral funiculus to the first thoracic segment (Gagel and Foerster).

2. HUMORAL MECHANISMS OF PUPILLARY DILATATION ("PARADOXICAL PUPILLARY DILATATION")

Pupillary reflex dilatation is, then, just as the light-reflex, an integrated movement wherein sympathetic-excitatory and parasympathetic-inhibitory mechanisms coincide. Two additional mechanisms of pupillary dilation remain to be considered.

When the superior cervical ganglion is removed, the pupil on the side of the lesion becomes smaller than the normal one, and pupillary reflex dilatation becomes slow and reduced (Fig. 12, dotted line). During the days following the operation, the miosis of the sympathectomized pupil becomes gradually less marked. When the animal is subjected to physical or emotional stress, the eye on the side of the lesion may show all signs of intense sympathetic irritation. During such reactions, the sympathectomized pupil may become maximally enlarged and it may remain even larger than its normal fellow-pupil for long periods of time. The possible mechanism of this "paradoxical pupillary dilatation" has been discussed since the turn of the century. The phenomenon, as well as similar reactions occurring in other systems, is explained as follows.

In the absence of its normal adrenergic innervation, the dilator pupillae develops an abnormal supersensitivity to adrenergic substances. Sensory or emotional stimulation elicits, reflexly, the liberation of such substances into the blood stream. They are carried to the eye and the hypersensitive denervated dilator pupillae contracts while the normal iris remains unaffected (cf. especially Cannon and Rosenblueth, 1949).

Physical and emotional stress are known to stimulate the adrenal output (Cannon, 1914 and later authors); the paradoxical pupillary response is therefore generally believed to be caused by adrenal epinephrine. But an analysis of the onset, rate and duration of the reactions showed that an additional, faster-acting humoral mechanism exists.

(i) The "paradoxically" increased dilatation movement brought about by the arrival of humoral substances in the iris begins within 2–3 seconds after the start of stimulation, and the reaction seldom requires more than 7 seconds to reach its maximum. When moderate stimuli are used, the responses begin to decline within less than 10 seconds (Fig. 12, dash-cross line). Adrenal epinephrine—as well as substances from all other organs discharging into veins—could not reach the eye in so short a time. Adrenergic substances are known to be liberated when the sympathetic nerves to the heart and the arteries are stimulated. These substances, reflexly poured out in response to sensory or emotional stimulation, are likely to enter the arterial circulation and to cause the paradoxical pupillary response.

(ii) In answer to strong or prolonged sensory or central nervous stimulation, adrenergic substances discharged into veins, such as adrenal epinephrine, reach the eye. Beginning about 8–15 seconds after the start of stimulation, they dilate the pupil and may cause it to remain large for long periods of time (cf. Fig. 12, dash-dot and solid lines).

When we consider the possible physiological importance of the "non-adrenal" and the adrenal humoral mechanisms which are revealed by "paradoxical" pupillary dilatation, we have to bear in mind that the non-adrenal mechanism is elicited in the intact, awake animal by moderate physiological stimuli. In contrast, the adrenal mechanism is brought into play only under conditions of unusually severe or long lasting stress, or upon powerful and prolonged central nervous stimulation. Under the circumstances of every-day life, man and animals are exposed to moderate psycho-sensory stimulation as long as they are awake. In contrast, catastrophic emergency situations which bring the adrenal mechanism into play occur relatively rarely. Therefore, the physiological role of the non-adrenal adrenergic mechanism must be more important than is generally believed today.

D. The Darkness-Reflex

When one or both eyes have been adapted to a given intensity of illumination, a short interruption of this illumination will bring about a darkness-reflex. It should be especially noted that this reaction is not identical with the pupillary *redilatation* that follows the contraction elicited by a short light-stimulus. The conditions differ insofar as, in the case of redilatation, the eye is adapted to darkness and a short flash of light is the stimulus, while in the case of the darkness-reflex the eye is adapted to light, and a short period of darkness is the stimulus. The two movements have different physiological mechanisms.

1. NATURE AND MECHANISM

In Fig. 13A, the solid line shows the normal pupillary reaction to a 1 second interruption of a moderately bright adapting-light. After a latent period of about 0.3–0.4 second the pupil dilates; it contracts and redilates when the darkness "stimulus" comes to an end, i.e., when light is re-admitted.

The normal darkness-reflex is, then, a triphasic movement. Comparison of the normal reaction with the simultaneous response of a sympathectomized pupil allows some insight into the mechanisms at work (Fig. 13A, broken line).

(i) While the eyes are in darkness, the sympathectomized pupil dilates slightly, the normal pupil more extensively (note the difference curve, dotted line of Fig. 13 A″). The dilatation in darkness is therefore due to relaxation of the sphincter pupillae of both eyes plus simultaneous sympathetic activity which reaches the normal iris alone.

(ii) Upon re-admission of light, the sympathectomized pupil's contraction begins slightly faster than that of the normal pupil (note the slight rise in the difference curve); but soon the contraction of the normal pupil catches up with that on the side of the lesion and the difference in size between the two pupils returns to the pre-stimulatory level.

(iii) During pupillary re-dilatation (third phase of the darkness reflex) the two pupils react nearly equally so that no more than the trace of a rise can be seen in the difference curve, although the dilatation movements of the two pupils are at least as extensive as those of the first dilatation phase.

The *efferent mechanism* of the first phase of the darkness reflex is therefore the same as that provoked by all other sensory stimuli with the exception of light, while contraction and redilatation have the same features as the light-reflex.

As to the *afferent mechanism*, the sudden change from light to darkness could be thought to elicit a psycho-sensory response. In normal subjects, however, the first dilatation phase of the darkness-reflex is a more vigorous movement, and more uniform upon repetition, than could be expected to result from a mild psycho-sensory stimulus. Moreover, the extensiveness of the darkness-dilatation is directly related to the intensity of the adapting light. When this light is dim, the dilatation is inextensive or absent while contraction and redilatation are relatively well preserved (Fig. 13B). The sudden change from dim light to darkness is as plainly visible as that from bright light to darkness and it should elicit pupillary dilatation if the mechanism of this movement were psycho-sensory in nature.

a. Electroretinogram

A possible mechanism is suggested by the electroretinogram. As can be seen from the electroretinogram of Fig. 13A′, the darkness-stimulus elicits an "off" response, reappearance of the adapting light an "on" response. If we assume the electrical action potential pattern to parallel a physiological

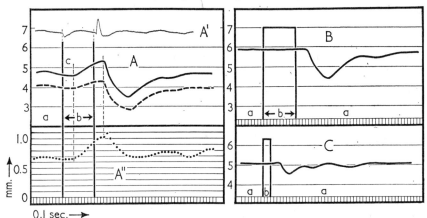

0.1 sec.→

FIG. 13. The Pupillary Reflex to Darkness. *A*: Pupillogram of a patient with left-sided (surgical) interruption of the cervical sympathetic path. At *a*, the eyes were adapted to light of 15 foot-candle intensity. During the period *b*, the light was turned off. The solid line shows the normal triphasic response to the 1-second interruption of the adapting light. During the dark interval, the pupil dilated; upon readmission of light, it contracted and redilated. The broken line represents the simultaneous response of the sympathectomized left pupil, while the dotted line in A″ shows the increasing and decreasing difference between the diameters of the two pupils (ordinate enlarged × 3). The curve A′ shows the normal electroretinogram elicited by a 1-second darkness stimulus (Kawabata, unpublished material; cf. discussion in the text).

B: Normal pupillary response to a 1-second interruption of dim adapting light. Note the large diameter of the pupil during light-adaptation (*a*), the absence of the darkness-dilatation (*b*) and the presence of contraction and redilatation phases.

C: Normal pupillary response to a short (0.23 second) interruption of bright adapting light. The darkness dilatation is missing, while contraction and redilatation appear.

afferent discharge, it is tempting to think that the "off" phenomenon triggers the first dilatation, the "on" response contraction and redilatation of the pupillary darkness-reflex.

The "on" discharge resembles the usual retinal response to stimulation by light, and the corresponding pupillary movement is—both in its appearance and clinically—identical with the light-reflex. The "off" discharge could be thought to be conducted to the inter-brain by one of the diencephalic roots of the optic tract or via other connexions; it would, as other diencephalic stimuli, elicit simultaneous inhibition of the Edinger-Westphal nucleus and sympathetic activation. Since the "on" response is much more vigorous than the "off" wave (Fig. 13A'), it would be easy to understand why the dilatation phase of the darkness-reflex is missing when the adapting light is dim (Fig. 13B) or when the darkness-stimulus is short (less than 0.3 second, Fig. 13C). In the one case, no effective "off" discharge would be generated; in the other, the pupillary dilatation elicited by the "off" reaction would be overpowered by the contraction evoked by the more intense "on" discharge.

E. THE LID-CLOSURE REFLEX

Under this name we group all pupillary movements that occur when the eyelids are closed for a short time either spontaneously, or voluntarily, or as a defensive reaction to various sensory stimuli, especially to stimulation by touch of the cornea or conjunctiva. In view of the diverseness of conditions that bring about closing of the eyelids it is not surprising that the associated pupillary movements vary.

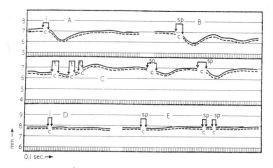

FIG. 14. Pupillary Lid-Closure Reactions (Normal Man). Pupillary diameter was recorded as the ordinate (in mm.) against time as the abscissa (in 0.1 second units), whereby the solid lines represent the right, the broken lines the left pupil. During the intervals c (outlined by double-arrows) the subject's eyes were closed, whereby i denotes intentional and sp apparently spontaneous closing of the lids, while t indicates lid closures elicited by touching the subject's cornea with a strip of paper tissue. During the experiments A, B and C, the eyes were in dim illumination, during the experiments D and E in complete darkness (cf. discussion in the text).

In Fig. 14 A, B and C the pupillary responses usually associated with short lid-closure reactions are shown. When the lid-closure is spontaneous, and often unconscious (sp), or intentional (i), the pupillary reaction consists of a short contraction and redilatation. In birds, who possess a striated pupillary sphincter, the reaction is remarkably fast and extensive. When the lid-closure is elicited by a sensory stimulus such as touching the cornea or conjunctiva (*t*), the pupils dilate. Quite often, this immediate reaction is followed by secondary blinks, which bring about pupillary contractions.

1. MECHANISM

The mechanism of the pupillary movements becomes clear when it is observed that in complete darkness spontaneous and intentional lid-closure reactions no longer affect the pupil (Fig. 14 D,E) while the lid-closure reactions due to sensory stimulation continue to be accompanied by pupillary dilatation. The contractions are, then, simply the pupillary response to the short darkness-stimulus brought about by the lid-closure. In the previous section the occurrence of pupillary contraction upon short interruptions of the illumination has been shown. The pupillary dilatation associated with the reactive lid-closure, on the other hand, is identical with psycho-sensory reflex dilatation elicited by other forms of sensory stimulation.

In any given lid-closure reaction, pupillary contraction or pupillary dilatation will result according to (i) the intensity of the psycho-sensory stimulus and of the illumination present during the examination and (ii) the duration of the lid-closure. When observed in light, longer intentional closing of the eyes (more than 0.3 second) will give rise to the dilatation phase of the darkness-reflex; *short* intentional or reactive lid-closures will dilate the pupils when they are accompanied by an emotional response and will contract them in the absence of a psycho-sensory reaction.

The literature abounds in erroneous descriptions and misconceptions about pupillary lid-closure reactions. For example, it is often stated that unilateral corneal stimulation will lead to predominantly or exclusively homolateral pupillary contraction ("oculo-sensory" or "trigeminal" reflex). In normal man, however, the two pupils *always* react in unison—at least as long as the stimulus is not intense enough to cause inflammatory reactions. It is true that in rabbits pupillary contraction can be elicited by stimulating the fifth nerve; but this phenomenon is not related to normal pupillary movements because it is not found in other mammals and is peculiar in many ways (Loewenfeld, 1958, p. 279).

Similarly, the "Piltz-Westphal phenomenon" was found to be caused by an experimental error. When a subject's eye is held open and he is instructed to attempt to close it forcibly, the pupils usually constrict (Westphal, 1899; Piltz, 1899). When the subject, however, is cautioned to continue, at all times during the reaction, to look at a far point, the pupillary contraction does not occur. The pupillary reaction therefore accompanied an involuntary and unconscious accomodative effort during the forced lid-closure, i.e., it was a near-vision reaction and not a distinct pupillary phenomenon.

F. "PUPILLARY UNREST" AND "HIPPUS"

It has been mentioned before that the pupil, when observed in diffuse light, is always found to be in activity. These movements, described under the names of *"pupillary unrest"* or, when more marked, of *"hippus"* have been discussed a great deal. Their absence as well as their presence were claimed to be indicative of various diseases. The movements were thought to be due to:

(i) spontaneous contractions of the sphincter pupillae, dependent or independent of its nerve supply;

(ii) changes in the blood vessels of the iris that were thought to be related to the pulse and/or respiration;

(iii) psycho-sensory stimuli.

The descriptions of these pupillary movements vary remarkably. To some authors they may appear as small, relatively regular oscillations; to others as slow, extensive, irregularly "jumping" waves of contraction and dilatation; to yet others as tortuous waves of contraction which, involving only part of the sphincter pupillae, creep around the pupillary circumference and cause slight, constantly varying changes in the shape of the pupil.

1. NATURE OF THE MOVEMENTS

When the pupillary movements are recorded, the following facts are revealed:

(i) Spontaneous, dynamic changes in pupillary shape do not occur normally. They are found in rare clinical cases with irritation or damage to a single long or short ciliary nerve, or with injury to small segments of the iris.

(ii) Neither pulse nor respiration has a direct influence upon the pupil. When pulse, respiration and pupillary oscillations are recorded simultaneously, no coincidence is found in timing of pulse and respiratory cycle on the one hand and pupillary movements on the other.

(iii) In darkness, the pupils of normal, alert subjects are usually large and show only few and shallow oscillations. However, when the subject is tired, large (up to several millimetres), relatively slow, irregular waves of pupillary contraction and dilatation accompany the waves of drowsiness and awakening of the individual.

(iv) When the eyes are exposed to long-lasting light-stimulation, the pupils contract, then redilate partially and begin to oscillate (cf. Fig. 2E). When the light is dim, the pupil may become as large and quiet as it was in darkness; with increasing area and intensity of the light, the mean diameter of the pupil will remain smaller, the rate of oscillations faster (maximally about 2 per second). To our knowledge, these movements continue indefinitely. Their mechanism is, to date, unknown. They are found in all normal subjects and are reduced or absent only (*a*) when the afferent or efferent path of the light reflex is impaired or (*b*) in the presence of spastic miosis.

(v) In all normal subjects, all the pupillary movements described are symmetrical on the two sides.

The last two sub-sections (E and F) may serve as examples of how inadequate observations of pupillary phenomena, combined with the confusion generated by a voluminous literature, have given rise to many misconceptions concerning the pupil. It is hoped that with the aid of modern, precise instruments for registration of pupillary size and movements the old misconceptions will gradually be replaced by a clearer understanding of pupillary mechanisms, so that full use can be made of the pupil as an exquisitely sensitive and accurate indicator of autonomic nervous events, both for research in neurology, ophthalmology, pharmacology, physiology, internal medicine, psychiatry and psychology, and, clinically, for the detection and localization of lesions in the brain-stem or in the afferent or efferent pathways of pupillary control.

References

A. REFERENCES CITED

Abelsdorff, G. (1900) Die Änderungen der Pupillenweite durch verschiedenfarbige Belichtung. *Z. Psychol. Sinnesorg.* **22**, 81–95.

Anderson, H. K. (1902). Effect on the pupil of excision of the ciliary ganglion. *Proc. Physiol. Soc.* May 10; *J. Physiol.* **28** (1902), XV.

Bard, P. (1928). A diencephalic mechanism for the expression of rage, with special reference to the sympathetic nervous system. *Amer. J. Physiol.* **84**, 490–515.

Bard, P. (1929). The central representation of the sympathetic system. *Arch. Neurol. Psychiat., Chicago.* **22**, 230–246.

Bender, M. B., and Weinstein, E. A. (1943). Functional representation in the oculomotor and trochlear nuclei. *Arch. Neurol. Psychiat., Chicago* **49**, 98–106.

Braunstein, E. P. (1894). " Zur Lehre von der Innervation der Pupillenbewegungen". Bergmann, Wiesbaden.

Budge, J., and Waller, A. (1851). Recherches sur le système nerveux. 1° partie. Action de la partie cervicale du nerf grand sympathique et d'une portion de la moelle épinière sur la dilatation de la pupille. *C.R. Acad. Sci.* **33**, 370–374.

Cannon, W. B. (1914). The emergency function of the adrenal medulla in pain and the major emotions. *Amer. J. Physiol.* **33**, 356–372.

Cannon, W. B., and Britton, S. W. (1925). Studies on the conditions of activity in endocrine glands. XV. Pseudoaffective medulladrenal secretion. *Amer. J. Physiol.* **72**, 283–294.

Cannon, W. B., and Rosenblueth, A. (1949). " The supersensitivity of denervated structures; a law of denervation". Macmillan, New York.

Engelking, E. (1919). Der Schwellenwert der Pupillenreaktion und seine Beziehungen zum Problem der pupillomotorischen Aufnahmerogane *Z. Sinnesphysiol.* **50**, 319–337.

Fuchs, E. (1885). Beiträge zur normalen Anatomie der menschlichen Iris. *v. Graefes Arch. Ophthal.* **31**, 3, 39–86.

Goltz, F. (1892). "Der Hund ohne Grosshirn". *Pflüg. Arch. ges. Physiol.* **51**, 570–614.

Grünhagen, A. (1863–93). 23 publications. *cf.* Loewenfeld, I. E. *Docum. Ophthal.* **12** (1958).

Harms, H. (1949). Grundlagen, Methodik und Bedeutung der Pupillenperimetrie. *v. Graefes Arch. Ophthal.* **149**, 1–66.

Harris, A. L., Hodes, M. C. R., and Magoun, H. W. (1944). The afferent path of the pupillodilator reflex in the cat. *J. Neurophysiol.* **7**, 231–244.

Henle, J. (1866). "Handbuch der systematischen Anatomie des Menschen. Vol. II: Eingeweidelehre". Braunschweig, Fr. Vieweg and Sohn, 634; qu. after Grunert and after 20 Ed. (1873), 661–662.

Hensen, V., and Völckers, C. (1878). Über den Ursprung der Accomodationsnerven, nebst Bemerkungen über die Funktion der Wurzeln des Nervus Oculomotorius. *v. Graefes Arch. Ophthal.* **24**, 1–26.

Hess, C. v. (1907). Untersuchungen über die Ausdehnung des pupillomotorisch wirksamen Bezirkes der Netzhaut und über die pupillomotorischen Aufnahmeorgane. *Arch. Augenheilk.* **58**, 182–205.

Hess, C. v. (1908). Zur Physiologie und Pathologie des Pupillenspieles. *Arch. Augenheilk.* **60**, 327–389.

Karplus, J. P., and Kreidl, A. (1909). Gehirn und Sympathicus. I. Mitt.; Zwischenhirn und Halssympathicus. *Pflüg. Arch. ges. Physiol.* **129**, 138–144.

Kawabata, H. (1960). Unpublished material.

Klinge, E. (1908). Die inneren Irisschichten der Haussäugetiere. Inaug. Diss Zürich and *Anat. Hefte* (1908), Abt. I, **36**, 601–710.

Langley, J. N., and Anderson, H. K. (1892). The action of nicotin on the ciliary ganglion and on the endings of the third cranial nerve. *J. Physiol.* **13**, 460–468.

Loewenfeld, I. E. (1958). Mechanisms of reflex dilatation of the pupil. Historical review and experimental analysis. *Docum. ophthal.* **12**, 185–448.

Lowenstein, O. (1937). "Der psychische Restitutionseffekt. Das Prinzip der psychisch bedingten Wiederherstellung der ermüdeten, der erschöpften und der erkrankten Funktion". Benno Schwabe, Basel.

Lowenstein, O. (1954). Alternating Contraction Anisocoria. A pupillary syndrome of the anterior midbrain. *Arch. Neurol. Psychiat. Chicago.* **72**, 742–757.

Lowenstein, O. (1955). Benign postinfectious disorder of anterior midbrain. *Arch. Neurol. Psychiat., Chicago.* **73**, 302–308.

Lowenstein, O. (1956). The Argyll Robertson Pupillary Syndrome. Mechanism and localization. *Amer. J. Ophthal.* **42**, No. 4 Pt. II, 105–121.

Lowenstein, O., and Loewenfeld, I. E. (1950). Mutual role of sympathetic and parasympathetic in shaping of the pupillary reflex to light. *Arch. Neurol. Psychiat., Chicago.* **64**, 341–377.

Lowenstein, O., and Loewenfeld, I. E. (1951). Types of autonomic innervation and fatigue. *Arch. Neurol. Psychiat., Chicago.* **66**, 580–599.

Lowenstein, O., and Loewenfeld, I. E. (1952). Disintegration of central autonomic regulation during fatigue and its reintegration by psychosensory controlling mechanisms. *J. nerv. ment. Disease.* **115**, 1–21; 121–145.

Lowenstein, O., and Loewenfeld, I. E. (1958). Electronic Pupillography. A new instrument and some clinical applications. *Arch. Ophthal. N.Y.* **59**, 352–363.

Lowenstein, O., and Loewenfeld, I. E. (1959). Scotopic and photopic thresholds of the pupillary light reflex in normal man. *Amer. J. Ophthal.* **48**, No. 1, Pt. II 87–98.

Magitot, A. (1946). "Physiologie oculaire clinique". Paris, Masson et Cie., 181.

Magoun, H. W., and Ranson, S. W. (1935). The afferent path of the light reflex. A review of the literature. *Arch. Ophthal. N.Y.* **13**, 862–874.

Piltz, J. (1899). Über neue Pupillenphenomene. *Neurol. Zbl.*, 248–261.

Polyak, St. (1957). "The Vertebrate Visual System". University Chicago Press, pp. 376–385.

Robertson, A. (1869). Four cases of spinal miosis; with remarks on the action of light on the pupil. *Edinb. med. J.* **15**, Pt. I, 487–493.

Rothmann, H. (1923). Zusammenfassender Bericht über den Rothmann'schen grosshirnlosen Hund, nach klinischer und anatomischer Untersuchung. *Zeitschr. f. d. ges. Neurol. & Psychiat.* **87**, 247–313.

Scheie, H. (1940). Site of disturbance in Adie's syndrome. *Arch. Ophthal. N.Y.* **24**, 555–581.

Schweitzer, N. M. J. (1955–56). Threshold measurements on the light reflex of the pupil in the dark adapted eye. (Thesis 1955: W. Junk, s' Gravenhage); also *Docum. ophthal.* **10**, 1–78 (1956).

Szentágothai, J. (1942). Die zentrale Leitungsbahn des Lichtreflexes der Pupille. *Arch. Psychiat. Nervenkr.* **115**, 136–155.

Westphal, A. (1899). Über ein bisher nicht beschriebenes Pupillenphänomen. *Neurol. Zbl.* **18**, 161–164.

B. GENERAL REFERENCES

Adie, W. J. (1932). Complete and incomplete forms of the benign disorder characterized by tonic pupils and absent tendon reflexes. *Brit. J. Ophthal.* **16**, 449–461.

Adler, F. H. (1953). "Physiology of the Eye". 2nd edition. Mosby, St Louis.

Anderson, H. K. (1903–5). The paralysis of involuntary muscle. Part I, *J. Phsyiol.* **30**, 290–310; Part II, *J. Physiol.* **33**, 156–174.

Bach, L. (1908). "Pupillenlehre. Anatomie, Physiologie und Pathologie. Methodik der Untersuchung". Karger, Berlin.

Barris, R. W. (1932). A pupillo-constrictor area in the cerebral cortex of the cat and its relationship to the pretectal area. *J. comp. Neurol.* **63**, 353–368.

Behr, C. (1924). Die Lehre von den Pupillenbewegungen. *In* "Handb. d. ges. Augenheilk". (Graefe-Saemisch). Springer, Berlin.

Behr, C. (1930). Der Anteil der beiden Antagonisten an der Pupillenbewegung bei den verschiedenen Reaktionen. v. *Graefes Arch. Ophthal.* **125**, 147–155 and **130**, 411–426.

Braunstein, E. P. (1925). Elektrische Aktionsströme der Iris. *Klin. Wschr.* **4**, 302–306.

Bremer, F. (1935). Cerveau "isolé" et physiologie du sommeil. *C.R. Soc. Bicl., Paris* **118**, 1235–1241.

Brown-Séquard, E. (1859). Recherches expérimentales sur l'influence excitatrice de la lumière, du froid et de la chaleur sur l'iris, dans les cinq classes d'animaux vertébrés. *J. de la Physiol.* (*Brown-Séquard*). **2**, 281–294; 451–460.

Budge, J. (1855). "Über die Bewegung der Iris, für Physiologen und Ärzte". Fr. Vieweg & Sohn, Braunschweig.

Bumke, O., and Trendlenburg, W. (1911). Beiträge zur Kenntnis der Pupillarreflexbahnen. *Klin. Mbl. Augenheilk.* **12** (Vol. 49), 145–150.

Clark, W. E. LeGros, and Meyer, M. (1950). Anatomical relationships between the cerebral cortex and the hypothalamus. *Brit. med. Bull.* **6**, 341–345.

Dale, H. H., and Laidlaw, P. P. (1912). The significance of the supra-renal capsules in the action of certain alkaloids. *J. Physiol.* **45**, 1–26.

Dogiel, J. (1886). Neue Untersuchungen über den pupillenerweiternden Muskel der Säugethiere und Vögel. *Arch. mikr. Anat.* **27**, 403–409.

9

Donders, F. C. (1864). "On the anomalies of accommodation and refraction of the eye". The new Sydenham Soc., London, Vol. 22 (cf. especially Chapter X).

Duke-Elder, W. S. (1933–1944). "Textbook of Ophthalmology", Vol. 1, 65–74; 417–418; 557–558; 561; Vol. 4, 3731–3805. Mosby, St. Louis.

Einthoven, Hoogerwerf, Karplus, J. P., and Kreidl. A. (1926–27). A: Die Aktionsströme des Halssympathicus. B: Hypothalamuserregung und Aktionsströme des Halssympathicus. *Pflüg. Arch. ges. Physiol.* **215**, 443–447; 447–452.

Eisler, P. (1930). Die Anatomie des menschlichen Auges. *In* "Schieck & Brückner's Handb. Ophthal". Springer, Berlin, 79–100.

Forsmarck, E. (1905). Zur Kenntnis der Irismuskulatur des Menschen; ihr Bau und ihre Entwicklung. *Mitt. Augenkl. Stockh.* **7**, 1–106.

Gabriélidès, A. J. (1895). Recherches sur l'embryogénie et l'anatomie comparée de l'angle de la chambre antérieure chez le poulet et chez l'homme. Muscle dilatateur de la pupille. Thèse de Paris; also *Arch. Ophthal., Paris* (1895), 176–193.

Gaskell, W. H. (1916). "The involuntary nervous system". Longmans, Green & Co., London.

Grunert, K. (1898). Der dilatator pupillae des Menschen, ein Beitrage zur Anatomie und Physiologie der Irismuskulatur. *Arch. Augenheilk.* **36**, 319–368.

Grynfeltt, Ed. (1899). Le muscle dilatateur de la pupille chez les mammifères. *Ann. Oculist., Paris,* **121**, 331–350.

Heerfordt, Chr. F. (1900). Studien uber den Musc. dilatator pupillae samt Angabe von gemeintschaftlichen Kennzeichen einiger Fälle epithelialer Muskulatur. *Arb. anat. Inst., Wiesbaden* **14**, 487–558 and **15**, 721.

Herzog, H. (1902). Über die Entwicklung der Binnenmuskulatur des Auges. *Ber. ophth. Ges. Heidelberg* **30**, 300–318; also *Arch. mikr. Anat.* **60**, 517, and *Z. Augenheilk.* (1901) **7**, 47–53.

Hess, W. R. (1939). Pupille und Zwischenhirn. *Klin. Mbl. Augenheilk.* **103**, 407–413.

Hess, W. R. (1947). Vegetative Funktion und Zwischenhirn. *Helv. physiol. acta,* Suppl. IV.

Hunter, J., and Jasper, H. H. (1949). Effects of thalamic stimulation in unanaesthetized animals. *Electroenceph. clin. Neurophysiol.* **1**, 305–324.

Ingram, W. R., Ranson, S. W., and Hannett, F. I. (1931). Pupillary dilatation produced by direct stimulation of the tegmentum of the brain stem. *Amer. J. Physiol.* **98**, 687–691.

Kowalewsky, N. (1886). Influence du système nerveux sur la dilatation de la pupille (Recherches critiques et expérimentales). *Arch. slaves Biol.* **1**, 92–121; 575–600.

Langendorff, O. (1900). Zur Deutung der "paradoxen" Pupillenerweiterung. *Klin. Mbl. Augenheilk.* **38**, 823–827.

Langley, J. N. (1892). On the origin from the spinal cord of the upper and thoracic sympathetic fibers, with some observations on the white and the grey rami communicantes. *Phil. Trans.,* 85–124.

Langley, J. N., and Anderson, H. K. (1892). On the mechanism of the movements of the iris. *J. Physiol.* **13**, 554–597.

Langley, J. N., and Dickinson, L. (1889). On the local paralysis of peripheral ganglia, and on the connexion of different classes of nerve fibres with them. *Proc. roy. Soc.* **46**, 423–431.

Levinsohn, G. (1902). Über die Beziehungen zwischen Grosshirnrinde und Pupille. *Z. Augenheilk.* **8**, 518–538.

Lewandowsky, M. (1899). Über die Wirkung des Nebennierenextraktes auf die glatten Muskeln, im Besonderen des Auges. *Arch. Anat. Physiol., Lpz.,* 360–366.

Lowenstein, O. (1956). Miosis in the Argyll Robertson Syndrome and Related Pupillary Disorders. *Arch. Ophthal., N.Y.* **55**, 356–370.

Lowenstein, O., and Loewenfeld, I. E. (1959). Influence of retinal adaptation upon the pupillary reflex to light in normal man. *Amer. J. Ophthal.* **48**, Pt. II, 536–549.

Lowenstein, O., Murphy, S. B., and Loewenfeld, I. E. (1953). Functional evaluation of the pupillary light reflex pathways. Experimental pupillographic studies in cats. *Arch. Ophthal., N.Y.* **49**, 656–670.

Magitot, A. (1921). "L'iris. Étude physiologique sur la pupille et ses centres moteurs". Doin, Paris.

Morone, G. (1959). "La pupilla". Soc. Oftal. Ital. (Soc. Ed. "Idea"), Rome.

Nawrocki, F., and Przybylski, J. (1891). Die pupillenerweiternden Nerven der Katze. *Pflüg. Arch. ges. Physiol.* **50**, 234–277.

Nussbaum, M. (1901). Die Entwicklung der Binnenmuskeln des Auges der Wirbelthiere. *Arch. mikr. Anat.* **58**, 199–230.

Parsons, J. H. (1904). The innervation of the pupil. *Roy. ophthal. Hosp. Rep.*, 20–61.

Redslob, M. E. (1928). Sur l'appareil dilatateur de l'iris. *Bull. Soc. franç. Ophtal.* **41**, 3–13.

Sachs, E., and Heath, P. (1940). The pharmacologic behavior of the intraocular muscles. *Amer. J. Ophthal.* **23**, 1199–1209; 1376–1387.

Salzmann, M. (1912). "Anatomie und Histologie des menschlichen Augapfels" (translated by E. V. L. Brown: "The anatomy and physiology of the human eyeball in the normal state"). Univ. Chicago Press.

Schultz, P. (1898). Über die Wirkungsweise der Mydriatica und Miotica. *Arch. Anat. Physiol.*, 47–74.

Spiegel, E. A., and Sommer, I. (1944). "Neurology of the eye, ear, nose and throat." Grune & Stratton, N.Y.

Stavraky, G. W. (1936). Responses of cerebral blood vessels to electric stimulation of the thalamus and hypothalamic regions. *Arch. Neurol. Psychiat., Chicago* **35**, 1002–1028.

Stiles, W. S., and Crawford, B. H. (1933). The luminous efficiency of rays entering the eye pupil at different points. *Proc. roy. Soc.* **112B**, 428–450.

Stotler, W. A. (1937). Innervation of the intrinsic muscles of the eye: an experimental study. *Proc. Soc. exp. Biol. N.Y.* **36**, 576–577.

Straub, H. (1910). Die Wirkung von Adrenalin in ihrer Beziehung zur Innervation der Iris und zur Funktion des Ganglion cervicale superius. *Pflüg. Arch. ges. Physiol.* **134**, 15–30.

Szily, A. v., Jr. (1902). Beitrag zur Kenntnis der Anatomie und Entwicklungsgeschichte der hinteren Irisschichten, mit besonderer Berücksichtigung des Musculus sphincter pupillae des Menschen. *v. Graefes Arch. Ophthal.* **53**, 459–498.

Wagman, I. H., and Gulberg, J. E. (1942). The relationship between monochromatic light and pupil diameter. The low intensity visibility curve as measured by pupillary movements. *Amer. J. Physiol.* **137**, 769–778.

Walsh, F. B. (1957). "Clinical Neuro-Ophthalmology". Williams & Wilkins, Baltimore.

Ward, A. A., Jr., and Reed, H. L. (1946). Mechanism of pupillary dilatation elicited by cortical stimulation. *J. Neurophysiol.* **9**, 329–335.

Wolfrum, M. (1931). Mikroskopische Anatomie des Uvealtraktes. I. Die Anatomie der Regenbogenhaut. *In* "Handb. ges. Augenheilk". (Graefe-Saemisch), Vol. 1, abt. 2, Kap. III, 1–218.

PART III

Secretion of Tears and Blinking

by

WILLIAM K. MCEWEN

Francis I. Proctor Foundation for Research in Ophthalmology, University of California San Francisco Medical Center, San Francisco, California, U.S.A.

CHAPTER 10

Secretion of Tears and Blinking

I. Introductory Remarks on Protective Mechanisms

Blinking and producing tears are often considered primarily as protective mechanisms to guard the eye against injury. It is obvious that these mechanisms play a part in protecting the eye. Objects small enough to pass the bony structure surrounding the eye are often stopped by the quick closure of the lids. Particles too small to initiate the blink reflex and to be stopped by the lids find themselves entrapped in the tear-fluid and washed away. Because of man's predominant reliance on sight in his daily life, there is a desire to protect this most valuable sense organ. This naturally leads to interpreting the mechanisms of tear production and blinking primarily as protective in nature.

The emphasis on protection tends to obscure the fundamental physiology of these mechanisms. Since the survival of an animal is based on its ability to make valid interpretations of its sensory signals and, in response, to act in a manner useful to its well-being, emphasis should be placed on the more positive interpretation of tear production and blinking as the means of keeping the eye functionally active. Tears and blinks are co-ordinated to maintain corneal integrity. Tears are necessary to keep the cornea and conjunctiva moist and to provide the metabolic needs of the epithelial surface of the cornea.

The lids act to distribute the tear-fluid over the eye and to provide an optically smooth surface over the cornea.

The true purpose of a mechanism cannot be determined at the present level of our knowledge. The particular viewpoint held by an investigator is usually a reflexion of his own feelings and orientation. As an illustration, Williams and Hecht (1955) describe a transparent window in each lower eyelid of a lizard and suggest that these windows act as "sunglasses" to protect the lizard's eyes from strong sunlight. Erickson *et al.* (1956) feel that conservation of moisture may be an equally valid "purpose" of such a device. Other examples may be given of divergent but equally valid viewpoints. In this chapter, maintenance of corneal integrity by tear production and blinking will be the particular viewpoint.

Material integrated from the classical texts cited under General References is given without specific reference being made to them.

II. Anatomical Aspects of Tear Secretion

The mucomembranous surface of the eyes of all animals living out of water is subjected to the drying effect of air. The loss of moisture is replenished by the secretion of glands. In animals the amount of fluid secreted is little more than is necessary to accomplish this purpose and only rarely does the amount secreted exceed the drainage capacity of the lacrimal passages. In man there is the added ability to weep, or lacrimate, which is an excessive outpouring of the lacrimal gland. Although this is an obvious and dramatic action it is not of great physiological significance to the normal eye. Montagu (1959) contends that natural selection favoured those infants who could produce tears and avoid the desiccation of nasal mucosa caused by rapid inspiration and expiration during crying episodes.

A. Lacrimal Apparatus

Tear-fluid is a mixture of the secretions of several glands. The fluid is conveyed mechanically by the lids across the surface of the eye and is normally drained away via the lacrimal passages. These mechanisms of secretion, distribution and outflow are usually described under the term lacrimal apparatus.

1. secretion

The glands whose secretions make up the tear-fluid are the lacrimal gland, the accessory glands of Krause and Wolfring (Ciaccio) and the goblet cells of the conjunctiva. Part of the secretion of the meibomian glands is found in tear-fluid as the oily outer layer of the precorneal tear-film (p. 272).

a. The Lacrimal Gland

This is a slightly pinkish tubuloracemose or tubular alveolar structure about 1 gramme in weight. The basement membrane of the acini is lined with a layer of short columnar secretory cells similar to the cells of the parotid gland. Secretory capillaries connect these cells and are themselves lined with either one or two layers of secretory cells depending on the size of the duct. In addition the ducts have myo-epithelial cells. The intermediate ducts

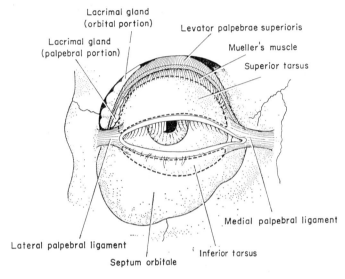

Lacrimal gland
(orbital portion)

Levator palpebrae superioris

Lacrimal gland
(palpebral portion)

Mueller's muscle

Superior tarsus

Medial palpebral ligament

Lateral palpebral ligament

Inferior tarsus

Septum orbitale

FIG. 1.

converge, not into a single large excretory canal, but instead empty into the upper fornix by means of from ten to twelve individual ducts. Occasionally one or two ducts may open into the lower fornix. The secretory cells contain the usual complement of enzymes (Kato, 1958). They also contain granules and fat droplets which tend to disappear during activity. These changes have been observed in the electron-microscope by Kobayashi (1958).

The lacrimal gland is placed superiorly and temporally in relation to the globe. It rests in a bony fossa in the roof of the orbit. Posteriorly it connects with orbital fat as far back as the posterior pole of the eye. Inferiorly it rests successively, from front to back, on the globe, and both on the palpebral muscle and on the external rectus. Anteriorly the extension of the levator in a groove across the gland appears to divide it into two portions. The superior or orbital portion is about twice the size of the inferior or palpebral portion. The palpebral part can be seen under the conjunctiva when the lid is everted. The ducts from the orbital part are intermingled with the palpebral

9*

portion so that extirpation of the inferior part of the gland practically destroys all ducts and is equivalent to total extirpation (see Fig. 1).

Blood is supplied to the gland by the lacrimal artery (a branch of the ophthalmic) and occasionally by a branch of the infra-orbital artery. A study of the distribution of the blood supply in the lacrimal gland was made by Parvis (1950). Venous return is by the lacrimal vein, a branch of the superior ophthalmic vein.

The nerves supplying the lacrimal gland will be discussed under the neural mechanisms of lacrimation and weeping.

b. The Accessory Glands

The accessory glands of Krause and of Wolfring (Ciaccio) are similar to, but much less developed than, the lacrimal gland (see Fig. 2). The glands of Krause are considered as a downward extension of the lacrimal gland. The glands of Wolfring lie further down on the lid. Secretions from these glands contribute to the composition of the tear-fluid.

c. The Conjunctival Goblet Cells

These cells are unicellular mucous glands found throughout the conjunctiva, particularly in the fornices. They are believed to be formed from the cylindrical cells of the conjunctiva. They enlarge as they pass toward the surface, discharge their contents and are destroyed (holocrine secretion). The secretion is mucinous and mixes with the tear-fluid secreted by the other glands.

2. DISTRIBUTION

The fluids secreted by the glands are elaborated at point sources distributed non-uniformly throughout the conjunctiva. If left to gravity alone very little fluid would reach the cornea. The lids mix and distribute the fluid so as to form an optically smooth liquid film over the cornea.

The conjunctival surface is a mucous membrane and as such is readily wet by water and watery secretions. The proteins in tear-fluid tend to lower the surface tension of water and cause it to spread more easily, but this effect is probably small in relation to the fundamental ease of wetting of the mucous membrane. The main site of mixing and distribution is along the tear-strips, which are concave cylindrical accumulations of fluid along the lid margins. This concave appearance is due to the wetting of the slightly separated orbital and palpebral conjunctival surfaces and is similar to the meniscus in a pipette. Here the liquid is confined by the oily secretion of the meibomian glands. Part of this meibomian secretion flows over the watery layer and is recognized in the slit lamp as the very thin outer layer of the precorneal tear-film. It is thought by Wolff (1954) that this oil-film on the surface of the watery layer retards evaporation.

The fluid is now distributed uniformly in a horizontal plane. There is a union between the fluids in the upper and lower fornices at the lacrimal lake and the outer canthus. Distribution in a vertical plane is accomplished by movement of the lids. Blinking lays down a thin layer over the palpebral

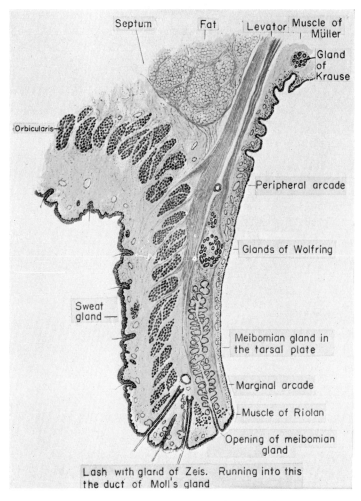

FIG. 2. Reproduced by permission from Wolff (1954).

opening. There is probably very little "squeegee" (i.e., wiping or polishing) action by the lids. Movement of the lids further mixes the components of the fluid, and contraction of the orbiculus orbicularis tends to move the tears along nasally.

When the lids distribute the tear-fluid over the surface of the eye, the secretions of the glands are not intimately mixed but appear by slit-lamp observation to be in layers. Wolff (1954) describes this precorneal film as a layered structure. The outermost layer is the thin oil-film from the meibomian glands as mentioned above. Next deepest is a watery layer of the lacrimal and accessory gland secretions. Innermost and lying directly over the cornea and conjunctiva is a mucinous layer derived from the goblet cells of the conjunctiva.

3. OUTFLOW

Four structures conduct the tears from the marginal tear-strips on the lids to the nose. These are designated as *puncta, canaliculi, lacrimal sac* and

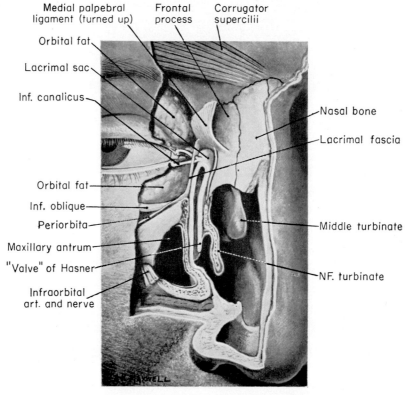

FIG. 3. Reproduced by permission from Wolff (1954).

nasolacrimal duct (see Fig. 3). The conjunctival membrane is continuous throughout. Many different viewpoints exist regarding the mechanism by which the fluid passes along these structures. Gravity, capillarity, siphoning and muscular action causing either a peristaltic action or a pump (suction) action have all been considered. The anatomy of the structures will first be described and then the various mechanisms of conduction of the fluid will be discussed.

a. The Puncta

The puncta are slightly raised papillae in the lid margins in line with the meibomian glands. They are found about 1 mm. nasal to the termination of the meibomian gland line. The upper and lower ones do not approximate upon lid-closure as the upper punctum is slightly nasal to the lower. The puncta are surrounded with avascular connective tissue which keeps them open and gives the papillae a whitish appearance. The puncta accept fluid from the marginal tear-strips and empty into the canaliculi.

b. The Canaliculi

The canaliculi have a short vertical path of about 2 mm., then turn a right-angle and pass nasally in the lid margins for a distance of from 7 to 8 mm. to empty independently in the lacrimal sac. The diameter of the tube is about $\frac{1}{2}$ mm. with a slight dilatation, or ampulla, at the bend. The canaliculi are composed of elastic tissue and are surrounded by the orbicularis muscle except anteriorly where it connects with the medial palpebral ligament.

c. The Lacrimal Sac

This is a membranous tube lodged vertically in the lacrimal fossa. The upper end is closed off and the lower end is demarcated by a slight constriction as it passes into the nasolacrimal duct. It is 4 to 8 mm. wide in a collapsed state and about 12 mm. long. Behind the sac are the lacrimal fascia and Horner's muscle. Anteriorly the medial palpebral ligament covers the upper part while the lower part is crossed by only a few fibres of the orbicularis.

d. The Nasolacrimal Duct

This duct is a continuation of the lacrimal sac for about 10 mm. in a bony lacrimal canal and then for another 5 mm. to empty into the inferior meatus of the nose. This mucomembranous tube has a fibro-elastic stroma and a double layer of epithelial cells. The stroma contains an exceptionally rich venous plexus which may dilate sufficiently to close the duct. Folds in the epithelium of the naso-lacrimal duct have been postulated as having a valve-like action.

e. The Mechanism of Outflow

The mechanism of outflow of tears along the lacrimal passages has been a problem for two hundred years. The difficulty lies in identifying the force or forces necessary to move the tear-fluid from the lacrimal lake into the nose. Several forces which might supply the needed pressure have been postulated.

Capillarity was first suggested by Molinelli (1773). Capillary force is a function of the surface tension of a liquid and only exists when there is an interface or an exposed surface of a liquid. This force may be postulated for getting the tears into the canaliculi but it will not promote flow. Another force is needed to move the liquid along.

Gravity is unavailable as a means of promoting flow. The hydrostatic pressure of fluid at the puncta is lower than at the opening of the canaliculi into the lacrimal sac. This can be shown anatomically. Siphoning is possible if the lacrimal sac is filled with fluid to a point below the level of the puncta. This force is easily disrupted if air gets into the "line" and siphoning can only be re-established by application of another force.

Some sort of pumping force appears necessary either in conjunction with capillarity and siphoning or alone in order to promote outflow of tears. von Arlt (1855) was one of the first to suggest a pump mechanism.

There is a minor distinction between two different types of pump action. Muscular action can cause a muscular ripple which results in a milking or peristaltic action, the pressures changing from atmospheric to positive pressures. Muscular action can also cause a dilatation of a structure with pressures varying from atmospheric to less than atmospheric. This suction action must make use of the "valves" in the lacrimal sac and the naso-lacrimal duct.

Apart from this distinction, the main unknown is the locus of action of the pump. Freiberg (1951) believes that the canaliculi and the lacrimal sac are involved and that muscular action of the fibres of the orbicularis produces a suction action. Nagashima (1954, 1958a, b) using manometry to measure the pressure changes, feels that lid movement causes peristaltic action in the sac and ducts. Jones (1957) observes that only one lid and Horner's muscle are needed for functioning of the pump. Hanney (1957a) studied the decreased passage of tears in cases of facial paralysis but points out (1957b) that upper lid movement is not necessary for functioning of the pump.

The pump mechanism appears established and further work will delineate the precise mechanism and the structures and changes of pressure involved.

III. Chemical Aspects of Tear Secretion

The term tears has been applied both to the secretion of the lacrimal gland alone and more generally to the liquid found between the palpebral and orbital conjunctiva. Tears, or tear-fluid, will be used in the more general sense and the term lacrimal secretion, or lacrimal fluid, will be applied to the secretion of the lacrimal gland.

The scantiness of the fluid, and the variation in its composition because of evaporation, inadequacy of mixing, and changes in the contribution of the individual glands making up the total secretion, severely limit the accuracy of the procedures and most of the analytical data should be considered as estimations, or approximations, and not precise determinations. When a sample of tears is taken for analysis the layered structure of the precorneal tear-film (p. 274) is physically destroyed but evidence for the three components—mucoid, watery and oily—is found analytically.

A. PHYSICAL-CHEMICAL PROPERTIES

1. RATE OF SECRETION

It is very difficult to estimate the rate of normal tear secretion. The usual value that is quoted in the literature of about 2/3 gm./16 hr. probably comes from Schirmer (1903). This is equivalent to a figure of about 0.7 μl./min., not subtracting the amount evaporated. This is an extremely low value and supports his contention that the lacrimal gland does not secrete unless stimulated. Szmt (1958) found a slightly higher value of 1.3 μl./min. Balik's (1952) values are even higher, 15 μl./min., while later Balik and Hradecky (1953) report 6 μl./min. Thaysen and Thorn (1954) give wide variations of from 10 to 100 μl./min. The amount of evaporation has been estimated at 50% (Veirs, 1955; Schirmer, 1903), and 25% (Szmt, 1958). It is not surprising that such divergent results are obtained for secretion rate, in view of the difficulty in controlling degree of irritation and evaporation. It appears that values around 10 μl./min. may be more in line with the flow of tears under the usual conditions of irritation and evaporation.

It is well known that the lacrimal gland is capable of secreting copious tears for prolonged periods under the stimulus of emotion or irritation. The ability of the lacrimal gland to be stimulated by irritation is deficient in the newborn (Sjörgren 1955), and confirmed by Kästner (1957). The gland is functioning at birth as shown by the presence of lysozyme in the tear-fluid (Staffieri et al., 1950) but the neural development has not in all cases proceeded to full development, which occurs from one to seven weeks after birth. Lacrimation is more profuse in the young than in adults (de Roetth, 1953) and more in the female than the male. The other glands contributing to the secretion of tears probably secrete at a uniform rate. Excessive mucous production in conditions of chronic irritation, such as in keratoconjunctivitis sicca, indicates an increased rate of secretion of the goblet cells.

2. pH

There is general agreement on the pH of tears. Swan et al. (1939) found a mean value of 7.3 which increased on lacrimation to 7.6. This normal value is confirmed by Vidal (1951) and by Pederson-Bjergaard and Smidt (1952) with values of 7.3 and 7.4 respectively. Hudelo and Mercier (1952) report a higher average of 7.8 with a range from 7.0 to 8.5. Recently Rexed (1958) determined the pH of the lacrimal secretion directly from the ducts. This was found to be 7.5. It is apparent that the tears are at least moderately buffered to yield such constant results and that they are about equivalent to the pH of serum. The slight increase in pH during lacrimation and the higher value from the lacrimal ducts may reflect the contribution of the basic protein lysozyme.

3. TEMPERATURE

The temperature of the tears has mostly been inferred from the temperature of the cornea. Markovitch (1951) found the low value of 30° C. while Amano (1954) found the temperature about 35° C. when the room temperature was 25° C. Undoubtedly several factors, such as ambient temperature, rate of evaporation, and blink-frequency, determine the temperature of the tear-film over the cornea.

4. OSMOTIC PRESSURE

The osmotic pressure of tears has been shown in recent years (Krogh et al., 1945) to be equivalent to plasma (0.9% NaCl). This has been confirmed by other investigators (Pederson-Bjergaard and Smidt, 1952 and Revol et al., 1952). The isotonicity of normal tear-fluid suggests that either the secretions are hypotonic and are concentrated by evaporation to tonicity or they are isotonic to start with and evaporation plays only a minor role.

5. SURFACE TENSION

The surface tension of tears was found by Cerrano (1910) to be about 0.7 times that of water. This is confirmation of the general property of proteins that they lower the surface tension.

6. REFRACTIVE INDEX

The refractive index of tears is given as 1.3362 to 1.3374 (von Röth, 1922).

B. COMPOSITION

The components of the tear-fluid may be conveniently divided into small and large molecules. The small molecules are the inorganic and low molecular weight organic substances. The large molecular weight components are classed as proteins, mucopolysaccharides and lipids. Unidentified material having enzymatic or immunological properties will be discussed under "other large molecules."

1. SMALL MOLECULES

Physiologically the concentration of small molecules in tear-fluid is most important when compared with their concentration in the blood as this comparison provides clues regarding their mechanism of production. The ratio of concentration of small molecules in tears to the concentration in blood provides three categories: (a) approximately equivalent; (b) greater in tears; and (c) less in tears. The physical properties and chemical composition of tears in man have recently been compiled by Altman (1961).

Sodium and urea were found to be about equivalent to the serum levels by Thaysen and Thorn (1954). They found the ratio of urea in the tears to urea in the plasma to remain unchanged despite a fourfold change in plasma urea. This they believe is evidence for diffusion of urea because a secretory mechanism would probably become saturated with increasing load. Balik (1959a, b) found both sodium and urea more concentrated in tears than in serum. He suggests that this increase is best accounted for by the contribution of the mucous glands which are rich in sodium.

Chloride was found to be slightly elevated by Thaysen and Thorn (1954), Giardini and Roberts (1950) and Balik (1955). Potassium is 3 to 5 times greater in tears than in serum as determined by Thaysen and Thorn (1954). The amino acid content of tears is also considerably greater than serum (Balik, 1958).

Both the total reducing substances and the glucose content of tears are much less than in blood. Giardini and Roberts (1950) found glucose to be at a level in tears of about 3 mg.% and it constituted about 41% of the total reducing substances. This is much lower than the concentration of 65 mg.% reported by Ridley (1940).

Several implications may be drawn from the work of these investigators. The definitely higher concentrations of potassium and amino-acids mean that these components are secreted. Metabolic work must be done to concentrate the potassium and amino-acids. The slightly higher concentration of chloride indicates that it was concentrated either by evaporation or by metabolic work. The glucose content of tears is surprisingly low from the data of Giardini and Roberts (1950). It is probable that the secretion of the lacrimal gland itself is low in glucose, as it is difficult to account for this reduction in glucose solely by the metabolism of the cornea. The low glucose content of tears suggests that it is a poor medium for bacterial growth and this has been cited as one of the reasons for the apparent relative immunity of the eye.

The change in concentration of the small molecules in tears with changes in the rate of tear secretion is difficult to assess. Thaysen and Thorn (1954) found that urea, sodium and chloride were independent of the rate of secretion while Balik (1958, 1959a, b) found urea, sodium and amino-acids decreased with increased tear production. The difficulty in determining the rate of tear production, the degree of irritation when obtaining samples and the effect of evaporation should be emphasized.

The small molecules are most important in supplying the metabolic needs of the cornea, both in furnishing metabolites and in carrying off waste products. Radio-isotopic tracer work (Maurice, 1951) has shown that the corneal epithelium is not a barrier to the diffusion of inorganic ions. Davson (1954) showed that metabolic work was necessary to maintain the cornea in its normal deturgesced state. The glucose and oxygen in tears supply the main nutrients of the corneal epithelium and the tear-fluid accepts and carries off carbon dioxide and other waste products. Interference with this transport system of the tears, such as by ill-fitting contact lenses, causes serious trouble.

The discussion of the physical properties of tear-fluid shows it to be a liquid of rather a constant environment possessing physical and chemical properties conducive to even flow over the conjunctiva and cornea. Consideration of the part played by the small molecules gives a dynamic aspect to the role the tears play in the physiology of the eye.

2. LARGE MOLECULES

The introduction of electrophoresis, particularly paper electrophoresis, vastly improved the ability of the biochemist to isolate and identify large charged molecules. The large molecules may be grouped under the headings proteins, mucopolysaccharides, lipids and other large molecules. Attention should be called to an excellent monograph on electrophoresis of tears by Krause (1959).

a. Proteins

The total proteins range from about 0.2 to 0.6% according to most investigators. This is about 1/20 of the concentration in blood serum.

It is difficult to obtain precise analytical data on a fluid that normally is small in amount and of a variable composition. The analysis of the individual proteins is made even more difficult by their low concentration. To overcome some of these difficulties investigators have resorted to chemical irritation, weeping, pooled tears, micro-methods, and irritation with subsequent concentration. Each method has its advantages and disadvantages. Stimulation of tearing, either psychic or chemical, gives a sample that is relatively closer in composition to the lacrimal fluid than the tear-fluid, but the larger quantities give better resolution in electrophoresis, particularly when concentrated. Pooling tears precludes individual analysis but approaches normal tear composition. Micro-methods use normal tear-fluid of a single individual but the individual proteins are difficult to resolve because of the low protein content. It should be borne in mind that stimulation is relative and with all methods there is probably some stimulation. With these precautions in mind the individual proteins can be discussed.

All investigators have found a similar general pattern in electrophoresis of tears. There is a fast anode moving group (albumin fraction), a cathode moving group (lysozyme fraction) and an intermediate group (middle fraction). From the earliest work of Miglior and Pirodda (1954) to the latest of Krause (1959) the middle fraction has been steadily resolved from one component to four components. Minor skirmishes have centred on the "albumin" fraction and the lysozyme fraction. The relative sizes of the three fractions, "albumin"/middle fraction/lysozyme, are roughly 20/50/30. Krause (1959) finds about 5% less "albumin" and correspondingly more lysozyme. Miglior and Pirodda (1954) and Erickson (1956) find 10% more "albumin" and correspondingly less of the middle fraction.

The *"albumin" fraction* has an electrophoretic mobility close enough to the mobility of serum albumin that it is tempting to omit the quotation marks. Erickson (1956) and McEwen et al. (1958) hold that there are two "albumins" in this fraction. The "albumin" found in normal tears has a faster mobility than serum albumin and has been designated tear albumin (Erickson, 1956). The "albumin" found in cases of keratoconjunctivitis sicca, where there is little functioning of the lacrimal gland, has a slower mobility than tear albumin and corresponds closely to serum albumin. Krause (1959), using concentrated stimulated tears, finds only one "albumin" and it travels at a slower rate than serum albumin. Brunish (1957) observed that the "albumin" fraction decreased from about 40 to 20% when excessive tear production was changed from emotionally stimulated tears to chemically stimulated tears. Although it is probable that the "albumin" in tears is an albumin, and the different rates of mobility may be explained by lower or higher molecular weights than serum albumin, the quotation marks should be left on this "albumin" fraction until more definitive work is done.

The *middle fraction* is particularly resistant to resolution into sub-fractions by paper electrophoresis. This may be due either to the polydispersity of the proteins (having a wide range of molecular weights) or to the presence of mucopolysaccharides. Krause (1959) succeeded in showing four different sub-fractions in this group. This was not a constant finding as tear samples were found which either were not completely resolved or were lacking one or two components. It should be noted here that the term "lacking," like "stimulation," is a relative term. "Lacking" as generally used means that only under the conditions of the particular test the component was not demonstrable. The sub-fractions of this middle group do not correspond in mobility with the globulins in serum and for the present must be designated in a non-committal fashion.

It is evident that this middle fraction is composed of sub-fractions which, under appropriate conditions, can be resolved into four components. These components vary in amount, and their variance has not been correlated with any particular factor in health or disease. As a group they are a constant and characteristic fraction of tear-fluid.

The *lysozyme fraction* is the most definitive and characteristic fraction of the electrophoretic pattern of tears. At the usual pH of 8.6 of the buffer, the lysozyme fraction moves to the cathode at a mobility equivalent to that of egg-white lysozyme. This material will lyse the saccharidic coat of *Micrococcus lysodeikticus*, which is a definitive identification of lysozyme. Lysozyme has been known to be present in the tears of man and animals since its discovery by Fleming (1922). It is more concentrated in man than animals as shown by its "lack" in most animals except the higher mammals (Erickson *et al.*, 1956). In the tear-fluid of the monkey there was found a fraction that had lysozyme activity but moved at a rate slower than the usual human lysozyme. Later, McEwen *et al.* (1958) identified statistically this slower moving fraction in human tear samples.

Lysozyme is widely distributed throughout the tissues of the body and because of its manifest enzymatic activity it has invited considerable interest and research particularly in Europe. Attention should be called to the excellent review of this subject by Schumacher (1958) and to the continuing Symposia on Fleming's Lysozyme (International, 1959). The interest in lysozyme in the eye has chiefly centred on its diagnostic and therapeutic usefulness in external diseases of the eye.

McEwen *et al.* (1958) consider the lack of lysozyme in their electrophoretic analytical method as pathognomic of kerato-conjunctivitis sicca and a useful tool in diagnosing early borderline cases. Krause (1959) feels that the lowering of the lysozyme concentration in keratoconjunctivitis sicca is only indicative of a general lowering found in all pathological conditions.

The therapeutic usefulness of lysozyme has strong proponents and opponents. The European groups feel that it has a wide spectrum of activity against infection while others feel its usefulness is limited. These attitudes reflect the earlier arguments regarding the ability of the eye to avoid infection: the presence of the bacteriolytic enzyme lysozyme or the unfavourable culture medium of tears and its continual flow. Further discussion of the therapeutic usefulness of lysozyme is beyond the scope of this book.

b. Mucopolysaccharide

Material staining as mucopolysaccharide was found in tear patterns by McEwen *et al.* (1958) and by Krause (1959). Apparently this material is associated with the protein components, principally component III of McEwen *et al.* and fraction 2 of Krause. It is likely that all of the mucopolysaccharide is bound to protein and that there is no pure mucopolysaccharide component. The components are resistant to the enzyme attack of trypsin, hyaluronidase, lysozyme and chitinase. The profuse stringy material in cases of keratoconjunctivitis sicca is also a mucoprotein. It is likely that these mucoproteins represent the mucoid layer of Wolff's structured tear-film.

c. Lipids and Other Large Molecules

There is evidence for the presence of *lipids* and other large molecules. McEwen *et al.* (1958) using the oil red–0 fat stain found neutral lipid at the origin of the electrophoretic pattern and a halo around the "albumin" spot. Here may be found the analytical evidence for the outer oily layer of the structured tear-film.

Storm (1955) identified plasmin in tear-fluid. Fleming and Allison (1925) showed tear proteins to be both organ- and species-specific. Agglutinins have been found by Hegner (1916); and later Putkonen (1930) showed the presence of *iso*-agglutinins and *iso*-agglutinogens. Thompson and Gallardo (1941) presented evidence for a component, other than lysozyme, that possessed antibacterial activity.

IV. Neural Mechanisms of Lacrimation and Weeping

Excessive secretion of the lacrimal gland may be elicited by two general mechanisms: (*a*) Irritation of the ophthalmic division of the fifth nerve, in particular the conjunctiva of the eye and the nasal mucosa, will produce a copious flow of tears. This reaction is stimulated in a reflex manner and is usually designated by the term lacrimation. Lacrimation is much more profuse in man than in animals (Mettier *et al.*, 1960). (*b*) The lacrimal gland may also be stimulated by impulses sent to it from the higher cortical centres of the brain when activated by certain emotional states. This process is often called emotional crying or psychic weeping. The simpler term weeping may be used to distinguish it from lacrimation. Crying might be reserved for the emotional showing of facial contortions and emitting sounds whether there is weeping or not. A newborn baby neither weeps nor lacrimates but is quite able to cry. An adult may weep silently with no evidence of crying. The ability to weep is lacking in animals. The peak of ability to weep is reached in childhood and gradually tapers off in adulthood (see Section III, 1).

The mechanisms by which lacrimation and weeping occur will be considered by describing the nerve supply of the lacrimal gland and the reflex pathways.

A. Nerve Supply of the Lacrimal Gland

Almost all of the nerve fibres to and from the lacrimal gland are incorporated in the lacrimal nerve. The lacrimal nerve is anatomically a branch of the ophthalmic division of the fifth, or trigeminal, nerve. On its passage through the gland to supply the lid, it gives off fibres to the lacrimal gland. Because the lacrimal nerve is anatomically a branch of the ophthalmic division there is a temptation to assume that the fibres which terminate in the gland have a neurological or functional connexion with the fifth nerve. There may be afferent pain fibres to the fifth nerve from the lacrimal gland or capsule, and Spooner (1957) suggests that the fifth nerve provides efferent fibres to the gland that have a trophic function in the control of cell growth and metabolism. It is probable that most of the efferent fibres in the lacrimal nerve that go to the lacrimal gland are the parasympathetic efferent nerve fibres of the great superficial petrosal nerve and the sympathetic efferent nerve fibres from the superior cervical ganglion.

1. PARASYMPATHETIC SUPPLY

The preganglionic fibres originate in a small area above the superior salivary nucleus in the lowest part of the pons (see Fig. 4). The secreto-motor fibres join with the sensory root (nervus intermedius) of the seventh nerve,

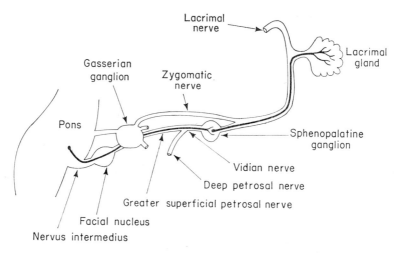

FIG. 4. Diagrammatic representation of parasympathetic supply to the lacrimal gland.

emerge from the lower body of the pons between the facial (motor) and auditory nerves having passed through the facial nucleus without synapsing. Incorporated in the greater superficial petrosal nerve, which arises from the facial (geniculate) ganglion, the fibres pass under the Gasserian (trigeminal) ganglion. They proceed as part of the Vidian nerve to synapse in the sphenopalatine ganglion (Meckel's ganglion). The Vidian nerve is a fusion of the greater superficial petrosal and the deep petrosal nerves as they pass through the pterygoid canal on emerging from the cranium.

The postganglionic fibres arising from the sphenopalatine ganglion are incorporated in the zygomatic nerve (a branch of the maxillary division of the fifth nerve) and thence, through the anastomosis of the zygomatic and lacrimal nerves, they reach the lacrimal gland. The fibres terminate in the gland between cells and around the ducts. Kato (1957) reports that the nerve

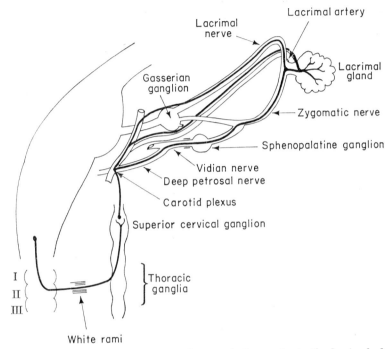

FIG. 5. Diagrammatic representation of sympathetic supply to the lacrimal gland.

fibres in the human lacrimal gland are chiefly non-medullated thin fibres. Cunningham (1931) suggests that there is a connexion by fine twigs directly from the sphenopalatine ganglion to the lacrimal gland. Mutch (1944) feels that the postsynaptic fibres go to the Gasserian (trigeminal) ganglion before entering the zygomatic nerve.

2. SYMPATHETIC SUPPLY

The preganglionic fibres arise in the hypothalamus, pass along the cervical cord, leave the central nervous system as white rami at the first, second or third thoracic level and ascend the cervical sympathetic chain to synapse in the superior cervical ganglion (see Fig. 5).

The postganglionic fibres join the carotid plexus and from there may reach the lacrimal gland by two or three routes. One path is by the deep petrosal nerve, the Vidian nerve, through the sphenopalatine ganglion and on to the lacrimal gland as described under parasympathetic supply. A second path is by entrance from the cavernous plexus into the ophthalmic nerve and via the lacrimal nerve to terminate in the lacrimal gland. A third route is via the carotid plexus and along the lacrimal artery. The fibres may either follow the artery to the gland or may enter the lacrimal nerve prior to the gland. Because of the general vasomotor function of the sympathetic system it is probable that the fibres terminate on arterioles supplying the gland.

B. Reflex Paths

Impulses that cause discharge in the efferent fibres to the lacrimal gland arise either peripherally (mostly from the fifth, occasionally from the second and seventh nerves) or centrally in the brain. The peripheral inputs are concerned with reflex lacrimation, whilst the cerebral inputs have much less of a reflex pattern and stimulate the gland in the act of weeping.

Since there are two efferent pathways to the lacrimal gland, it is not clear in every case whether one or the other, or both, are stimulated. Early work by numerous investigators has developed the concept that secretory stimulation of the lacrimal gland is primarily by way of the parasympathetic fibres. It has been shown that stimulation of the parasympathetic system will produce lacrimation even when the sensory root of the fifth nerve is cut (Mutch, 1944). Conversely, no tearing will take place when the sphenopalatine ganglion is blocked, but the fifth nerve intact. Pharmacological data support these findings. Parasympathomimetic drugs such as pilocarpine, muscarine, acetylcholine and physostigmine stimulate secretion and the parasympatholytic drug, atropine, inhibits the activity.

A minor indefinite regulatory role is assigned to the sympathetic system. The sympathetic fibres provoke vasoconstriction and have a less active and a less constant effect on secretion than do the parasympathetic fibres.

It is clear that the parasympathetic is responsible for the gross production of tears in lacrimation or weeping, but what neural control there is for the normal secretion of tears is not definite. All possible mechanisms have been implicated: parasympathetic, sympathetic, direct fifth nerve innervation and no control. The sympathetic, through its vasomotor function, may provide tonic stimulation of normal secretion. During sleep there is little or no lacrimal secretion.

Until more information is obtained regarding the connexions between the afferent and efferent paths, only the sites, stimulation of which will produce tears, can be given with certainty. These sites are usually remote from the gland itself.

1. FIFTH NERVE STIMULATION

Most reflex lacrimation originates from irritation of the ophthalmic division of the fifth nerve. This includes all painful diseases of the eye and stimuli such as injuries, foreign bodies and other irritants. Certain diseases, such as herpes simplex, will desensitize the cornea, whilst other diseases, such as kerato-conjunctivitis sicca, may progress to the point of rendering the lacrimal gland incapable of functioning. Both processes will give an apparent decrease in the reflex. Two relatively new agents have appeared to irritate the eye and to cause lacrimation: smog and contact lenses. Much distress is caused in localities where an eye-irritating smog exists and lacrimation is a major complaint of patients wearing ill-fitting contact lenses. Experience with both these agents has indicated that there is a wide variation in the threshold of individuals to painful stimuli.

"Eye strain" and accommodative strain have been implicated in causing lacrimation (Duke-Elder, 1952). Painful stimuli at sites other than the eye are well-known producers of tears: nose tickling, painful teeth and nasal sinuses.

2. STIMULATION VIA OTHER NERVES

Looking at a bright light causes lacrimation. The pathway for this stimulus is the optic nerve. The impulses travel to the visual cortex and are reflected back to the superior colliculus. Connexion is then made via the longitudinal fasciculus to the parasympathetic system.

Tasting of highly spiced food causes lacrimation. Stimulation of the taste-buds produces impulses that travel along the seventh nerve (see Fig. 6). Because of the close approximation of the seventh nerve with the para-sympathetic supply to the lacrimal gland, such a connexion might be conceded. There is a particularly interesting pathological association between lacrimation and salivation known as "crocodile tears." During recovery from seventh nerve paralysis, a considerable number of patients find that stimulation of salivation produces an excessive flow of tears. It is presumed that regenerating salivary fibres of the facial nerves are misdirected to the lacrimal gland. Dereux (1953) considers that the "crocodile tear" syndrome is not rare. This syndrome must be differentiated from the overflow of tears accompanying seventh nerve paralysis where improper functioning of the orbicularis and the pump mechanism leads to an inadequate drainage of the normal tear secretion.

The central inputs for the act of weeping are unknown. However, Pfuhl (1953) feels that the centre for weeping is in the second gyrus of the frontal lobe while Loewenberg (1945) believes that the hypothalamus is the centre for psychogenic stimulation of tears. Mizukawa et al. (1954) report that stimulation of the ventromedial hypothalamic nucleus in the rabbit will cause lacrimation. In some individuals the act of weeping is under voluntary control.

Lacrimation accompanies the large convulsive acts of vomiting, coughing, yawning and laughing. Synkinesis with the vagus and glossopharyngeal nerves probably accounts for this effect.

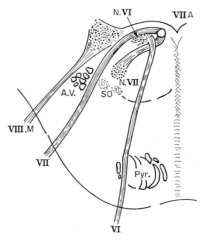

Fig. 6. Plan of the origins of the sixth and seventh cranial nerves. (Reproduced by permission from Wolff, 1954)

V. Anatomical Aspects of Blinking

The lids act as a variable-speed shutter that is under both involuntary and voluntary control. There are two types of involuntary control of the eyelids: the centrally controlled closing and reopening of the lids, termed the periodic blink, and the peripherally stimulated action of the lids referred to as the reflex blink. The lids may be voluntarily opened or closed either quickly or slowly. The reflex control of the lids takes precedence over the voluntary control. The voluntary action is usually bilateral although most people are able to blink one eye, which is termed a wink. The condition in which a partial or full wink is caused by involuntary muscle twitching (tic) is socially embarrassing as the performance is often construed as voluntary with all the implications of a wink. Squeezing the eyes shut is an extreme forceful closure of the lids using the orbicularis and accessory muscles and may occur voluntarily or reflexly and, when involuntarily, is called *blepharospasm*. During waking hours the eyes are open except for the periods of periodic blinking, reflex blinking and purposeful closure.

The open position is a dynamic balance between the muscles that open the lids and the muscle that closes the lids.

A. MUSCLES OF LID-OPENING

1. MUSCLES LIFTING UPPER LID

The major muscle concerned is the levator palpebrae superioris. It is assisted in its task by Müller's muscle. In extreme position of upward gaze the occipito-frontalis, an accessory muscle of the face, helps the levator to elevate the lid.

a. Levator Palpebrae Superioris

This muscle may be considered in three sections: (i) the contractile part and its origin, (ii) the aponeurosis (a widened tendinous part) and (iii) the insertion.

The contractile portion arises in the posterior orbit from a short tendon attached to the lesser wing of the sphenoid bone near the optic foramen, and is blended with the origin of the superior rectus muscle. This muscle continues between the roof of the orbit and the superior rectus to about the position of the upper fornix and terminates at the aponeurosis. Just before this juncture of the aponeurosis and the body of the levator, the whole muscle is enveloped in a thick fascial sheath, which fuses with the sheath of the superior rectus and the conjunctiva at the upper fornix. Despite this fusion, there is sufficient play in the tissues so that the two muscles work independently. Evidence of this is given in sleep when the upper lids are down and the eyes are turned up. It is doubtful whether upper lid retraction, during extreme upward gaze, is aided by contraction of the superior rectus.

The aponeurosis, a tendinous connective tissue membrane, fans out to the width of the orbit and turns downwards to follow the curvature of the globe. The two ends of the base of the aponeurosis are called horns. The more prominent lateral horn passes through a groove in the lacrimal gland and is attached to the orbital tubercle of the zygomatic bone. The medial horn makes an indefinite connexion to the medial palpebral ligament and thence to the bone. The front edge of the band sends fibrous attachments to the skin of the upper lid.

The fibres from the aponeurosis traverse the fasciculi of the orbicularis muscle in order to reach the skin of the lids. They attach in a definite layer in front of the tarsal plate. A few of the fibres are attached to the tarsal plate.

b. Müller's Lid Muscle (Superior Palpebral Muscle)

This is a thin band of smooth muscle lying underneath and in close apposition to the aponeurosis of the levator. Its fibres arise from the body of the levator and terminate by elastic tendons to the upper border of the tarsus. This is the main muscle attachment to the tarsus. The juncture of the tarsal and orbital portions of the lid is demarcated on the outside of the lid by the superior palpebral furrow. This fold of skin allows rapid retraction of the lid.

c. Frontalis Muscle

The frontalis muscle may be considered an accessory lid-opening muscle. Contraction raises the eyebrows and wrinkles the skin of the forehead. Distally, its fixed point is at the galea aponeurotica, which is a thin tendon joining the frontalis with the occipital muscle. The fibres of the frontalis terminate in the skin of the eyebrows and are mixed with fibres of the orbicularis, corrugator and pyramidalis. These last three muscles are antagonistic to the lid-opening muscles. On extreme upward gaze, or when the lids seem "heavy," the frontalis muscle is brought into action to help retract the lids.

2. MUSCLES DEPRESSING THE LOWER LID

The lower lid does not have a muscle corresponding to the levator muscle of the upper lid. On downward gaze the lower lid can open or drop only about 5 mm. from its normal position just below the lower limbus. This action is mediated by the inferior palpebral muscle which is analogous to Müller's muscle (the superior palpebral muscle) of the upper lid.

a. Inferior Palpebral Muscle

The fibres of this muscle arise from the fascial sheath of the inferior rectus muscle. The fibres terminate in the lower lid but apparently do not reach as far as the tarsus. The opening of the lower lid on downward gaze is mediated primarily through the inferior rectus muscle with additional help from the inferior palpebral and the inferior oblique (Jones, 1960). Unlike the upper lid, the fusion of the muscle sheaths of the ocular muscles and the lower-lid muscle is direct enough to provide co-operative action.

B. MUSCLES OF LID-CLOSURE

The obicularis oculi is the chief muscle employed for closing the eyes. Since, in contrast to the levator, it is well represented in both the upper and lower lids, both lids will be discussed together. The two facial muscles, the corrugator and the pyramidalis, may aid the orbicularis in lid-closure.

1. ORBICULARIS OCULI

The orbicularis muscle is ordinarily considered in two portions: the palpebral part, which is essential for lid-closure, and the orbital part, which serves a supplementary function. The strength of the orbicularis was measured by Jacobs (1954) and was found to be quite variable in different individuals.

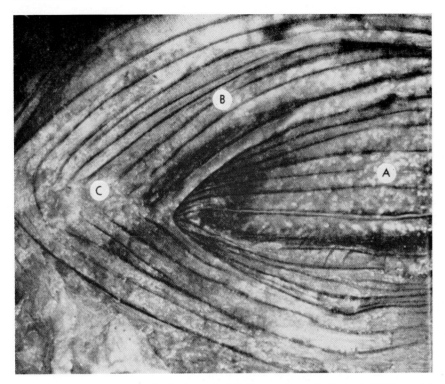

FIG. 7. Lateral part of palpebral muscle. (A) Pretarsal muscle (upper). (B) Preseptal muscle (upper). (C) Lateral palpebral raphé. (Jones, 1960.)

a. Palpebral Portion

The fasciculi of the muscle fibres are arranged in a semi-elliptical layer in both lids. The palpebral portion of the orbicularis may be divided into three groups: the preseptal fibres, the pretarsal fibres (including Horner's muscle) and the muscle of Riolan.

The preseptal fibres are arranged peripherally and cover the septum orbitale. The fibres arise partly from the medial palpebral ligament and adjacent bone. Some of the deeply placed medial fibres are in close relation and make contact with the fascia covering the lacrimal sac. The lateral termination is at the lateral commissure where the fibres cross and are interlaced.

The pretarsal fibres are joined to, and cover, the tarsal plate. These fibres at the medial end form a well-defined muscle-fibre mass which passes with the medial palpebral ligament behind the lacrimal fossa and attaches to the posterior lacrimal crest. This part of the pretarsal muscle is often called Horner's muscle, or the pars lacrimalis of the orbicularis muscle (see Figs. 7 and 8). The fibres at the lateral commissure are intermingled with the preseptal fibres at the lateral palpebral raphe. Jones (1960) considers that the pretarsal fibres of the upper and lower lids join to form a common tendon which inserts into the lateral orbital tubercle.

Another part of the pretarsal portion of the orbicularis has been given the name of Riolan. The muscle of Riolan is a group of extremely fine fibres which lie along the free margin of the lids and behind the eyelash follicles. The fibres are separated from the rest of the pretarsal portion by the glands of Moll.

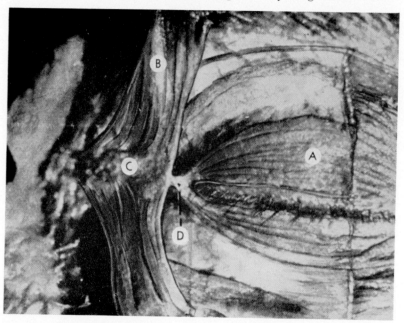

FIG. 8. Attachment of lateral palpebral raphé. (A) Pretarsal muscle. (B) Preseptal muscle. (C and D) Attachment of medial end of lateral palpebral raphé to common tendon of (A). (Jones, 1960.)

b. Orbital Portion

The orbital part of the orbicularis extends for a considerable area around the eye. It is attached on the medial side to the supra-orbital notch and the medial palpebral ligament. The fibres encircle the eye and are reattached at the malar bone of the cheek.

During their passage around the eye they extend into the eyebrow region, the temple and the cheek. When the orbital part is used to squeeze the eyes tightly shut, the skin is drawn toward the medial side where the muscle is firmly anchored.

2. ACCESSORY MUSCLES OF LID-CLOSURE

The corrugator pulls the eyebrows towards the nose. This action aids in shading the eyes from bright lights shining above.

The pyramidalis pulls the eyebrows down and is antagonistic to the frontalis muscle. Both the corrugator and pyramidalis muscles often work in conjunction and aid the orbicularis in squeezing the eyes tightly shut.

VI. Neurophysiology of Lid Movement

The degree and rate of lid-closure and opening are subject to precise voluntary control. Involuntary action of the lids may be stimulated subcortically or from several peripheral sites. The innervation of the lid muscles will be considered first, followed by a discussion of the voluntary and involuntary lid movements.

A. EFFERENT PATHWAYS (MOTOR)

1. INNERVATIONS OF LID-CLOSURE

All muscles of lid-closure, main and accessory, are innervated via motor divisions of the seventh nerve.

The seventh nerve nucleus lies in the midportion of the pons. The fibres, instead of passing directly out, go in a dorso-medial direction, ascending and encircling the sixth nerve nucleus and emerge from the ventro-lateral surface of the brain-stem above the olive and below the restiform body.

From this point of exit, the nerve passes in the posterior cranial fossa to the internal meatus of the temporal bone with the pars intermedius, the sensory root of the seventh nerve. The nerve continues through the facial canal, leaving the skull through the stylomastoid foramen, and passes into the parotid gland where it divides into its terminal branches. The upper temporal branch goes forward and upward over the zygoma to supply the upper part of the orbicularis and the accessory muscles: the corrugator, pyramidalis and frontalis. The lower zygomatic branch crosses the malar bone and connects with the lower part of the orbicularis.

2. INNERVATION OF LID-OPENING

The third nerve is the principal nerve that stimulates the levator to contract. The levator is also supplied by sympathetic fibres from the cavernous plexus. The accessory frontalis muscle is innervated by the seventh (facial) nerve. The lid-opening nerves are therefore the third and seventh cranial nerves and the autonomic sympathetic supply.

The *third cranial* (*oculomotor*) *nerve pathway* has been described elsewhere; it is only necessary here to discuss the peripheral pathway of the fibres to the levator, and to identify the origin of these fibres in the central nervous system.

The superior division of the third nerve enters the ocular surface of the superior rectus. From here fibres pass to the levator either by piercing the medial edge of the superior rectus or by winding around its medial border. The inferior division of the third nerve terminates in the inferior rectus and the inferior oblique. Stimulation of this division causes opening of the lower lid secondarily, by contraction of these extrinsic muscles.

The *sympathetic supply* to the superior and inferior palpebral muscles of the lids is derived from postganglionic fibres arising in the superior cervical ganglion. These fibres pass upward as the carotid plexus and then join the third nerve at its division into the superior and inferior branches. The sympathetic fibres follow the third nerve divisions and are carried thus to the palpebral muscles of the upper and lower lids. The preganglionic sympathetic pathway is similar to that described under sympathetic supply (p. 285).

The *seventh nerve* supplying the accessory lid-opening muscle, the frontalis, has been described above (p. 293).

3. SUPRANUCLEAR CO-ORDINATION OF LID MOVEMENT

Wherever antagonistic muscle groups exist, the body provides integrated reciprocal innervation so that both sets of muscles do not act at the same time. In 1896, Sherrington showed that the levator was inhibited during contraction of the orbicularis in the act of blinking. The reciprocal inhibition between the third and seventh nerves means that there is an integrating mechanism between these nerves.

Recent electrophysiologic studies of Gordon (1951) and of Björk and Kugelberg (1953) have revealed more details regarding the innervation mechanism. When the eyes are open and looking straight ahead there is a continuous firing of the motor units in the levator. On upward gaze the activity increases and on downward gaze there is decreased firing. On extreme downward gaze, or when the lids are closed, the muscle motor units are at rest. Lowering of the lid upon downward gaze is not accompanied by contraction of the orbicularis but by relaxation of the levator alone. During the rapid closing and opening of the lids in blink action the initiation of the act is the inhibition of the motor units of the levator. These remain inhibited until the orbicularis has had time to contract and relax. Gordon (1951) believes there are specific motor units located in the pretarsal region that are alone responsible for the blink action. More will be said about the blink later.

Sustained positioning of the lids is controlled by units in the preseptal region of the lids.

B. AFFERENT PATHWAYS FOR REFLEX LID MOVEMENTS

Lid action is initiated by a wide variety of stimuli, both peripherally and centrally. Most stimuli cause the eyelids to close or blink by reflex innervation of the seventh nerve. There are few instances of stimuli causing the eyelids to open.

1. PERIPHERAL REFLEX INPUTS

Peripheral stimuli with reflex connexions to the lids are carried by the trigeminal, optic and auditory nerve pathways.

The ophthalmic division of the fifth nerve is the major afferent path in the reflex circuit. The most sensitive areas for activation of the blink reflex are the cornea, conjunctiva and lid lashes. Depending upon the degree of irritation, lid-closure may be prolonged, and in the extreme, blepharospasm will occur. Blepharospasm brings all the lid-closure muscles into play. The corneal reflex is one of the last to be abolished under anesthesia. Irritation of the mandibular and maxillary divisions is much less provocative of a reflex action. Kugelberg (1953) showed a blink reflex by initiating an afferent impulse along the fifth nerve as a result of tapping on the face.

Inputs along the optic nerve, occasioned by the approach of a foreign body or a bright light, probably pass to the visual cortex, then back to the superior colliculus. Intercalary neurones in the posterior longitudinal fasciculus transmit them to the seventh nerve nucleus. The approach of a foreign body promotes a conditioned reflex for blinking and involves learned pathways which earlier were reinforced by stimuli from the fifth nerve. The corrugator and pyramidalis muscles aid in producing a narrow palpebral fissure in response to a bright light or glare.

The auditory nerve plays a complex role in lid-reflexes. Moderate noise will tend to startle or alert a person causing widening of the palpebral fissure. Loud noise, on the other hand, initiates a blink-reflex. Peripheral fibres of the cochlear division of the eighth (auditory) nerve have their cell bodies in the spiral ganglion. The fibres travel centrally and enter the brain-stem lateral and superior to the seventh nerve. Interconnexions between the eighth and seventh nerves probably exist in the medial longitudinal fasciculus. A supranuclear connexion to the cortex may also be interposed in this reflex. Toguchi and Imai (1954) describe a vestibulopalpebral reflex that is activated through the vestibular division of the eighth nerve.

Movements of the eyelid, eye and facial muscles are all intimately related. During waking hours, the accessory muscles, along with the lids, provide facial expression and animation. As the eyes move up and down the lids follow simultaneously. When the lids close rapidly, as in a blink, the eye also moves. Ginsborg (1952) showed that eye movements are probably synchronous with lid-closure. When a blink occurs with the eyes in the primary position, the eye moves inward (20–100' of arc) and upwards (40–70' of arc). Later Ginsborg and Maurice (1959) showed that when the eyes were not in the primary position, the eyes rotated toward the primary position at the beginning of the blink.

2. CENTRAL REFLEX INPUT

Voluntary and many involuntary lid movements are initiated centrally. There is a wide range of voluntary lid movements, from slight adjustments to wide opening or tight closure. The voluntary control is for the most part subsidiary to the reflex control, and the reflex lid-movements can be only partially inhibited by one's desire to do so. The rate of the periodic blink may be slowed voluntarily but not obliterated. Once the blink action starts, whether voluntarily or involuntarily, it completes its action without interference.

There are connexions from the cerebral cortex to the seventh and third nerve nuclei. Corticobulbar connexions with the seventh nerve nucleus descend in the pyramidal tract and cross in the pons to the seventh nerve nucleus on the opposite side. Cerebral inputs to the oculomotor nucleus arrive from the frontal and occipital lobes and probably the basal ganglia.

Complicated acts such as vomiting, yawning and sneezing probably cause lid-closure by synkinesis at a subcortical level. A bright light or nasal irritation may cause a reflex blink apart from the sneeze, but closure of the lids just prior to the explosive phase of the sneeze is the characteristic sneeze lid-closure reflex. It will be remembered that similar complicated acts promote lacrimation (p. 288).

C. THE PERIODIC BLINK

A blink of the lids initiated voluntarily cannot be distinguished objectively from the involuntary form. For the most part a blink is an unconscious periodic reflex movement and it will be discussed from that point of view.

None of the peripheral inputs mentioned above (second, fifth or eighth nerve inputs) initiates the periodic blink The mechanism and the central nervous system centre for the blinking movement mediated through the seventh nerve are unknown. The periodic blink is absent, or of very low frequency, in infants. In adults there is a wide variation in the frequency of the blink. Emotional states affect the frequency of the periodic blink. Most noticeable is the inhibition of the blink-frequency in persons with a "vacant

stare when lost in deep thought." Sleep abolishes the periodic blink, but resting with the eyes closed does not alter the blink rate (i.e., the twitching of
the lids) according to Lawson (1950). In some diseases, such as Parkinsonism,
the rate of periodic blinking is retarded.

The blink mechanism starts with an involuntary stimulus of central origin
that inhibits the levator. The levator starts to descend and its rate of descent
rapidly increases as the orbicularis muscles are innervated. After closure,
the orbicularis relaxes and the levator lifts the lid. Kisin (1956) believes
that the superior palpebral muscle acts as the trigger for activating the
levator.

The average rate of blinking has been found by King and Michels (1957) to
be 12.5 blinks/min. Gordon (1951) found the blink lasted about 0.3 second.
Kawaoka (1956) found a lower value of about 0.2 second for the duration of
the blink. These data suggest that vision is interrupted every 5 seconds with
an 0.3 second blackout (Lawson, 1948), which would mean that an average
person is without vision 6% of his waking hours. However, the lid does not
obscure the iris during the whole blink period. There is a relatively slow
movement of the lid downwards as the levator relaxes and before the orbicularis accelerates the movement. The actual time during which the lid cuts
out the light has been estimated by Gordon (1951) to be closer to 0.13 second.
This gives a lower blackout index of about 3%. It is true that the high speed
missiles and aircraft of today may cover considerable distance in the blink
of an eye, but fatigue and inattention are of more importance in aeroplane
accidents, according to Evrard (1957), than blinking. A person is usually
unaware of this periodic blink which has a pattern of 4,870 msec. of light
followed by 130 msec. of darkness. Regular intermittent stimuli such as
used in critical fusion frequency tests are observable at a rate of about 40
cycles/sec. or a pattern of 12 msec. of light followed by 12 msec. of darkness.
Awareness of the individual of the 12 msec. dark period of flicker and
unawareness of the 130 msec. darkness of the blink has several explanations.
The lower brain-centres may suppress the information from the retina and
not allow it to reach the higher conscious centres. A physiological explanation
may be found in the duration of the primary image. The primary image,
after being formed, lasts from 50 to 200 msec. depending upon various factors.
The period of the blackout is for the most part within the range of the persis-
tence of vision and is a rather isolated event as it has about 5,000 msec. of
light preceding and following it. In flicker tests the periods of lightness and
darkness are regular. It may be that in flicker the primary image has not had
a sufficient exposure to light to become well established so as to persist a
sufficiently long time.

Psychologists have particularly been interested in the periodic blink mechanism, from the standpoint of its purpose and its alterability. Only brief

mention can be made of this work, which is found mainly in the psychological literature. In recent literature the reasons given for the periodic blink, in addition to protection, are the increased visual perception (Nannarelli, 1955), the prevention of dizziness and to rest the eyes (Haberich, 1956). As regards the factors that affect the rate, several authors are in agreement that anxiety or tension causes an increase (Meyer *et al.*, 1953; King and Michels, 1957; Doehring, 1957). Poulton and Gregory (1952) indicate that inattention slows the blink rate, while Wood and Bitteman (1950) felt that blinking did not correlate with visual fatigue.

VII. Summary

The production of tears and the movement of the lids have been considered separately but there are many similarities and indeed the co-operative integration of these two mechanisms is important for the physiological functioning of the eye. Their association and interrelation may be considered at three levels. Weeping and lid-closure are only loosely associated at the voluntary and emotional level, closely associated at the reflex level and intimately interrelated at the normal functioning level where there is the constant production of tear-fluid and the periodic blink.

Voluntary control of weeping is difficult but may be accomplished by certain individuals, while weeping is a cardinal sign of grief. Bilateral lid-movements are under voluntary control but some people have difficulty in learning unilateral control of the wink. Emotions affect the blink-rate but this change is minor compared to the effect on lacrimal secretion (weeping). Severe emotional discharges stimulate both mechanisms.

Various peripheral reflexes, particularly stimulation of the ophthalmic division of the fifth nerve, produce tears and lid-closure. A blink alone may be produced reflexly, as by a loud noise, but it is seldom that lacrimation from peripheral stimuli is unaccompanied by simultaneous peripheral stimulation of the lids. It is at this level that the mechanisms of tear production and blinking have been considered as protective. The tear production and blinking reaction of animals to peripheral stimuli is an obvious protective device. The obviousness of this type of reflex action is apt to overshadow the physiological aspects of these mechanisms, which are constantly and continually subserving the needs of the cornea and conjunctiva.

It is at the unconscious vegetative level that the tear production and the periodic blink are integrated for normal functioning of the eye. The lacrimal apparatus constantly produces a particular fluid to meet the metabolic requirement of the cornea and provides a drainage system to dispose of the used fluid. The periodic blink brings this fluid into contact with the cornea and pumps it out by way of the drainage system. During this total process the fluid must be distributed over the cornea so that it provides a smooth optical surface; and the means of doing it, the blink, must not interfere with vision. The meeting of these requirements by the interrelated actions of secretion and blinking provides the physiological basis for tear production and the periodic blink-mechanism.

Acknowledgment

I am greatly indebted to many persons in the Department of Ophthalmology and the Francis I. Proctor Foundation for Research in Ophthalmology for their criticism and advice.

References

A. GENERAL

Adler, F. H. (1959). "Physiology of the Eye", 3rd edition. The C. V. Mosby Co., St. Louis.

Davson, H. (1950). "The Physiology of the Eye" (reprinted). J. & A. Churchill, Ltd., London.

Duke-Elder, W. S. (1940 and 1952). "Textbook of Ophthalmology", Vols. I and V. The C. V. Mosby Co.

Maximow, A. A., and Bloom, W. (1957). "A Textbook of Histology", 7th edition. W. B. Saunders Co., Philadelphia.

Spooner, J. D. (1957). "Ocular Anatomy". The Hatton Press, Ltd., London.

Whitnall, S. E. (1932). "The Anatomy of the Human Orbit", 2nd edition. Oxford University Press, London.

Wolff, E. (1954). "The Anatomy of the Eye and Orbit", 4th edition. H. K. Lewis and Co., Ltd., London.

B. SPECIFIC

Altman, P. L. (1961). "Blood and other Fluids". Federation of American Societies for Experimental Biology, Washington D.C.

Amano, J. (1954). Research on the influence of environmental conditions on local temperature of the eye. Acta Soc. ophthal. jap. 58, 332–339, as cited in Ophthal. Lit. 8, No. 3088 (1954).

Balik, J. (1952). The lacrimal fluid in keratoconjunctivitis sicca. A quantitative and qualitative investigation. Amer. J. Ophthal. 35, 773–782.

Balik, J. (1955). Secretion of chloride ions in tears. Csl. ofthal. 11, 256–259, as cited in Ophthal. Lit. 9, No. 1616 (1955).

Balik, J. (1958). The amino acid content of tears. Sborn. lék. 60, 332–336, as cited in Ophthal. Lit. 12, No. 4847 (1958).

Balik, J. (1959a). The sodium level of tears. Ophthalmologica, Basel 137, 95–102.

Balik, J. (1959b). The excretion of urea in tears. Acta ophthal., Kbh. 37, 103–111.

Balik, J., and Hradecky (1953). The protein level in tears. Csl. ofthal. 9, 102–107. Cited in Ophthal Lit. 7, No. 335 (1953).

10

Björk, A., and Kugelberg, E. (1953). The electrical activity of the muscles of the eye and eyelids in various positions and during movement. *Electroenceph. clin. Neurophysiol.* 5, 595–601.

Brunish, R. (1957). The protein components of human tears. *A.M.A. Arch. Ophthal.* 57, 554–556.

Cerrano, E. (1910). Recherches physico-cliniques sur les larmes par rapport a l'emploi des collyres. *Arch. ital. Biol.* 54, 192–196.

Cunningham's Text-book of Anatomy (1931), 6th edition (Arthur Robinson, ed.) p. 688. Oxford University Press, London.

Davson, H. (1954). Hydration of the cornea. *J. Physiol.* 125, 15P–16P.

Dereux, J. (1953). Postparalytic prandial homolateral lacrimation. Syndrome of crocodile tears. *Rev. neurol.* 88, 120.

de Roetth, A., Sr. (1953). Lacrimation in normal eyes. *A.M.A. Arch. Ophthal.* 49, 185–189.

Doehring, D. G. (1957). The relation between manifest anxiety and rate of eyeblink in a stress situation. *U.S.N. Sch. Aviat. Med. Res. Rep. Proj. No. NM* 13 01 99, *Subtask No.* 1, *Rep. No.* 6, as cited *Ophthal. Lit.* 11, No. 4120 (1957).

Duke-Elder, W. S. (1952). "Textbook of Ophthalmology", Vol. V, p. 5204. C. V. Mosby Co., St. Louis.

Erickson, O. F. (1956). Albumins in lacrimal protein patterns. *Stanf. med. Bull.* 14, 124.

Erickson, O. F., Feeney, L., and McEwen, W. K. (1956). Filter-paper electrophoresis of tears. II. Animal tears and the presence of a "slow-moving" lysozyme. *A.M.A Arch. Ophthal.* 55, 800–806.

Evrard, E. (1957). Blinking, a possible cause of accidents in aerial navigation. *Méd. aéro,* 12, 151–159.

Fleming, A. (1922). On a remarkable bacteriolytic element found in tissues and secretions. *Proc. roy. Soc. B93,* 306.

Fleming, A., and Allison, V. D. (1925). On the specificity of the protein of human tears. *Brit. J. exp. Path.* 6, 87.

Freiberg, T. (1951). The role of the lacrimal sac and caruncle in the mechanism of lacrimal drainage. *Ophthalmologica, Basel* 122, 193–206.

Giardini, A., and Roberts, J. R. E. (1950). Concentration of glucose and total chloride in tears. *Brit. J. Ophthal.* 34, 737–743.

Ginsborg, B. L. (1952). Rotation of the eyes during involuntary blinking. *Nature, Lond.* 169, 412–413.

Ginsborg, B. L., and Maurice, D. M. (1959). Involuntary movements of the eye during fixation and blinking. *Brit. J. Ophthal.* 43, 435–437.

Gordon, G. (1951). Observations upon the movement of the eyelids. *Brit. J. Ophthal.* 35, 339–351.

Haberich, F. H. (1956). The significance of blinking for vision. *Berl. Med.* 7, 7–8.

Hanney, F. (1957a). Disturbances in the draining away of tears in facial paralysis. *Klin. Mbl. Augenheilk.* 130, 684–687.

Hanney, F. (1957b). The drainage of tears in restriction of the movement of the upper lid. *Klin. Mbl. Augenheilk.* 131, 69–72.

Hegner, C. A. (1916). Uber das Vorkommen von Agglutininen in der Tränenflussigkeit. *Klin. Mbl. Augenheilk.* 57, 48.

Hudelo, A., and Mercier, J. (1952). A study of the lacrimal pH as a function of the local and general state. *Ann. Oculist, Paris* 185, 764–771.

International Symposium on Fleming's Lysozyme, 1st Milan (1959). (Abstracts of Relations and Communications.)

Jacobs, H. B. (1954). Strength of the orbicularis oculi. *Brit. J. Ophthal.* **38**, 560–566.

Jones, L. T. (1957). Epiphora. II. Its relation to the anatomical structures and surgery of the medial canthal region. *Amer. J. Ophthal.* **43**, 203–212.

Jones, L. T. (1960). The anatomy of the lower eyelid and its relation to the cause and cure of entropion. *Amer. J. Ophthal.* **49**, 29–36.

Kästner, M. (1957). Observations on premature babies. *Klin. Mbl. Augenheilk.* **130**, 304–310.

Kato, Y. (1957). Distribution of the nerve fibers in the human lacrimal gland. *Acta Soc. ophthal. jap.* **61**, 2264–2287, as cited in *Ophthal. Lit.* **11**, No. 3414 (1957).

Kato, Y. (1958). Histochemical observation of the human lacrimal gland. *Acta Soc. ophthal. jap.* **62**, 175–184, as cited in *Ophthal. Lit.* **12**, No. 27 (1958).

Kawaoka, H. (1956). The blinking movement and its electro-oculographic analysis. *Acta. Soc. ophthal. jap.* **60**, 1039–1045, as cited in *Ophthal. Lit.* **10**, No. 1578 (1956).

King, D. C., and Michels, K. M. (1957). Muscular tension and the human blink rate. *J. exp. Psychol.* **53**, 113–116.

Kisin, P. Y. (1956). The functional relationship of the upper tarsal muscle and the palpebral levator. *Vestn. oftal.* **1**, 19–22, as cited in *Ophthal. Lit.* **10**, No. 539 (1956).

Kobayashi, M. (1958). Studies of the lacrimal gland by electron microscopy. *Acta Soc. ophthal. jap.* **62**, 230–241, as cited in *Ophthal. Lit.* **12**, No. 471 (1958).

Krause, U. (1959). A paper electrophoresis study of human tear proteins. *Acta ophthal. Kbh. Suppl.* **53**.

Krogh, A., Lund, C. G., and Pedersen-Bjergaard, K. (1945). The osmotic concentration of human lacrymal fluid. *Acta physiol. scand.* **10**, 88–90.

Kugelberg, E. (1952). Facial reflexes. *Brain* **75**, 385–396.

Lawson, R. W. (1948). Blinking: Its role in physical measurement. *Nature Lond.*, **161**, 154–157.

Lawson, R. W. (1950). Blinking and sleep. *Nature Lond.*, **165**, 81–82.

Loewenberg, H. (1945). Psychosomatic relations in function of lacrimal glands. *J. clin. Psychopath.* **6**, 473–475.

McEwen, W. K., Kimura, S. J., and Feeney, M. L. (1958). Filter paper electrophoresis of tears. III. Human tears and their high molecular weight components. *Amer. J. Ophthal.* **45**, 67–70.

McEwen, W. K., Kimura, S. J., Feeney, M. L., and Li, J. G. (1959). "Lysozyme in tears and leukemic leukocytes". *In* International Symposium on Fleming's Lysozyme, 1st Milan (1959). (Abstracts of Relations and Communications), p. 19.

Markovitch, A. (1951). Considerations sur la division de l'appareil lacrymal. *Ann. Oculist.*, *Paris* **184**, 803–810.

Maurice, D. M. (1951). The permeability to sodium ions of the living rabbit's cornea. *J. Physiol.* **112**, 367–391.

Mettier, S. R. Jr., Boyer, H. K., Hine, C. H., and McEwen, W. K. (1960). A study of the effects of air pollutants on the eye. *A.M.A. Arch. indust. Hyg.* **21**, 1–6.

Meyer, D. R., Bahrick, H. P., and Fitts, P. M. (1953). Incentive, anxiety and human blink rate. *J. exp. Psychol.* **45**, 183–197.

Miglior, M., and Pirodda, A. (1954). Indigani elettroforetische sulla composizione proteica delle lacrime umane normali. *G. ital. oftal.* **7**, 429.

Mizukawa, T., Takagi, Y., Kamada, K., and Hama, H. (1954). Study on the lacrimal function. *Tokushima J. expertl. med.* **1**, 67–72, as cited in *Ophthal. Lit.* 8, No. 4101, (1954).

Molinelli (1773). *Mém. Acad. Sc. Bologna* **11**, 1, as cited by Duke-Elder (1940) "Textbook of Ophthalmology", Vol. I, p. 653. The C. V. Mosby Co., St. Louis.

Montagu, A. (1959). Natural selection and the origin and evolution of weeping in man. *Science* **130**, 1572–1573.

Mutch, J. R. (1944). The lacrimation reflex. *Brit. J. Ophthal.* **28**, 317–336.

Nagashima, K. (1954). A study on the function of the lacrimal pathway. *Acta Soc. ophthal. jap.* **58**, 936–942, as cited in *Ophthal. Lit.* **8**, No. 2588 (1954).

Nagashima, K. (1958a). Studies on the function of the lacrimal passages. *Acta. Soc. ophthal. jap.* **62**, 9–19, as cited in *Ophthal. Lit.* **12**, No. 1142 (1958).

Nagashima, K. (1958b). Studies on the function of the lacrimal passages. *Acta Soc. ophthal. jap.* **62**, 578–596, as cited in *Ophthal. Lit.* **12**, No. 1142 (1958).

Nannarelli, V. (1955). The influence of the blink reflex on the visual perception of form and movement. *Acta neurol., Napoli* **10**, 96–108, as cited in *Ophthal. Lit.* **9**, No. 3387 (1955).

Parvis, V. P. (1950). Arrangement for the regulation of blood circulation in the human lacrimal gland. *Biol. latina* **3**, 250–284, as cited in *Ophthal. Lit.* **4**, No. 6198 (1950).

Pederson-Bjergaard, K., and Smidt, B. C. (1952). Electrolytic conductivity, osmotic pressure and hydrogen ion concentration of human lacrimal fluid. *Acta derm. -venereol., Stockh.* **32**, 261–267.

Pfuhl, W. (1953). Weeping in worry, pain and emotion. *Med. Mschr.* **7**, 547–549.

Poulton, E. C., and Gregory, R. L. (1952). Blinking during visual tracking. *Quarterly J. exp. Psychol.* **4**, 57–62.

Putkonen, T. (1930). Über die gruppenspezialischen Eigenschaften verschiedener Körper-flussigkeiten. *Diss. Helsingfors*, cited by Krause (1959).

Revol, L., Nouvel, G., and Jaumard, A. (1952). Osmotic pressure of the lacrimal fluid. *Toulouse méd.* **52**, 748–751, as cited in *Ophthal. Lit.* **6**, No. 4655 (1952).

Rexed, V. (1958). The pH of the lacrimal fluid determined by a capillary micro-glass electrode. *Acta ophthal., Kbh.* **36**, 711–718.

Ridley, F. (1940). "Modern Trends in Ophthalmology". Ridley and Sorsby, eds. Hoeber, New York, 1940.

Schirmer, O. (1903). Studien zur Physiologie und Pathologie der Tränenabsonderung und Tränenabfur. *Albercht v. Graefes Arch. Ophthal.* **56**, 197–291.

Schumacher, H. (1958). Neue Erkenntnisse über die Biochemie des Lysozyms und ihre Klinische Bedeutung für die Augenheilkunde. *Fortschr. Augenheilk.* **8**, 142–211.

Sherrington, C. S. (1896). On the reciprocal innervation of antagonistic muscles. *Proc. roy. Soc.* **64**, 179–181 (1898), as cited in Björk, A., and Kugelberg, E. (1953).

Sjörgren, H. (1955). The lacrimal secretion in newborn premature and fully developed children. *Acta ophthal., Kbh.* **33**, 557–560.

Spooner, J. D. (1957). "Ocular Anatomy", p. 99. The Hatten Press Ltd., London.

Staffieri, M., Zorzi, M., and Sburlati, L. (1950). Behavior of bacteriolysis of lysozyme in tears, saliva and nasal secretion of full term and premature infants. *Boll. Ist. sieroter. Milano*, **29**, 139–147, cited *Ophthal. Lit.* **4**, No. 5395 (1950).

Storm, O. (1955). Fibrinolytic activity in human tears. *Scand. J. clin. Lab. Invest.* **7**, 55.

Swan, K. C., Trussell, R. E., and Allen, J. H. (1939). pH of secretion in normal conjunctival sac determined by glass electrode. *Proc. Soc. exp. Biol. N.Y.*, **42**, 296–298.

Szmt, J. (1958). Lacrimation Tests. *Klin. Oczna* **28**, 195–201, cited in *Ophthal. Lit.* **12**, 472 (1958).

Thaysen, J. H., and Thorn, N. A. (1954). Excretion of urea, sodium potassium and chloride in human tears. *Amer. J. Physiol.*, **178**, 160–164.

Thompson, R., and Gallardo, E. (1941). The antibacterial action of tears on staphylococci. *Amer. J. Ophthal.* **24**, 635–640.

Toguchi, M., and Imai, H. (1954). Vestibulopalpebral reflex. A blink related to head movement. *Nippon Seirigaku Zassi* **4**, 7–14, as cited in *Ophthal. Lit.* **8**, No. 4181 (1954).

Veirs, Everett R. (1955). "The Lacrimal System", p. 4. Grune & Stratton, New York.

Vidal, F. (1951). pH of tears. *Arch. Oftal. B. Aires*, **26**, 430, as cited in *Ophthal. Lit.* **5**, No. 5810 (1951).

von Arlt, F. (1855). *A.F.O. i* (2) 135 as cited by Duke-Elder (1940). "Textbook of Ophthalmology" Vol. 1, p. 653. The C.V. Mosby Co., St. Louis.

von Röth, A. (1922). Uber die Tränenflüssigkeit. *Klin. Mbl. Augenheilk.* **68**, 589–604, as cited by Krause, A. C. (1934). "The Biochemistry of the Eye", The Johns Hopkins Press, Baltimore.

Williams, E. E., and Hecht, M. K. (1955). Sunglasses in two anoline lizards from Cuba. *Science* **122**, 691.

Wolff, E. (1954). "The Anatomy of the Eye and Orbit", 4th edition, pp. 212–213. H. K. Lewis and Co., Ltd., London.

Wood, C. L., and Bitterman, M. E. (1950). Blinking as a measure of effort in visual work. *Amer. J. Psychol.* **63**, 584–588.

AUTHOR INDEX

Numbers in italics indicate the page on which a reference is listed.

Gaskell, W. H., *266*
Génis-Gálvez, J. M., 219, 220, *227*
Gesell, A., 142, *146*, 186, *187*
Giardini, A., 281, *302*
Gillessen, P., 210, *227*
Ginsborg, B. L., 65, 67, 72, 97, 107, *145*, *146*, 298, *302*
Gliddon, G. H., 103, 112, *143*
Gobar, F., 115, *151*
Goldmann, H., 195, 196, 215, *227*
Goldsmith, R. I., 213, 214, *225*
Goltz, F., 256, *263*
Goodman, L. S., 166, *175*
Gordon, G., 296, 297, 299, *302*
Granit, R., 45, *61*
Graybiel, A., 77, 78, 79, 109, *143*, *146*, *151*
Graves, B., 199, *227*
Green, E. L., 115, *150*
Gregory, R. L., 300, *304*
Grenacher, H., 3, *5*
Grimes, P. A., 166, *175*
Grünhagen, A., 232, 246, *263*
Grunert, K., *266*
Grynfeltt, Ed., *266*
Gulberg, J. E., *267*
Gullstrand, A., 195, 202, 205, 209, 210, *227*
Gunter, R., 166, *174*

Haberich, F. H., 300, *302*
Haidinger, W., 5, *5*, 64, *146*
Haines, H. F., 115, *146*
Hama, H., 289, *303*
Hamasaki, D., 208, *227*
Hannett, F. I., *266*
Hanney, F., 278, *302*
Harms, H., 239, *263*
Harrigan, R. F., 215, 218, *228*
Harris, A. L., 246, *264*
Hartman, A. P., 106, 135, *144*
Hartman, T., 138, *147*
Hartson, L. D., 158, *175*
Harvey, A. M., 154, 166, *174*
Hatano, S., 43, *61*
Hayhow, W., 44, *62*
Heath, P., *267*
Hebbard, F. W., 118, 129, *146*
Hecht, M. K., 272, *305*
Hegner, C. A., 285, *302*

Heerfordt, Chr. F., *266*
Heinemann, E. G., 119, 138, *146*
Helmholtz, H., 203, *227*
Helmholtz, H. L. F. von., 15, 18, 25, *26*
Henderson, J. W., 54, 57, 58, 59, *60*, *61*
Henderson, T., 199, *227*
Henle, J., 233, *264*
Hensen, V., 198, 199, *227*, 250, *264*
Hering, E., 9, *12*, 21, 25, *26*, 37, *61*, 91, 108, *146*
Hermans, T. G., 25, *26*
Herzau, W., 110, *146*
Herzog, H., *266*
Hess, C., 200, 211, 214, 216, *227*, 239, *264*
Hess, W. R., *266*
Higgins, E. L., 7, *12*
Higgins, G. C., 72, 74, *146*, *147*
Hine, C. H., 285, *303*
Hines, M., 42, 44, *61*
Hirsch, M. J., 115, 131, *143*, *146*
Hodes, M. C. R., 246, *264*
Hofman, H., 166, *175*
Hofmann, F. B., 105, 109, *146*
Hofstetter, H. W., 112, 119, 120, 137, 140, *143*, *146*, 208, 211, *227*
Home, E., 194, *227*
Hoogerwerf, *265*, *266*
Howe, L., 30, *61*, 139. *146*
Hradecky, 179, *301*
Huber, G. C., 44, *61*
Hudelo, A., 280, *302*
Humphrey, T., 54, 55, 58, *60*
Hunt, G. C., 45, *61*
Hunter, J., *266*
Hyde, J. E., 51, 52, *61*, 67, 87, 88, 101, *146*

Iarbus, A. L., 72, *146*
Ilg, F. L., 142, *146*, 186, *187*
Imagawa, T., 43, *61*
Imai, H., 297, *304*
Ingram, W. R., *266*
Irvine, S. R., 41, *61*, 167, *175*
Ittelson, W. H., 137, *146*
Ivanoff, A., 104, *147*, 202, *227*

Jablonski, M. D., 135, *150*
Jacobs, H. B., 293, *302*

SUBJECT INDEX

12²

AB